INCENTIVE

How the conditions of reinforcement affect the performance of rats

INCENTIVE

How the Conditions of Reinforcement Affect

the Performance of Rats

by FRANK A. LOGAN

New Haven: YALE UNIVERSITY PRESS, *1960*

Preface

SCIENTIFIC PROPOSITIONS, as a rule, are tentative and incomplete and this book is no exception. The various conditions of reinforcement have not been studied sufficiently to permit very confident general statements about their effects, and the theoretical approach is still in the early developmental stages. To publish under such circumstances is to risk being outdated before the publication is off the press. To wait for a conclusive, finished product, however, is to risk not publishing at all.

This book could be called a progress report covering the first five years of an ongoing research program. During that time the goals have been largely exploratory, intended to develop fruitful lines for future theoretical and research activity. It is hoped that a second edition of this book can be written, perhaps a decade hence, to cover the problem area more intensively and more extensively.

Acknowledgments

MODERN SCIENCE, as a rule, is a cooperative venture and the research program reported in this book is no exception. I have only incompletely acknowledged this fact here and in the following text. I am sure that I have adapted and adopted many ideas of other people, some of which have lost their identity in the ongoing activity of the program. Unfortunately, there is nothing to do about this fact except to admit it.

Before mentioning substantive contributors, I should like to acknowledge an immeasurable debt to the two men whose teachings, advice, and encouragement are largely responsible for my arriving at the point of publishing this book. Kenneth W. Spence and Neal E. Miller have gone far beyond the ordinary relationships of a mentor and a colleague. Professor Spence is not only a master at science-making but is unusually capable at transmitting the attitudes, techniques, and motives of the scientist. Professor Miller has an extraordinary ability to converse creatively at the frontiers of another psychologist's thinking after only a few moments briefing. I could not possibly count how many of the ideas expressed in this book were borrowed from or stimulated by these men, but I am reconciled by the fact that, however large the number here, it is but a small portion of their output.

It is also fitting that I should acknowledge the late Clark L. Hull. Although I had the opportunity to know Professor Hull personally only during the last few months of his life, his influence has been profound. Indeed, the theoretical approach described in this book will be recognized as a direct descendant of Hull's theory.

Many colleagues have aided the program in one way or another. In particular, William Kessen was a continuing source of encouragement and made many valuable suggestions about an early draft of this book. In addition I am indebted to Robert P. Abelson, Norman H. Anderson, Frank A. Beach, William N. Dember, Kay C. Montgomery, Arlo K. Myers, and Burton S. Rosner.

The most vigorous and tangible support of the research program has come from students. In particular, Eileen M. Beier served as my research assistant and general project supervisor and should be considered to be a genuine coauthor of several of the empirical chapters of this book. Others have become actively engaged, at one time or another, with various phases of the program. Simply to mention their names hardly does justice to the contributions of Herbert Barry III, Gordon H. Bower, John R. Brooks, Bennett D. Dodd, Robert A. Ellis, Louis M. Gonzalez, Peter Hill, Wendell D. Kincaid, Arthur Kover, Mark McLellan, Richard Peckham, George Rosenwald, Milton A. Trapold, and Robert F. Weiss.

The primary source of financial support for the program was the National Science Foundation. Grants from that agency were used to build the apparatus, pay salaries, and cover the multitude of living expenses of such a program. The unrestricted and flexible nature of these grants made them ideal for a program of this kind.

The research on punishment was supported in part by PHS research grant M-1760 from the National Institute of Mental Health, Public Health Service

Yale University supported this research, not only in general as the host institution, but also in a number of specific ways. Through the Institute of Human Relations and its director, Mark A. May, the very beginnings of the program were supported and part of the cost of preparing this manuscript was covered. Through the Department of Psychology and its chairman, Claude E. Buxton, portions of the equipment, supplies, clerical work, and salaries were provided. Through the work scholarship program and Ruth M. Rowe, executive secretary for student employment, Financial Aids Office, invaluable research assistance was provided. First Edgar S. Furniss, and then Norman S. Buck, as provost, smoothed over several valleys in outside support. And the Yale Press was exceptionally cooperative in the publication stages of the book.

A number of people have been involved in the mechanical aspects of the research program and the preparation of this book. Gus Ogren helped build and maintain many parts of the apparatus. Lee Robinson helped maintain the animals. Dorothy Badger kept financial records and solved many clerical problems. Virginia Simon drew the final graphs. Jane Olejarczyk and Pat Cunningham prepared a mimeographed draft of the book and Susan Henry prepared the final copy. Finally, but most especially, my wife Julia not only tolerated me while this book was in preparation, but she spent many tedious hours working on data and drawing graphs.

New Haven, Connecticut
September 1, 1959   F. A. LOGAN

Contents

CHAPTER 1

Introduction

ANYONE can affect what other people do if he has something they want. This is because rewards, or reinforcements, play an important role in determining behavior. Children are affected by a parent's love, students by a teacher's grade, employees by an employer's wages, lovers by a partner's caresses, salesmen by a customer's purchases, and everyone, in general, by the approval of their peers. In these and countless other situations, people learn how to perform in order to obtain rewards.

There are many possible conditions of reinforcement, or ways that rewards can be given, ranging from the simple ones, in which a constant reward is given every time the response occurs, to the more complex conditions, in which the amount of reward depends upon how well the response is made. All conditions of reinforcement are not equally effective: some lead to a high and stable level of performance while others produce lower and more variable performance. Even among conditions that produce equal performance, some are more efficient in the sense that they do so with less reward. One can therefore pose the practical question: What are the best conditions of reinforcement to use to get the best performance for the least reward?

The scientist is interested in a somewhat different and more general question: How is behavior affected by the way rewards are given, or, to say the same thing somewhat more formally, what is the relationship between performance and the conditions of reinforcement? The effect of any condition of reinforcement is interesting regardless of whether it happens to be an efficient utilization of rewards. From the systematic study of a wide variety of conditions of reinforcement, the scientist attempts to formulate principles from which he can predict the effects of new conditions. To the extent that these principles are correct they can be used to answer such practical questions as how to get maximum performance with a minimum of reward.

A great deal of work has been done on the general problem of how performance is affected by the conditions of reinforcement, but the range of conditions used is small relative to the possible conditions that can be devised. Most extensively studied have been the simple, constant conditions in which a regular reward is given; some subjects may be given a larger reward than others, or some may be given the reward sooner than others, but for any one subject the reward is constant. Less research has been done on conditions in which the reward is varied from time to time for the same subject: sometimes a large reward may be given and sometimes a small one, or the subject may be given the reward immediately part of the time and required to wait for it the rest of the time. The most complex conditions involve correlated reinforcement, in which the reward depends upon the *way* the response is made. When reward is correlated with response, the subject can affect the amount of reward he receives by the speed and vigor with which he responds.

The three types of conditions of reinforcement can be studied using animals in the laboratory. In the research reported here, hungry rats were each day given one or more trials in which they ran from a starting box down a short straight alley to a goal box. Their running speed was automatically recorded to provide a measure of performance. Food reward was given in the goal box under constant, varied, or correlated conditions, and the data show how the various conditions affected the rats' running speed.

One might question whether the *principles* governing the rat's behavior in such a situation also apply to human behavior. In the last analysis this is a question of fact, and the evidence on it is still incomplete. There are no data known to the author that clearly disprove the affirmative hypothesis; neither can those of us who entertain it yet argue very convincingly that it is true. However, it can be seen in the present work that the rat's behavior shows more of the characteristics of human behavior as the conditions under which the rat is observed are made more similar to those under which people typically behave.

The most general principle suggested by the data to be reported is this: Rats behave in such a way as to maximize reward while at the same time minimizing effort. Some version of this principle is probably as old as the earliest analyses of human behavior. However, it requires a great deal of systematic elaboration in order to be generally useful as a predictive principle. It is not known, a priori, which events are most rewarding and which responses are least effortful; these must be determined empirically. Furthermore, other variables that affect performance have to be considered. Past learning may interfere with the occurrence and learning of the optimal response. The level of drive may affect the effort the organism will expend for a particular reward. And whether the subject will accurately maximize reward depends partly upon his ability to discriminate the optimal response from similar ones, which in turn depends upon the distinctiveness of the feedback (i.e. response-produced) cues.

The remainder of this chapter will be devoted to an informal description of the kinds of conditions studied, the type of results obtained, and the general nature of the proposed theoretical approach. This relatively casual summary is intended to provide a general overview of the entire project. In order not to interrupt the development, related research by others is not explicitly identified; such references are given in the later chapters along with a detailed account of the empirical laws and a more rigorous and formal presentation of the theory.

THE CONCEPT OF INCENTIVE

It will be useful first to distinguish the present use of the concept "incentive" from the related words "reward" and "reinforcement." The last two are used interchangeably to designate such events as giving food to a hungry rat. A condition of reinforcement is simply the empirical relation between the response and the reward.

"Incentive" is a hypothetical concept referring to what might popularly be described as the subject's expectation of reward. If a rat's performance in an alley is differentially affected by the reward he has previously received in the goal box, then some internal consequent of the reward must be present while he is in the alley before the reward is received. "Incentive" is our word for this consequent.

The distinction between incentive and reward is important for several reasons. First, incentive must be learned just as the response itself is learned; the rat learns not only to run down the alley but also to expect food at the end of the alley. Whereas the conditions of reinforcement can be stated in advance and held constant for a number of trials, incentive may be changing as the subject learns these conditions.

Secondly, equal differences in reward do not produce equal differences in incentive. For example, the difference between two pellets and four pellets equals the difference between twelve and fourteen pellets. But the difference in incentive produced by the latter difference in reward is much smaller than that produced by the former.

Finally, and perhaps most important, the subject's incentive may imperfectly represent the actual conditions of reinforcement. Incentive can be acquired only on the basis of experience with reward in the situation, and the subject's behavior cannot be affected by the consequences of untried responses; the experimenter's intentions to reward may not all be reflected in incentive. Furthermore, incentive depends partly upon the distinctiveness of the feedback cues relative to the conditions of reinforcement. As an extreme but clear example, if a rat were rewarded on trials when the number of tenths of a second that he took to respond were even and not rewarded were that number odd, his incentive would be the same as if he were being rewarded on a random half of the trials, because of his inability to make so fine a discrimination of his speed of running.

Incentive, then, is an intervening variable determined by previous experiences of reward and determining current performance. Because of the informal manner of presentation in this chapter, it might seem as if incentive were thought of as conscious expectation of reward. Though this use of the vernacular is sometimes convenient, it should be recognized that incentive will be developed in later chapters in more formal and mathematical terms.

CONDITIONS OF CONSTANT REINFORCEMENT

In the simplest conditions of reinforcement the reward is the same every time the response occurs. In an experimental setting such as the straight alley, a constant amount of food is available in the goal box and the hungry rat has merely to run down and get it. Some rats may be given a large reward and others a small one, and some may be rewarded immediately while others are required to wait for a fixed time of delay before they get the food.

Human behavior is seldom performed under such constant conditions. Perhaps an infant's early attempts at such behavior as using a spoon receive more or less indiscriminate parental reward. And some later activities, say making correct responses on objective tests, are followed by a fixed and predetermined reward. However, even though such conditions are relatively infrequent in the natural environment, their systematic study in the laboratory provides a reference level for comparison with the effects of more complex conditions.

Our data, as well as those from a number of previous studies, show that rats run faster the bigger the reward they are given and also the shorter the time they are required to wait for it in the goal box. Both the amount and delay of reward show diminishing returns. A constant difference in amount of reward produces less difference in running speed the larger the absolute amounts involved. Similarly, a constant difference in time of delay shows less differential effect on performance for long delays than for short ones.

CONDITIONS OF VARIED REINFORCEMENT

The number of possible conditions of reinforcement is greatly increased if the reward is varied from trial to trial. The most frequently studied of these conditions is partial reinforcement, in which the reward is omitted on part of the trials. Either the amount or the delay of reward can be varied separately, i.e. a large reward can be given sometimes and a small one other times, or the reward can be given immediately sometimes and delayed other times. And, of course, both amount and delay of reward can be varied simultaneously.

Variation in reward is much more common than constant reward in the natural environment. A parent may not reward the child every time he makes his bed or remembers to close the door. Most gambling situations offer variations in reward with calculable probabilities. Going to the theater may be entertaining on some occasions and boring on others. Cramming before an examination is sometimes successful. A blind date is not always unpleasant. Indeed, everyday examples of varied reward can be found in almost any type of human behavior.

Before describing how rats perform when reward is varied, let us consider two of the possible reactions to such conditions. At one extreme, incentive for the ensuing trial would be based on some kind of average of the rewards encountered on all the previous trials; at the other extreme, incentive would be based solely on the immediately preceding trial, as if whatever happened last will happen again. If the over-all conditions of reinforcement never change, then an organism that was built on the former principle would be most adaptive since its behavior would be relatively stable in the face of chance temporary fluctuations in reward. An organism built on the latter principle would show unstable behavior at the whim of what the reward on the previous trial happened to be. However, if the conditions of reinforcement sometimes change, then the former type of organism is at a disadvantage since it would re-adjust to the new conditions only slowly (and, indeed, never completely).

Rats are intermediate between these two extremes: their performance is reasonably stable when the reward is varied and yet they are able to readjust to altered conditions. Incentive apparently depends upon a finite sample of the previous trials, the reward on the last trial contributing the most with progressively less contribution from the rewards on more remote trials. We find that performance varies from trial to trial in accordance with the variation in reward, but the change is incomplete, and a number of consecutive trials with the same reward is required to shift performance completely to the appropriate level.

Although behavior is somewhat variable under conditions of varied reinforcement, we may nevertheless ask questions about the performance level by averaging over enough trials to include the range of variation in reward. Thus, we can compare average performance when reward is given on only half the trials with performance under constant reward even though the behavior of the subjects receiving partial reinforcement shows trial-to-trial fluctuations depending on whether the previous trial was reinforced or not.

It is also necessary to specify the portion of the response that is being considered. This is because varied reward affects behavior differently at different distances from the goal, leading to higher relative performance far from the goal than near it. One could almost say that rats start optimistically as if anticipating the better reward but end up pessimistically as if now anticipating the poorer reward. The following description applies to average behavior over the entire response.

We have data on only a few cases of irregular variation between two equally likely values and hence we can give only a tentative and partial description of the effects of varied reinforcement. When the delay of reward is varied between two equally likely values, then among conditions with the same average delay, performance is better the wider the range of variation in delay. For example, constant 10-second delay is inferior to variation between 9 and 11 seconds, which in turn is inferior to variation between 8 and 12 seconds, etc. The limiting case, and hence the best condition, is when the reward is given immediately on half the trials.

The effects of varying the amount of reward are somewhat more complex. If the average amount is large, the rule is the opposite of that given above for varied delay: among conditions with the same large average amount, performance is better the smaller the range of variation in amount. For example, 20 pellets is a large reward to a rat, and constant 20-pellet reward is better than variation between 19 and 21 pellets, which in turn is better than variation between 18 and 22 pellets, etc. However, if the average amount is small, a moderate degree of variation in amount is better than either constant or very widely varied amounts. For example, a constant 4-pellet reward is inferior to variation between 3 and 5 pellets, but the latter is better than 2 and 6 pellets or 1 and 7 pellets.

The widest range of variation in amount of reward is partial reinforcement when the amount is zero on half the trials. Under some conditions partial reinforcement seems to be consistent with the above description since it produces poorer performance than constant reward. Under other conditions, however, different factors are apparently introduced, because we find that rats may run faster if they are given reward on only part of the trials than if the reward is constant.

Clearly, had we not restricted the discussion to variation between two equally likely values, the number of possible conditions of varied reinforcement would have been indefinitely large.

Whether the rules given here are sufficiently general to handle all such conditions, or whether more comprehensive rules must be found, is one of the many questions for future research.

CONDITIONS OF CORRELATED REINFORCEMENT

The conditions of reinforcement which offer the largest number of possibilities are those in which the reward is not merely varied from trial to trial but where variations in the reward are correlated with variations in the response. Thus, one might give a rat more food the faster he runs down an alley. Since speed varies from trial to trial the reward will also vary, but the reward will have been given differentially, fast responses getting larger rewards. When using such conditions the experimenter cannot tell in advance what reward the rat will get on any particular trial. Instead, the experimenter states a *terms* function describing how much the rat will get depending on how fast he runs. The terms function, then, tells what the rat gets for what he does.

Systematically to enumerate the possible terms functions would require a great deal of space; a few examples must therefore suffice. The amount of reward may be correlated with the rat's speed of running either positively, so that the rat can maximize reward by running fast, or negatively, so that the rat gets more reward if he runs slowly. In either case, any of a number of terms functions can be used to determine, in general, how much improvement in performance is required to achieve a specified increase in reward.

The previous research on correlated reinforcement has used discontinuous terms functions: a predetermined reward is either given or not, depending on whether the response was performed within the range specified by the experimenter as correct. It should be recognized that more finely graded, or continuous, terms functions can also be used: the reward is larger the closer the response is to the correct one.

Similarly, any of a variety of terms functions can be used to relate delay of reward to speed; i.e. how quickly the reward is given can be correlated with how fast the rat runs. Futhermore, both amount and delay of reward may be correlated with speed simultaneously. When this is done, the effects may be complementary (the same behavior that gets the most reward also gets it the quickest) or antagonistic (the rat must choose between getting more reward and getting it sooner).

"Response speed" is a gross concept that may refer to a number of molecularly different aspects of the response. There are at least five senses in which a response is commonly called "slow": a gradual but continuous motion, e.g. to move one's arm slowly; a delayed start, e.g. to answer a question slowly; many repetitions of various parts of the response, e.g. to eat slowly; a spacing of the various parts of the response, e.g. to talk slowly; and a prolongation due to interfering activities, e.g. to dress slowly. All these examples have in common the notion of a long time elapse before the response is completed; they differ in how the time is consumed.

In the remainder of this book, "speed" will refer to the time taken to complete a response with no distinctions made between the various ways this time was spent. The same score may be assigned to responses which are topographically quite different. We will say that the rat ran slowly if he took a long time to get to the end of the alley even though, in another sense, he may have run rapidly back and forth before getting to the end.

When generalizing on the results of our studies, it is assumed that the principles governing behavior under conditions of correlated reinforcement are the same for all quantitative aspects of the response. Only to the extent that this hypothesis is true can the data on the rat's adjustment to conditions in which he has to take time in the alley (i.e. to run slowly) be used to make interesting statements about other skills. There are no data that disprove this hypothesis; indeed, the internal consistency of our data lend support to it. However, it remains an assumption requiring more varied testing.

The rewards for most human behavior are of the correlated type: it is typically not only what one does but how one does it that matters. This is most obvious in those activities we commonly call skills. For example, the skilled pianist must not only strike the right keys in the right order but must do so with the proper force and speed. The golfer must swing with just that force which hits the ball the right distance. Furthermore, the bulk of day-to-day behavior is performed under conditions of correlated reinforcement. We learn how hard to press the pencil against the paper, the razor against the skin, the foot against the brake pedal. We learn how rapidly to talk, to dance, to swat flies. We learn how vigorously to assert our opinions, how eagerly to raise a bet in poker, how quietly to retire after staying out late. As a matter of fact, it is difficult to think of instances in which reward is not somehow correlated with the way the response is made.

Such conditions provide the most obvious application of the principle that the organism will maximize reward while minimizing effort. Generally, we have found that the rat will run fast if he can get more reward by doing so or will run slowly if he has to in order to get reward. There are, however, a number of qualifications which must be considered.

Attention must be given not only to how much reward the rat can get by responding a particular way but also to how quickly he can get it. Suppose, for example, that a rat is given more food when he runs slowly, but that he can get some reward sooner by running fast. He may prefer to get the smaller reward quickly than to wait for the larger one, and which he chooses depends systematically on how much more he can get by running slowly and how much longer he has to wait for it.

The optimal behavior must occur sufficiently often if it is to be learned. For example, conditions in which the rat gets reward only if he runs fast will not succeed if used from the beginning of training simply because there are no provisions to get him to try running fast so that he can learn that he will be rewarded. Some conditions are such that, if the rat is performing at an inefficient level, the consequences tend to drive him in the right direction. For example, if the rat is rewarded only when he runs slowly, then if he runs fast he will not be rewarded and will tend to slow down. If this self-correcting feature is not inherent in the condition, then performance must be shaped to the desired level by the use of graded criteria. Here, the rat is rewarded if he does well for his present performance level; as this reward draws his performance in the desired direction, the criterion is changed so that he must improve still further.

The use of graded criteria is familiar to all parents and teachers. The question arises whether performance is better if the criterion is kept fairly low so that the subject will receive reward frequently, or if it is held well ahead of the subject's average performance so that he will succeed only occasionally. Our evidence on this problem is still very sketchy, but it suggests that high and difficult standards are more likely to elicit outstanding performance from rats.

Learning to respond properly depends upon the correct response being clearly distinguishable by the subject from incorrect responses. This, in turn, is affected by the distinctiveness of the feedback cues. If the organism is to attain the optimal level of performance, the stimuli produced by the optimal response must be different from those produced by other responses. Presumably different organisms, and different muscle systems within the same organism, may differ in the ease of, and the capacity for, such learning. We may assume that performance will be improved if distinctive external cues are added to tell the organism whether or not he is responding optimally.

If the feedback cues are not highly distinctive and only an imperfect response discrimination can be formed, then performance will vary from trial to trial among the similar responses. The principle of maximization of reward is therefore better stated in terms of average reward, although the psychological average may not correspond to any conventional measure of central tendency such as the mean. The implication of this can best be shown by an example: Suppose a rat is rewarded only if he takes 5 seconds or more in the alley. His average time will, in fact, be somewhat greater than 5 seconds (actually about 5.4 seconds), but with a variance such that he runs too fast on 20 to 25 percent of the trials. Why doesn't he achieve 100 percent reinforcement?

To answer this, we must observe that the proprioceptive feedback cues of his speed of running are not sufficiently distinctive to eliminate variability in performance and, therefore, to achieve 100 percent reward he would have to average a response time of about 8 seconds to insure that he never took less than 5 seconds. While this would maximize amount of reward, it would not maximize how quickly he got it, on the average, since he would frequently take much longer than necessary. The rat, as it were, is willing to risk occasionally missing reward altogether in order to get it as soon as he can.

It might be noted that an organism that adjusts so well as to get reward 100 percent of the time in such a condition may be at a disadvantage if the over-all conditions of reinforcement change.

Thus, in the previous example, if the cutoff were removed and the rat could get food if he ran fast, or if the conditions were changed so that he would get more food if he ran fast, then a rat who was perfectly adjusted to the original conditions could get no experience that would permit readjustment. But this is a part of the general topic of changes in the conditions of reinforcement.

CHANGES IN THE CONDITIONS OF REINFORCEMENT

After initial training under any of the previously discussed conditions of reinforcement—fixed, varied, or correlated—the conditions may be changed. The number of possible changes is even larger than the number of original conditions. The most frequently studied of these is experimental extinction, the switch from a condition involving some reward to constant nonreward. The effects of increasing and decreasing a constant amount or delay of reward have also been studied previously. Of course, several changes may be made at the same time, e.g. both the amount and delay of reward may be increased. And the conditions may be changed from one kind to another, e.g. a subject who has learned to run slowly under correlated reinforcement may now be given a constant reward regardless of his speed.

Changing conditions of reinforcement are certainly common in the natural environment. During childhood, there is a gradual shift from typically lenient conditions to relatively more demanding ones. Optimal behavior in earlier situations may not be optimal in new but similar situations. Throughout life old ways of responding must be abandoned in favor of new solutions.

There are three general questions of particular interest in this context. First, how does the ultimate stable performance level after a change to a particular condition compare with that shown by other subjects who have been trained only under that condition? Secondly, given such a statement of where the performance level is headed, how rapidly does it attain this level? Finally, we may also be interested in the path it traces on the way. Let us deal with each of these questions separately.

What is the stable performance level after a change in the conditions of reinforcement? Because there are so many possible changes, we can give only a tentative answer to this question. All the results in our laboratory and the bulk of prior work suggest that performance shifts to precisely the level maintained by subjects trained under that condition initially, *if* the new condition insures experience with the optimal performance. The principle, then, is the same in predicting performance after a change in the conditions of reinforcement as it is in predicting performance in original training. The subject starts at the performance level produced by the previous condition rather than at that of a naïve subject, but his performance will attain the new appropriate level unless the previous training prevents the subject from ever responding correctly.

If the new condition is constant reward, the change will be encountered unless the prior conditions have completely eliminated the response. Similarly, there is typically little problem with a change to varied reinforcement although, if the condition involves infrequent reward, the response may have to be shaped, as during initial training, to the stage where it will occur often enough to provide experience of the range of variation in the reward.

It is primarily with correlated reinforcement that we must be sure that the new conditions involve a change in the reinforcement actually encountered by the subject before predicting whether performance will shift. As long as the subject gets the accustomed reward while continuing to perform as usual his performance will not shift, even though some change in the reward conditions has been made outside his range of performance. One common example is the student whose early teachers tended to give better grades for long answers to essay questions; he may then persist in making long responses for later teachers who are less influenced by the sheer length of a reply. A college teacher may find that just giving good grades for short answers is not enough to change this behavior, but that he must also penalize discursive replies by reducing the grade given them.

How fast does performance shift after a change in the conditions of reinforcement? The principle which seems best to describe the resistance to change in reward is this: The shift is more rapid the greater the change in reward that the subject encounters. If there is no change in the rewards actually received, performance will shift at an infinitely slow rate, i.e. there will be no change at all. A few examples will make this principle clearer.

At the simplest level, suppose fixed reward is simply changed

in amount. The new and different reward will then be encountered on each trial and, to describe it informally, the subject can
tell immediately that the reward has been changed. Such changes
do, in fact, produce the fastest shifts in performance.

Suppose, however, that the reward was varied during original
training, say 50 percent large and 50 percent small. If the new condition is 100 percent small, the change is less severe than if the
original condition had been 100 percent large. It might be said
that the subject has been accustomed to getting a small reward.
The well-known effect of partial reinforcement on resistance to
extinction is a special case of this instance, where the small reward
is zero. Presumably this effect can also be seen in the other direction, i.e. partial reinforcement should lead to as slow an adjustment
to 100 percent reward as to 100 percent nonreward.

Even greater resistance to change may follow training with correlated reinforcement. For example, consider the rat who has first
learned to respond slowly in order to get reward and is then rewarded regardless of his speed. This change means only that the
few faster speeds which would originally have been nonreinforced
are now reinforced, and a very large number of trials is required
for performance to adjust to the new condition. Similarly, the conditions can be changed in the other direction so that a rat who has
first learned to respond slowly in order to get reward is not rewarded no matter how he responds. Performance also changes very
gradually in this case. It is as if a nonreinforcement is taken not
to mean that the environment has changed but that the response
was not made properly. And so the rat persists in trying to make
what is no longer an adaptive response.

The principles concerning resistance to change in reward may
pertain even when the over-all conditions of reinforcement remain
the same. Unless the reward is fixed, variations in reward occur
within the same condition. For example, there is no real difference
between the first ten trials of extinction and a sequence of ten nonreinforced trials in a condition of partial reinforcement. A response that is highly resistant to extinction is precisely one that
can be maintained with a low frequency of reinforcement. Or in
general, the more resistant the response is to changes in the conditions of reinforcement, the more stable it will be in the face of

fluctuations in the reward received while the over-all condition of reinforcement remains unchanged.

The fact that correlated reinforcement produces responses that are resistant to change is particularly relevant to understanding the persistence and stability of everyday behavior. The prevalence of correlated reinforcement in the natural environment would be expected to lead to just such a state of affairs. For example, a response such as aggression may be learned in childhood under correlated reinforcement, since the more vigorous the aggression, the more likely it is to succeed. Aggression may then persist as a stable personality trait even though it is subsequently rewarded only occasionally.

What is the path traced by performance after a change in the conditions of reinforcement? In addition to our concern with where the performance level is headed and how rapidly it is going to get there, we may also be interested in the course through which performance shifts after a change in reward. Some changes lead to a gradual and direct shift to the new appropriate level, but two other paths have also been observed.

The most well-known of these is the "overshoot," in which performance shifts more than is appropriate and then recovers to the appropriate level. This path seems particularly likely following a change to a smaller amount of constant reward.

Another unusual path has occasionally been found during extinction when performance, rather than beginning to decrease immediately, actually increases at first and then ultimately declines. This path is most likely following correlated reinforcement where no reward was given if the response was not performed properly. When the subject cannot get reward no matter how he performs, he may not only try again and again, as we have seen, but also try still harder. Thus, a rat that has learned that he gets the reward only if he runs fast will, during extinction, attempt to run even faster. And one who was required to run slowly for reward will run even more slowly early in extinction.

This tendency for performance first to shift away from the ultimate extinction level can be understood if we observe what the subject learned to do when he did not get rewarded during initial training. Since he learned that trying harder the next time did get rewarded, he will do this also during the early trials of extinction. It not only takes many trials to extinguish a response learned under correlated reinforcement but during these trials there is little or no decrement in performance. Typically, however, when performance does finally begin to extinguish, it does so quite rapidly: the subject either responds the way he learned he had to, be it fast or slow, or performs at the extinction level. The intermediate ways of responding, having been eliminated during training, do not occur during extinction. Perhaps this phenomenon is related to abrupt changes in human behavior, such as when a previously outspoken individual suddenly becomes mild and submissive.

Speculations on extremely efficient conditions of reinforcement

Using the principles presented here, let us now return to the problem of designing efficient conditions of reinforcement that will maximize the ratio of the performance to the reward. The most efficient conditions would combine varied and correlated reinforcement so that, first, the response must be performed correctly in order to have a chance of being rewarded and, secondly, even if performed correctly the response is rewarded only part of the time. Once an organism has been induced to perform under such conditions, extinction should be exceedingly slow (or the probability of reward can be reduced to near zero without materially affecting performance).

The condition can be extended a step further by deliberately building in the idea of the gambler's fallacy, by correlating the amount of reinforcement with the number of responses since the previous reward: the longer the persistence in the face of failure, the greater the eventual reward.

It is not hard to find analogous conditions in the everyday world. How many good shots does the weekend golfer require to keep him playing? For how long will the amateur fisherman persist without catching anything? Or, to look at it another way, how miserable it is to take on a hunting trip a person who has not yet been trained to the conditions of reinforcement and who therefore describes more objectively his loss of sleep, his discomfort, and his lack of success! However, given a few successes he may get hooked too. Find a man who thinks he knows something about horses but recognizes that, of course, the best horse doesn't always win the race, and there's a man who's hooked. To modify a familiar saying: "There's a sucker trained every minute."

One instructive illustration of the application of these principles is in the designing of a better slot machine. The element of skill could be added in a number of ways, but the most profitable would be to correlate the probability of payoff with the speed of playing. The machine can pay off more frequently and still earn more money if the rate of playing is increased. Furthermore, the size of the payoff can independently be correlated with persistence, i.e. the longer the run without payoff, the larger the eventual payoff. Optimal adjustment to these conditions is to play as fast as possible and to keep on playing in the face of mounting losses.

The assumption made in designing a slot machine is that the player and the owner are interested in different things: the former in the reward per play, the latter in income per hour. To illustrate this same idea mathematically, imagine the game of betting on the toss of a die. If the player gives the house $1 before each toss, and the house returns $5 if he is correct, the player should average a loss of $1 every six plays since he can expect to be right one-sixth of the time. Normally in such a game, a player who paid $2 would receive $10 for a correct call. If, however, the payoff were $10.50 on a $2 bet, the percentage payoff would be higher and the player might be induced to increase the size of his bet in order to obtain the more favorable odds. His loss, as a result, would be greater on an absolute basis, $1.50 rather than $1 every six plays. The important point is this: the principle of maximization of reward does not imply that the subject will behave in the most adaptive way under all conditions. Indeed, the principle can be used to select conditions in which the reward is correlated with performance in such a way that the subject should minimize reward (or maximize losses).

It seems possible that a few chance rewards, if taken as correlated with the way the response is performed, can also form the basis of magical and superstitious beliefs. It is certainly not argued that superstition and the examples of complex human behavior that have been mentioned can be understood solely in terms of the conditions of reinforcement under which they are performed. It is held, however, that the complexities look somewhat less formidable when the principles described here are taken into account.

PUNISHMENT

Once suggested, it will be obvious that all the kinds of conditions we have studied with positive reward can also be used with punishment. Thus, punishment can be fixed, either severe or mild, immediate or delayed. The punishment may be varied from trial to trial in several ways, including partial punishment, varied amount of punishment, etc. The punishment can be correlated with performance according to some terms function so that the amount or likelihood of punishment depends upon the way the response is made. Also reward conditions and punishment conditions can be combined in any way.

Punishment can be conceived of as producing negative incentive. Rats run more slowly if they are given an electric shock in addition to food at the end of the alley. They appear to minimize punishment when it is correlated with speed in much the same way that they maximize reward. For example, if a hungry rat running down the alley for food is shocked when he runs fast, he will learn to run slowly.

There are two other ways in which punishment affects performance. The punishment, as a stimulus, typically evokes some response that will, through the principle of anticipatory responding, in later trials tend to occur before the punishment. An electric shock at the end of the alley produces a reflexive withdrawal that subsequently appears in the rat's hesitant approach to the food cup. In addition, punishment may serve as a cue to enhance the learning of the preceding response. For example, we find that, contrary to common-sense expectation, if a rat is required to run fast in order to get reward and is shocked whenever he does run fast, he may develop a higher and more persistent level of performance than if no punishment is involved.

The over-all effect of punishment on performance represents a combination of the negative incentive value with the stimulus and cue values. If these act in opposite directions the combined effect may not be predictable. Consider the effect of spanking a boy to teach him not to cry when he gets hurt. As negative incentive, the spanking should weaken the tendency to cry; as a stimulus, the spanking should enhance the tendency to cry because it evokes more crying; and as a cue, the spanking may be followed by an unusual display of affection and hence acquire reward value. The magnitude of these separate effects would have to be estimated in order to predict the outcome of the punishment procedure in such a case.

In presenting a general picture of the present research program, the nature of the problem, and the types of results obtained, it has been necessary to anticipate some of the conclusions these results suggest. It is hoped that this introduction will facilitate tracing the logic of the research program through the variety of experiments to be reported.

It should be re-emphasized that the principles have been stated very loosely and informally. From the foregoing discussion it might appear that the rat consciously attends to the conditions of reinforcement, figures them out, and behaves accordingly. While people may sometimes do this, it is very unlikely that rats do. A more formal and rigorous formulation of the theoretical mechanisms underlying such learning is necessary in order to predict, objectively and correctly, the extent to which performance will match the intuitively optimal level.

The current version of the micromolar theory is presented in Chapter 5. One aspect of this approach, the definition of the response, is discussed somewhat more extensively in Chapter 6. A major alternative to the micromolar theory, the equilibrium model for correlated reinforcement, is developed in Chapter 7.

Six data chapters follow the description in Chapter 2 of the general methods and procedures of the researches. Four report the effects of the various reward conditions: Chapter 3 deals with constant reinforcement, Chapter 4 with varied reinforcement, Chapter 8 with correlated reinforcement, and Chapter 9 with changes in the conditions of reinforcement. Chapter 10 reports the relatively small amount of data on the effects of punishment. Chapter 11 describes the free behavior situation, in which rats living in a box had to work for whatever water they received by pressing a bar. Correlated reinforcement gives the rat control over the amount of reward he obtains on any particular trial, and the free behavior situation gives the rat control over the amount of reward he accumulates over the day.

Because this book reports the present status of an ongoing research program rather than a finished project, some of the problems for future research are indicated in Chapter 12. It will be apparent throughout that the work to be done far exceeds the amount already done. Nevertheless, the results now are sufficient to provide a reasonably extensive picture of the effects of the various conditions of reinforcement and to provide enough tests of the theoretical approach to suggest its potential usefulness.

CHAPTER 2

Method

IN MOST of our studies we used the same apparatus and followed similar general procedures. Those aspects of the method which apply, by and large, to all studies are described in this chapter. More specific details of design and procedure are given briefly where the data are presented, and a complete summary has been collected in the Appendix.

A number of modifications were made during the first several years of the research to provide greater apparatus flexibility, to promote experimenter convenience and reliability, or to eliminate counterbalancing some variables that had been found to be relatively trivial. The method is described here, as finally evolved, except that changes are noted that might reasonably be expected to be important in interpreting the data.

LABORATORY

The main laboratory was a windowless, air-conditioned room with a hung acoustical-tile ceiling and double door that effectively muffled most sounds from the corridor and nearby rooms. The laboratory was not maintained on a regulated light/dark cycle, the prevailing level of illumination being complete darkness. When rats were being run the room was dimly lighted from seventeen shielded 7-watt bulbs (run on 50 percent voltage) on the clocks and data table, indirectly from five shielded 7-watt bulbs inside the apparatus, and from a bank of six red 7-watt bulbs on a portable stand. An overhead light was on only when an experimenter was preparing (or repairing) the apparatus or servicing cages.

The blower unit of the air conditioner ran continuously and the standard setting of the thermostat was 80° F. Because the thermostat was set below 60° F. when rats were being run to insure a constant sound from the compressor as a masking noise, the temperature dropped several degrees during the run. However, the change was small because heat was generated by the apparatus, and no systematic effect was noted.

The free behavior and activity studies were run in an adjacent laboratory which was served by the same air-conditioner and maintained at approximately the same temperature. It was also used when there was not enough room in the main laboratory to house all the rats being run at any particular time.

SUBJECTS

The subjects were hooded and albino male rats ranging from 90 to 150 days of age when brought to the laboratory. They were obtained from several commercial sources. Within any particular study, rats were assigned randomly to the various conditions except that, when several shipments were used in the same design, rats from different shipments were counterbalanced among conditions.

Rats were housed in individual cages with water freely available at all times. As noted above, most of the rats were housed in the main laboratory.

APPARATUS

The floor plan of the apparatus is shown in Fig. 1. In most of the studies one alley was blocked off so that the apparatus was functionally a single alley, i.e. any individual rat ran in only the white or the black alley. Each alley was 4″ wide and 4″ high.

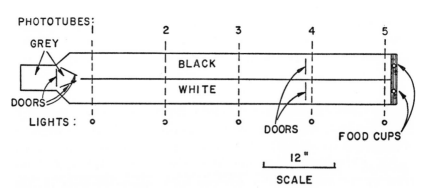

Figure 1. Floor plan of the double alley maze.

The sides were lined with glass to provide a continuous surface, and the top and bottom were of ½″ hardware cloth.

The apparatus was suspended inside a box, five sides of which were Celotex. The top was hinged and constructed of glass covered with one-way vision cellophane. The inside of the Celotex box was painted median grey. A pan of sawdust was 12″ below the floor of the alley. In addition to the five shielded 7-watt bulbs (white light) that activated the phototubes, a red 7-watt bulb was mounted 8″ centrally above the food cups.

A delay-box unit was on a table near the apparatus. There were two main divisions of this unit, one used preceding and the other following a rat's trial in the alley. Each of these main divisions had two 9″ x 18″ compartments, so that a rat could be put into one compartment at the same time that the previous rat was taken out of the other. The unit was 4″ high with a ½″ hardware-cloth floor and top and was painted median grey throughout.

Response measures. The rat's speed of running was timed automatically on Standard Electric timers controlled by a microswitch under the start door and by the succession of phototubes. Seven measures of performance will be referred to by letters. Five are independent of each other: starting time (S) between opening the start door and breaking the first photobeam, and running time separately over the four successive feet of the alley between the photobeams ($A, B, C,$ and D). The two aggregate measures are running time (R) cumulated over the four feet between the first and last photobeams, and response interval time (I) between opening the start door and breaking the last photobeam. The phototubes were wired with holding circuits so that, once a clock was stopped, it was not reactivated during that trial. Therefore, if a rat stopped and/or retraced, time continued to accumulate on the clock for the segment from which the rat retraced until it ultimately broke the succeeding photobeam.

Each of these times was taken on a separate clock and the aggregate times could be used to check the accuracy of the readings. Each time score was converted to its simple reciprocal as a measure of response speed, and all data will be presented as arithmetic means of these speeds. In the later experiments, reciprocals were read by the experimenter directly from extended faces on the clocks which contained the reciprocals in concentric circles.

The reaction time of the phototube units was dependent on the setting of a potentiometer controlling the bias across the tube. Variations in this adjustment, as well as aging of the lights and phototubes themselves, would affect the readings since a "slow" tube would slightly increase the time for the preceding segment and correspondingly reduce the time for the succeeding segment. A master circuit to permit adjustment of these settings was available, but it was impracticable for daily use. These settings could make an appreciable difference for the middle segments of the alley, where very short times (.1 to .2 seconds) were frequently observed, and quantitative comparisons using them must be restricted to groups being run concurrently. The longer, aggregate times are relatively free of this source of variance.

Reward mechanism. The food pellets used as reward were prepared by the P. J. Noyes Co., Lancaster, New Hampshire. They were cylindrical in shape and weighed 42–43 mg. The pellets were of uniform size, and the amount of reward was varied by varying the number of pellets given on a trial. The appropriate number of pellets were loaded into the reward mechanism by the experimenter and dropped automatically into the food cup at the end of the alley. The food release was accompanied by the distinctly audible click of a bell solenoid (see Bugelski, 1938).

The delivery of the food could be timed from the opening of the start door or from the breaking of any of the 5 phototube beams by means of a programming circuit containing Hunter timers. In addition, a cutoff time could be selected so that reward was delayed (or withheld altogether) if the rat ran faster (or slower) than the designated speed. The relay of the last phototube was wired in series with the reward mechanism so that, under all conditions, the food could not be delivered until the last beam was broken. This was done to prevent the rats from learning, under some conditions, to wait in the alley until the mechanism clicked.

The pellets had to fall approximately 8″ through a tube to reach the food cup. The time of release of the food will be referred to as the time of reward, although there was a slight minimal delay before the pellets reached the cup. Since the rat had to complete the inch of the alley after the last photobeam and get in position for the food, this minimal delay was virtually zero.

Both alleys were equipped with comparable feeding mechanisms. A selector switch determined which mechanism was activated on any trial.

Shock mechanism. A grid floor could be inserted in the last foot of the black alley. The grids were of $\frac{1}{16}''$ diameter stainless steel wire and were spaced $\frac{1}{4}''$ apart so that each paw singly would complete the electric circuit. The shock was provided by 100 VAC transformed to 450 volts and then stepped down by a potentiometer to the voltage level desired. A 150K-ohm resistance was wired in series with the rat.

A condensor-discharge timing circuit controlled the duration of the shock. It was administered when the rat broke the last photobeam in the alley. The occurrence of the shock could be determined by the experimenter, or a cutoff speed could be designated so that the occurrence of the shock depended upon the rat's speed.

Taming and Establishment of Hunger Rhythm

Upon arrival from the breeder, rats were housed in group cages in the main colony room until needed, for as long as 30 days, during which time both food and water were freely available. When brought to the laboratory the rats continued on ad libitum food and water for 2 to 4 days, after which the food was removed and a 24-hour feeding schedule begun.

For the next 5 days each animal was removed from its home cage, placed in the first delay box for about a minute, placed in the second delay box for another minute, and then returned to its home cage where the day's ration of food was available. This ration had been put in a glass caster and was composed primarily of Purina laboratory chow supplemented by 3 to 20 reward pellets as needed to balance the scale on which the food was weighed. During the preliminary taming period, a somewhat larger number of reward pellets was given in order to increase the experience of eating them. Subsequently, extra pellets were added to the day's ration to counterbalance, within a single experiment, any differences in amount of reward given in the alley.

Thus, by the time of its first trial in the alley, each rat had been shuttled between the delay boxes 5 times, had been on a 24-hour deprivation cycle for 5 days, and had been accustomed to eating the reward pellets. No other special taming or pretraining procedures were used.

EARLY TRIALS IN THE ALLEY

The first few trials in the alley differed from the later trials in two ways. First, the designated reward conditions were typically not instituted until the third or fourth trial, the reward being placed in the food cup and available immediately. This was done to avoid adding the noises of the feeding system to an already fear-inducing situation. In some of the early studies the pellets were moistened for these trials to increase odor cues.

The second way in which early trials differed from the later ones was the schedule. In order not to disrupt the hunger rhythm or to interfere with other studies in progress on the alley, the full schedule could not be run on the early trials. A typical procedure for 24 rats scheduled to run 1 trial a day was to run 8 rats on each of the first 3 days, 12 on the next 2 days, and only then (each rat's third trial) the full 24. Rats running more than one trial a day followed a similar procedure and were then promoted in stages to the designated number of trials a day.

RUNNING PROCEDURE

The procedure for each rat involved three stages: Detention in the first delay box, the trial in the alley, and detention in the second delay box. While the duration of these was fairly constant from trial to trial, some variation occurred. The schedule followed the following pattern: rat #1 placed in delay box #1; rat #2 placed in delay box #1, rat #1 removed, run in the alley, and placed in delay box #2; rat #3 placed in delay box #1, rat #2 removed, run in the alley, and placed in delay box #2, rat #1 removed and returned to its home cage; and so on. Each rat was fed its daily ration after two other rats had run the alley.

Rats running more than one trial a day were shuttled between delay box #2 and the alley until they had completed their scheduled trials, after which the next rat was brought into the above sequence. Such a procedure therefore gave a longer period of detention in delay box #1 for rats running several trials a day than for those running only one trial a day.

Between trials the experimenter read and reset the clocks, reset the apparatus, and weighed the rat's food ration. If all the clocks were being read, the total procedure took 2 to 3 minutes per rat if one trial a day was given, and another 1 to 1½ minutes per additional trial a day. It took approximately 30 seconds less per trial if only 1 or 2 clocks were read.

The rat was placed in the start box and the one-way vision glass door of the Celotex box was closed. The start door was raised manually when the rat was facing it. (A counterweight was used to guide the speed of opening the door, but some variation within and between experimenters in this act undoubtedly occurred.) The two guillotine doors in the alley could be used to prevent retracing. The rat was typically removed from the alley immediately upon finishing its reward pellets although a small reward (up to 4 pellets) could be consumed in less than the 3 to 5 seconds required by the experimenter to get to the goal end and open the doors.

In order to keep on schedule, the experimenter could gently shove a rat that refused to run, or remove a rat that did not complete the alley during extinction. The rat was allowed up to 5 minutes in each segment of the alley, and even then was not disturbed if it was actively responding in any way (i.e. not lying immobile). Because of the leniency of this criterion, it was very rarely invoked.

During extinction, and on nonreinforced trials during acquisition, the rat was typically removed 3 to 5 seconds after breaking the last photobeam. The feeding mechanism did not click on such trials.

Many of the studies were run by several experimenters according to a regular weekly schedule. All of the experimenters followed the same general procedures as described here or as noted in the Appendix.

Missing Data

When a rat died during the course of the experiments the data obtained before its death were typically discarded in preparing the report of the results. For statistical tests that required proportional N's, the mean of the available scores was used as a fake score without increasing the number of degrees of freedom.

Another source of missing data arose within a rat's record. The apparatus might have failed, the experimenter might have neglected to read or reset the clocks, the rat might have been turned or turning around when the start door was opened, unusual noises might have penetrated the laboratory, the home cage water bottle might have been empty, etc. The available information on that and adjacent trials was used to estimate these missing scores.

NOTE: ON A COMPARISON BETWEEN THE WHITE
      AND BLACK ALLEYS

The apparatus had two alleys but, for most of the research, any individual rat ran in only one of them. The alleys were closely similar except that one was painted black and the other white. Because of the familiar brightness preference among rats for black and the possibility of a stimulus intensity dynamism effect, one may ask whether the data were quantitatively affected by the brightness of the alley.

Most of the early studies in the apparatus were run with half of the rats in each condition running in one alley and the other half in the other. Performance curves aggregated across reward conditions in Expers. 54A, 54B, 55D, 55E, 56D, and 56E are shown in Fig. 2.

Sizable differences do indeed appear, with rats starting somewhat faster into the black alley but running somewhat faster in the white alley. These differences are reliable because of the large number of subjects involved.

However, within any single study, the effects of alley brightness are small in comparison with the effects of reward conditions, and there is no apparent tendency for reward to interact with alley. An analysis of Exper. 55D justifying these contentions is given in Table 1.

Alley brightness will not be attended to further in the subse-

Table 1. Results of an analysis of variance of Exper. 55D broken down to test the statistical significance of the effect of alley brightness.

Source	d.f.	m.s.	F
Reward conditions	11	.1193	5.52 **
Alley brightness	1	.0277	1.28
Conditions x alley	11	.0230	1.06
Error	84	.0216	

NOTE: In all analysis of variance tables, a single asterisk is used to indicate significance at beyond the .05 level, and a double asterisk to indicate significance at beyond the .01 level.

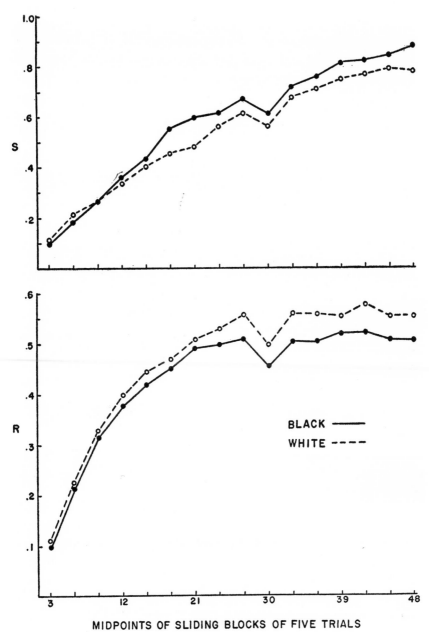

MIDPOINTS OF SLIDING BLOCKS OF FIVE TRIALS

Figure 2. Starting and running speeds aggregated across reward conditions to show speed in the white and black alleys separately. (Expers. 54A, 54B, 55D, 55E, 56D, and 56E)

quent chapters, but it should be borne in mind when making quantitative comparisons between experiments. A record of the alleys used in the various experiments is included in the Appendix.

NOTE: ON A COMPARISON BETWEEN HOODED AND
   ALBINO RATS

Some of the experiments were run using hooded rats and others using albinos. One may ask, therefore, whether there are differences between these two types of rats that should be considered in interpreting the various results. Many experimenters reported their observation that the hooded rats are more fearful and are tamed less quickly and fully.

Several experiments included both hooded and albino subjects, although the hooded rats were typically fed a smaller quantity of food. The above-mentioned anecdotal evidence is supported by the performance of the two types of rats during the early trials in the alley. The upper graphs of Fig. 3 show the relative performance, aggregated across reward conditions, of the hooded and albino rats in Exper. 56C. It will be seen that the albinos were somewhat faster on the first trial and became even more so during the early trials.

The lower graphs of Fig. 3 show the asymptotic speeds of the hoods and albinos as a function of delay of reward as obtained in Expers. 55D and 56C. The functions are closely comparable. A difference was found at short delays (at 1 sec. delay, $t = 2.33$, d.f. $= 20$, $p < .05$), but since these points appear to be out of line with their functions, the difference is interpreted as being due to sampling fluctuations.

These findings support the belief that, while there are differences between hooded and albino rats in their initial reaction to being handled and run in the alley, their ultimate performance levels are very similar. There has been no indication that different principles apply to the behavior of the two types of rats, and the distinction will generally be ignored.

NOTE: ON THE ROLE OF FEAR IN THE ALLEY

The performance curves to be presented include the extinction of fear in addition to the learning of the running response. The belief that fear is involved is based on the observation that, early

in training, the rats crouch and preen, stretch cautiously forward
and withdraw, and frequently defecate. Futhermore, notwithstanding their state of hunger and their familiarity with the reward pellets, the rats take several minutes (not infrequently 10 to 15 minutes) to start eating the first time they are in the goal box.

Fear can directly affect the performance curve because of the
time consumed by the fear-induced behavior. In addition, if fear
interferes with the immediate eating of the food, the reward may
be so long delayed that it would be expected to have relatively little direct effect on the running response.

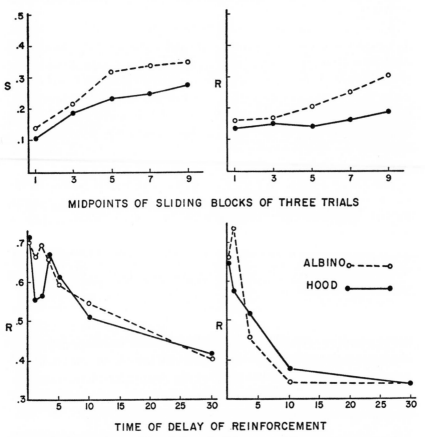

Figure 3. Comparison of hooded and albino rats. The upper graphs show
starting and running speeds during the first ten trials in the alley aggregated
across reward conditions. The lower graphs show terminal running speed as
a function of time of delay of reinforcement. (Expers. 55D and 56C)

In an experiment by Bower (1959), the conventional pretraining procedures were supplemented in two ways: (1) rats were allowed to roam the maze without reward before training was begun and (2) they were then placed directly in the goal box, which contained reward pellets. These experiences would be expected at least partially to extinguish the fear evoked by the apparatus and to train the rats to eat in the goal box (see Karn and Porter, 1946). The effect should be to increase speed initially and to permit the reward to show an effect sooner.

The performance over the early trials by the group receiving this special treatment is shown in Fig. 4, along with a group that

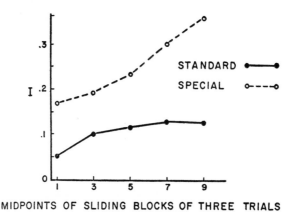

MIDPOINTS OF SLIDING BLOCKS OF THREE TRIALS

Figure 4. Performance during the first ten complete trials of a group run by Bower (1959) that was given preliminary adaptation training in the alley and with the feeding mechanism, compared with performance of a group given the standard pretraining procedure. (Exper. 57D)

had received the conventional pretraining and was running under comparable conditions. The expected differences clearly occurred.

One could argue that the pretraining procedures used by Bower would provide "latent learning." The difference shown in Fig. 4 could therefore be attributed to learning to run the alley (or learning a field map of the alley) rather than to the extinction of fear and the training to eat. These accounts are not incompatible and both may well be involved. If so, then the present data provide an indication of latent learning in a straight alley (see also Barry and

Logan, 1957). Conversely, however, one might also note the possible relevance of the account proposed here to some conventional latent learning studies (e.g. Blodgett, 1929; and Tolman and Honzik, 1930).

NOTE: ON EXPERIMENTER DIFFERENCES

In an experimental setting like the one used in the present research, there is considerable interaction between the subject and the experimenter. An experimenter's technique of handling rats may produce effects that appear in the obtained data. Specifically, for example, rats that are handled by an "affectionate" experimenter might be considerably less emotional than ones handled by a "nervous" experimenter. Since the rat must run shortly after being handled and is running into a goal box from which it must ultimately be removed, this difference in emotionality might readily appear in performance.

Furthermore, the procedures used in the present research permit slight differences in the time the rat spends in the start box before the door is opened, the rat's degree of orientation toward the door, and the speed with which the door is opened. Any of these could have a direct effect upon performance.

This problem is of concern when quantitative comparisons are made between experiments run by different experimenters. The available data do not permit evaluating this possibility, and such comparisons must therefore be made with caution.

Data are available concerning possible experimenter differences within the same experiment. Many of the studies were run by several experimenters—not with different experimenters running a part of the animals all of the time, but with different experimenters running all of the animals a part of the time. One can ask, therefore, whether some of the day-to-day variability in performance can be attributed to consistent differences among experimenters.

The data from Exper. 56C were selected for this comparison since they were collected by four experimenters who differed appreciably in their techniques with the rats. Asymptotic R-speed for the groups running at 0 seconds and 30 seconds delay were separated according to experimenter, and the results are tabulated in Table 2. It can be seen that the differences among the experimenters were small relative to the effects of reward.

Accordingly, the subsequent data have been averaged over trials without regard to which experimenter was running the rats on those trials. However, since the homogeneity obtained may have resulted from effects on the rats which generalized among the experimenters, no conclusion can be drawn concerning experimenter differences that might appear between different experiments.

Table 2. Mean terminal R-speed with immediate and delayed reward, separated to show the results obtained by each experimenter. (Exper. 56C)

Experimenter	0″ delay	30″ delay
FL	.67	.32
EB	.63	.31
HB	.69	.33
RW	.65	.34

NOTE: ON THE INCENTIVE VALUE OF THE REWARD PELLETS

The prepared pellets used as reward in the alley are a preferred food. When the daily ration was placed in the cages, the rats invariably ate the few pellets in the cup before eating the Purina checkers. This preference could result from the size, texture, and/or sweetness of the pellets.

Rats were not routinely satiated on these pellets, the major portion of their diet being Purina checkers. Some indication that the pellets may also be relevant to a specific hunger was obtained by Barry (1958). In a preliminary study, two groups were run that differed in hours of deprivation but had not been satiated on the reward pellets as a part of their diet. Barry's major experiment differed mainly in that the subjects were satiated on the reward pellets before the scheduled deprivation began. (There was also a small change in hours of deprivation and in maintenance schedule.) The terminal R-speeds are shown in Table 3. It will be seen

Table 3. The effect of hours of deprivation on R-speed depending on whether the rats were or were not satiated on the reward pellets as a part of their daily ration. (Data from Barry, 1958)

	2–3 hours deprivation	26–27 hours deprivation
Not satiated	.584	.650
Satiated	.307	.459

that after satiation the rats ran slower, and that the differential effect of hours of deprivation was larger under these conditions.

Another aspect of the way amount of reward was manipulated in the present studies is that the number of pellets was increased in order to increase the amount of reward. A given weight of food may have different incentive value depending on the number of units in which it is given (see Wolfe and Kaplon, 1941). Data consistent with this possibility were obtained in a study started by Kover (Exper. 54C). Two groups of six rats each were run to the same weight of food reward. For one group this amount was given in one piece while the other group received the same amount in six pieces.

At the end of 70 trials, the 6-pellet group was running slightly but not reliably faster than the 1-pellet group. The reward conditions were then reversed and performance reversed accordingly so that, after 24 additional trials, the current 6-pellet group was significantly faster than the 1-pellet group (.623 vs. .489, t = 2.532, d.f. = 10, p < .05). Accordingly, the incentive value of the reward probably was greater than it would have been if the rats had been routinely satiated on the pellets and if the number of units had been held constant.

Note: On Changes in Drive during Performance

Many of the performance curves that will be presented in the later chapters show an initial rise to a fairly high level and then a gradual and prolonged drift toward still higher speeds. The most obvious interpretation of the latter rise is continued learning to run in the alley and/or further development of incentive based on the reward received in the goal box. There is evidence, however, that such a gain might result, at least in part, from a gradual increase in drive level, since rats apparently adapt slowly to the type of deprivation cycle used in these experiments (see Reid and Finger, 1955).

This finding was replicated as a part of Exper. 58A. Five rats were permitted ad libitum food and water while living in standard individual activity wheels, and daily records were kept of food and water intake as well as weight and activity. They were then placed on the deprivation cycle (12 grams given at the same time each day) used in the alley research. The effects of this procedure on the other three measures are shown in Fig. 5.

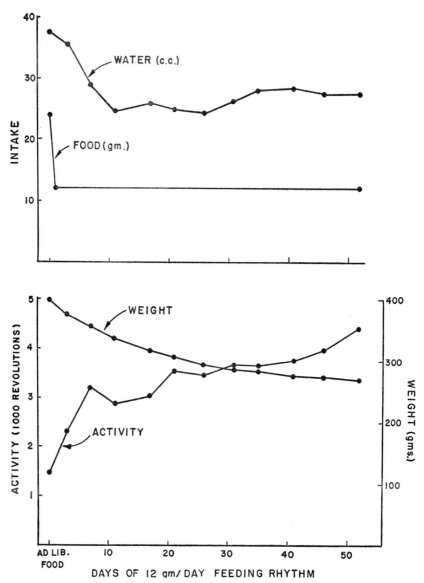

Figure 5. The effect on water intake, weight, and activity of the change from ad libitum food to a 24-hour food deprivation cycle. (Exper. 58A)

It will be seen that water intake decreased fairly gradually but had attained a reasonably stable level within 10 to 12 days. However, weight continued to decline and activity to increase over the entire span of 52 days of observation. Accordingly, if the latter measures are interpreted as indicative of the prevailing level of drive (see Finger, Reid, and Weasner, 1957), then the 5-day preliminary adaptation to the feeding rhythm given during the alley research was not sufficient to establish a stable hunger cycle. Some of the observed increases in performance could therefore reasonably be attributed to this fact.

NOTE: ON THE PROBLEM OF ERROR VARIANCE IN RUNNING SPEED

In attempting to determine the functions relating average running speed to the various conditions of reinforcement, we confront two major sources of error variance. One of these is the day-to-day fluctuation in performance found within an individual rat. The other concerns individual differences in running speed among rats ostensibly under the same experimental conditions.

The first of these presents the lesser problem. It is easier to run a few additional trials to get a better estimation of an individual rat's average speed than to run additional rats to get a better estimation of the average effect of a condition. Furthermore, the procedures and apparatus permit enough control over the stimulus and antecedent conditions so that reasonably stable within-rat levels of performance were typically obtained.

The procedures used, however, do not minimize between-subject variance. Although an experiment may show a statistically significant difference between two reward conditions, it is by no means uncommon for the range of speeds within a condition to exceed the maximum treatment differences obtained.

Both sources of variance can be virtually eliminated under certain reward conditions. For example, if the reward is maximal within a narrow but easily attainable band of performance, then all rats on all trials will zero in on this level. But this, of course, does not provide a general solution to the problem.

One approach to reducing between-subject variance would be to use highly inbred subjects. Subjects that were genetically almost identical might be expected to respond almost identically to a selected set of conditions. As a preliminary exploration of this approach, Exper. 57E was run using six mice from a highly inbred strain. Except for the insertion of a ¼″ hardware-cloth floor which raised the mice so that they would break the photobeams, the procedures were as closely comparable to those used with the rats as possible.

The results with the mice were as variable as those typically obtained with rats. Consistent individual differences in running speed appeared which, while absolutely somewhat smaller, were

Table 4. The various scores obtained from rats living in activity wheels first with ad libitum food and then under food deprivation conditions, and after training in the alley first without reward and then with 8-pellet reward. (Exper. 58A)

			Rat #1	*Rat #2*	*Rat #3*	*Rat #4*	*Average*
After 60-day ad lib. food		Food intake	21.1	21.6	28.4	22.1	23.4
		Water intake	34.9	34.7	43.7	33.3	36.7
		Weight	374.4	320.4	494.4	368.7	389.5
		Activity	659	5613	110	292	1668
After 52-day food deprivation cycle		Food intake	12.0	12.0	12.0	12.0	12.0
		Water intake	31.0	34.2	24.1	25.5	28.7
		Weight	256.9	175.6	320.0	280.5	258.3
		Activity	4475	10710	2176	597	4489
After 32 trials without reward		S	.52	.30	.14	.92	.47
		A	.36	1.10	1.66	.60	.93
		B	2.72	1.66	2.46	1.10	1.99
		C	1.15	.85	1.75	.67	1.11
		D	.40	.94	.84	.52	.67
		R	.072	.266	.338	.150	.207
		I	.054	.106	.092	.122	.093
After 32 trials 8-pellet reward		S	1.59	1.05	1.40	1.62	1.41
		A	2.54	1.52	2.16	1.64	1.97
		B	3.88	1.98	3.10	2.52	2.87
		C	2.86	1.76	2.44	1.92	2.25
		D	1.70	1.42	1.48	1.64	1.56
		R	.628	.416	.536	.464	.511
		I	.450	.298	.384	.362	.373
	Terminal weight		260.1	231.5	301.1	266.6	264.8

relatively as large as those found with rats because the mice typically took longer to run the alley.

Another approach to dealing with individual differences in running speed is to accept their existence and to partial them out statistically. If, before running an experiment, it could be determined which animals were relatively fast and which were relatively slow, then a treatment-by-levels design could be used in assigning rats to the various conditions. This would presumably reduce the error variance relevant to the treatment effects.

A search for such a covariant term was included as a part of Exper. 58A. Four rats first lived in individual activity wheels with ad libitum food and water, and weight and activity as well as food and water intake were recorded. These same observations were again made following 52 days of maintenance on a 12-gram deprivation schedule. The rats were then run 32 trials without reward in the alley, followed by 32 trials with an immediate 8-pellet reward. All the available speed measures were recorded for the last 5 trials without reward and similarly for the last 5 trials with reward; the data are presented in Table 4. There are no obvious and striking relationships between absolute or relative measures obtained in the activity wheels and performance in the alley.

Both of these approaches to controlling for individual differences in running speed deserve more detailed and systematic testing. The preliminary evidence presented here, however, is not very encouraging.

CHAPTER 3

Conditions of Constant Reinforcement

REINFORCING events vary in a number of dimensions, the two most familiar being the amount and delay of reward. That is, rewards may be large or small and they may be immediate or delayed. In conditions of constant reinforcement, the subject is given the same selected amount of reward at the same selected delay on every trial. The empirical question is: How is the rat's speed of running affected by the amount and delay of reward received at the end of the alley?

Fairly extensive data on this question are already available in the literature. The major purpose of the present studies was to provide control information for comparison with the effects of the more complex conditions of reinforcement to be dealt with in the later chapters.

The amount and delay of reward are not independent dimensions at the point of nonreinforcement, since a zero amount cannot be given at different delays. For that matter, they may not be completely independent at other values since larger amounts take longer to consume and hence involve longer within-reward delay. However, if delay is defined by the point in time when the reward is made available, then the amount and delay can be varied independently except at the point of nonreinforcement. Because of this, the nature of the interaction between them must be considered, i.e. is the detrimental effect of delaying the reward the same for large and small amounts? In analogous fashion, it is important to consider the interaction between reward and drive, i.e. is the difference between a large and small reward, or an immediate and delayed reward, the same for highly motivated subjects as for mildly motivated ones? Some data bearing on these interactions have been included in the present chapter.

PERFORMANCE WITHOUT REWARD

Hungry rats will run down an alley even if they are never given food (or other obvious reward) in the goal box. This is akin to the "operant level" observed in the bar-pressing situation (see e.g. Skinner, 1938, p. 66, and Schoenfeld et al., 1950) and provides a baseline against which the effects of the various conditions of re-

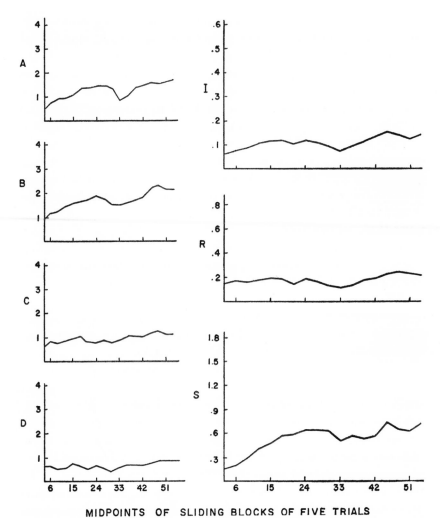

MIDPOINTS OF SLIDING BLOCKS OF FIVE TRIALS

Figure 6. Performance at one trial a day with a 30-second detention in the empty goal box without reward. (Exper. 56C)

inforcement can be evaluated. The performance of a group of rats run one trial a day without reward is shown in Fig. 6. The *I*-speed of this group showed a slight but distinct "learning" curve, the improvement from the first three to the last five trials being statistically significant (t = 2.28, d.f. = 9, p < .05). The greatest gain occurred in *S*-speed and in the early sections of the alley, while speed in the goal section (*D*-speed) showed little consistent change over trials.

The most promising interpretation of this phenomenon is that running is high in the initial hierarchy of responses to hunger and is also relevant to an "activity" need (see Hill, 1956). The increase in the speed of running is assumed to result from the extinction of the initial fear of the apparatus, a gradual increase in the drive level, and the reduction in the amount of time-consuming exploratory behavior.

As an alternative account, the experimenter's removing the rat from the alley could be assumed to be a reinforcing event (see Bernstein, 1957). Being handled may have acquired reward value, and involves removal from a fear-inducing situation and ultimate return to the home cage. This interpretation seems unlikely because there was so little increase in speed near the goal where this event occurred. Furthermore, if this analysis were correct, handling could be expected to have properties similar to those of other rewards, one of which is that the effectiveness of a reward is reduced the longer it is delayed.

As a test of this implication, Gonzalez (Exper. 58D) ran two groups without food reward. The rats in one group were removed immediately upon breaking the last photobeam in the alley (it required about 3 seconds to open the doors and get the rat); the rats in the other group were detained for 30 seconds in the empty goal section before being removed. The results are shown in Fig. 7.

There was very little difference in the performance of the two groups over the major portion of their trials. The small difference that did appear near the end of training was not statistically significant, and it was in the reverse direction from that expected by the hypothesis that nonrewarded rats run to the secondary reward of being picked up; the group for which this event was delayed ran faster than the group that was removed immediately.

The terminal performance of these groups was appreciably

above that shown in Fig. 6. One factor which may partially account for this difference is the size of the home cages in which the rats lived. The home cages used by Gonzalez were less than half the size of those used in Exper. 56C, and they very severely constricted the animals' movement. A study of the activity potential of the home cage is needed to determine the importance of this factor.

That some variables affect both speed of running without reward and running speed under conditions of reinforcement is indicated by the fact that the rats that run fastest without reward

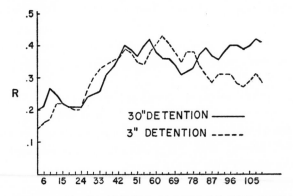

MIDPOINTS OF SLIDING BLOCKS OF FIVE TRIALS

Figure 7. Performance at one trial a day with 3-second or 30-second detention in the empty goal box without reward. (Exper. 58D)

tend also to run fastest with reward. The nonrewarded rats in Exper. 56C were shifted after the 57 trials shown in Fig. 6 to a condition of 12-pellet reward, and the correlation (product-moment r) between their speeds under the two conditions was .78.

One variable that affects running speed whether reward is given or not is the level of the hunger drive. In Exper. 54D, rats run without reward showed performance curves comparable to those already presented. After 91 trials under standard 24-hour deprivation conditions, the rats were given 9 test trials at 48-hour deprivation, 9 trials at 3-hour deprivation, and 9 additional trials at 24-hour deprivation. Performance under 48-hour deprivation showed no consistent difference from that under 24-hour deprivation, but both S-speed and R-speed were significantly reduced under the

3-hour deprivation condition (t = 4.14 and 4.73 for S-speed and R-speed respectively, d.f. = 5, p < .01 for both).

Another variable that almost certainly affects the level of performance without reward is the distribution of practice, although no studies have been directly aimed at showing its effect. All the studies referred to in this section were run one trial a day, and the rats never refused to run. Nor did they under conditions of extinction at one trial a day. However, rats that are extinguished with several massed trials a day typically run progressively slower on successive trials and, after two or three trials, may not complete the alley within a reasonable period of time. Presumably, comparable behavior would be observed in rats given several nonrewarded trials a day from the beginning of their experience with the alley.

By way of summary, these data suggest:

1. There is a baseline (operant) level of performance in the alley that is maintained without obvious reward. This level is above that observed on the first few trials in the alley.

2. Rats performing without reward run fairly quickly from the start box and through the early segments of the alley, but complete the later segments more slowly.

3. This baseline level of performance is directly related to the level of the hunger drive, is markedly reduced by additional massed trials, but is unaffected by the time of detention in the empty goal box each trial.

The phenomenon of stable performance without reward is not only interesting in its own right, but is important because it sets a lower limit on the range within which typical conditions of reward can show their differential effects. At the other extreme is a physiological limit at the maximum speed at which rats can run. Performance under the various conditions of constant reward is constrained to fall between the two limits.

DELAY OF REWARD

It is generally recognized that performance is inferior if the reward is delayed and that the nature of this function is such that the difference between, say, a 2-second and a 5-second delay is greater than that between a 12-second and a 15-second delay. Among the studies of this variable are those by Brown and Gentry (1948),

Logan (1952), and Perin (1943). The particular parameters of this function may vary considerably with a number of other factors.

For example, it is clear from the work of Brown et al. (1949) and Carlton (see Spence, 1956, pp. 160 ff.) that the effect of delaying the reward depends partly on what the subject does during the delay period. Specifically, if he has the opportunity to, and indeed does, make responses incompatible with the instrumental response itself during the time of delay, then the delay is more detrimental to instrumental performance than if he is constrained during the delay.

A special case of this factor is involved in the distinction between nonchaining delay (delay imposed at the end of a behavior chain) and chaining delay (delay imposed on the early links of a chain because the remaining links must be completed before the reward is received). An alley necessarily involves chaining delay since the primary reinforcement for running in the early sections of the alley is delayed at least for the time taken to run the rest of the alley. With a relatively homogeneous behavior chain, such as running in an alley, the detrimental effect of chaining delay would be expected to be less than that of an equal delay imposed at the end of the chain because the rat makes the same response during chaining delay (i.e. running) as the response for which the reward is delayed.

This section is concerned with nonchaining delay, i.e. with the time the rat is required to wait in the goal box before the reward is delivered. The factor most often emphasized as determining the effect of nonchaining delay is the amount of secondary reinforcement that is present in the situation (see Spence, 1947). Delayed reward is progressively more detrimental to performance as the presence of external cues that can provide secondary reinforcement are minimized (Grice, 1948; Perkins, 1947). Thus, performance suffers less from a delay imposed in a goal box into which the food is dropped than if the reward is given in a radically different situation from the delay situation.

Therefore, it is important to have data on the effect of the delay variable in the present apparatus using our standard procedure. The two most relevant aspects of this procedure were: (1) secondary reinforcement was high because the food cup was present during the delay, and (2) the length of time the rats stayed in the goal box was also different for groups receiving different delays in that each rat was removed as soon as it had consumed the reward.

Speed as a function of delay of reward. Two independent esti-

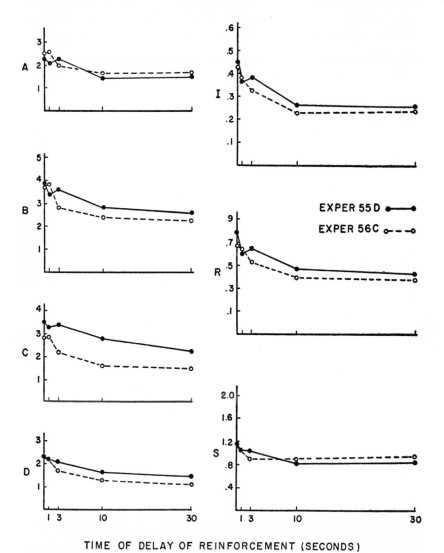

TIME OF DELAY OF REINFORCEMENT (SECONDS)

Figure 8. Performance as a function of the time of delay of reinforcement. (Expers. 55D and 56C)

mates of the function relating speed to delay of reward were obtained as parts of Expers. 55D and 56C. In Exper. 55D, seven groups of ten rats each had delays of 0, 1, 2, 3, 5, 10, or 30 seconds respectively; in Exper. 56C, five groups of twelve rats each had delays of 0, 1, 3, 10, or 30 seconds respectively. The other relevant major variables were the same for all groups in both experiments: standard 24-hour feeding cycle, 2-pellet reward, training at one trial a day.

Speed at the end of the 57 acquisition trials is shown as a function of delay of reward for both experiments in Fig. 8. At a gross descriptive level, the functions agree with each other and with the body of literature on the subject, since speed was found to be a concave upward, decreasing function of the time of delay of reward. There are, however, rather large quantitative discrepancies at the longer delays in the middle and end of the alley.

Several minor differences between the experiments could have contributed to these discrepancies. There were three experimenters in Exper. 55D and four in Exper. 56C, two of whom were common to both; the rats in Exper. 55D were run in rotated order while those in Exper. 56C were run in the same order each day; and the larger reciprocal-reading clocks, which added a slightly audible click as the rat passed each photobeam, were installed between the experiments.

Of perhaps greater importance is the possibility that the groups differed in the extent to which they had attained stable levels of performance. In Fig. 9, the learning curves for the combined 1, 3, and 30 second delay groups are plotted. It can be seen that some curves, particularly those for S-speed, were still rising even after 57 trials and that other curves, particularly those near the goal for the 30 second delay group, were showing a distinct decline during the later trials. On balance, then, the functions shown in Fig. 8 probably do not reflect asymptotic performance; the shorter delay groups might have gained from additional training, and the longer delay groups might have lost.

To establish statistically that a performance curve is nonmonotonic is difficult with a single group, because one would have to select, post hoc, the trials to be tested. As an alternative indication of the reliability of this phenomenon, the performance curves of all the groups in the various experiments for which the reward was long delayed are collected in Fig. 10. Nonmonotonicity is clearly the rule.

The available data do not permit confident systematic statements about this phenomenon. Detailed analysis of the data suggests that the decrease sets in earlier the longer the delay of reward, that it occurs first near the goal and tends to move back toward the

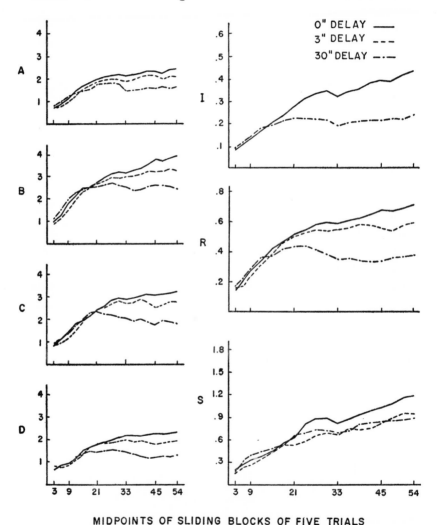

MIDPOINTS OF SLIDING BLOCKS OF FIVE TRIALS

Figure 9. Performance curves of groups receiving reward after 0-second, 3-second, or 30-second delay. (Expers. 55D and 56C)

start, and that delays as short as two or three seconds may show some of this effect. However, larger groups will have to be run for more trials to establish such propositions.

Without systematic data, there is little justification for making elaborate speculations to explain the finding. Theories (e.g. Spence, 1956, p. 153) that attribute the effects of delayed reward to incompatible responses during the delay period can attribute the decrease in speed to the growing strength of competing responses. Hull's theory (1943) can imply nonmonotonicity if one

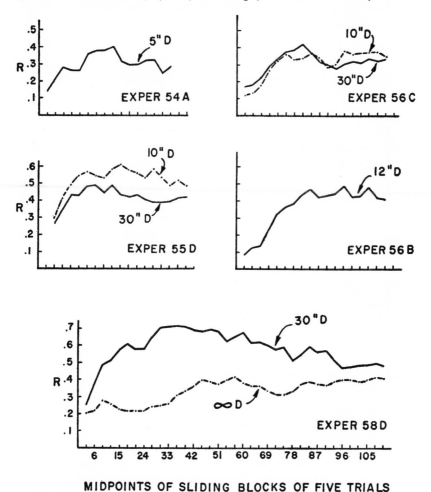

MIDPOINTS OF SLIDING BLOCKS OF FIVE TRIALS

Figure 10. Performance curves of groups from several experiments for which the reward was appreciably delayed.

assumes that both habit and conditioned inhibition are developed during delayed reward training, but at different rates. A theory which includes a learned variable based on the effort required by the response (e.g. Tolman, 1955) can similarly predict nonmonotonicity if the incentive and effort factors are learned at different rates.

The fact that the functions shown in Fig. 8 may not reflect stable terminal levels makes uncertain any conclusion about whether or not the asymptote of the delay function is at the baseline level of performance without reward. Specifically, is a very long delayed reward better than no reward at all? The data suggest that it is, since the functions appear to be leveling off well above the baseline. Furthermore, the 30-second delay group in Exper. 58D remained superior to the unrewarded group even after the hundred trials shown in Fig. 10 (t = 3.04, d.f. = 12, p < .02).

The superiority of long delayed reward over nonreward can be deduced from a theory like that proposed by Spence (1947), in which the effects of delayed reward are related to the secondary reinforcing properties acquired by the cues present at the completion of the instrumental response. According to such a theory, delayed reward means that secondary reinforcement is directly conditioned to cues that have changed since the instrumental response was completed. Under conditions in which the subject is left in the goal box during the delay, the change results primarily from the dissipation of the response-produced cues of having entered the goal box, and the maximal change possible is for these cues to have completely disappeared. But even at that stage, the goal-box-without-instrumental-response-produced cues is sufficiently similar to the goal-box-with-instrumental-response-produced cues that secondary reinforcement will generalize from the former to the latter. Since some secondary reinforcement will occur upon entry into a goal box even though the reward is long delayed, there will be greater incentive to run than if there were no reward at all.

The data in this section may be summarized as follows:

4. Response speed in all sections of the alley is a concave upward, decreasing function of the time of delay of reward. The asymptote of this function appears to be above the level produced by nonreinforcement.

5. Response speed changes nonmonotonically over trials if the

reward is delayed. There is a suggestion that this decline in speed appears first near the goal, starts earlier in training, and is more extensive the longer the delay of reward.

Individual differences in the delay function. The functions given in Fig. 8 were based on average performance for different groups of subjects and do not necessarily show how the speed of any individual rat is affected by delayed reward. Obtaining an individual function would require testing each rat at a number of different delays. This would not only take a prohibitive amount of time (see Seward and Weldon, 1953) but would also involve the further assumptions that a rat changed from one delay to another reaches the same performance level as if it had been trained on the second delay from the beginning of training, and that the confounded differences in age do not have an appreciable effect on performance.

While adequate counterbalancing might permit evaluating the soundness of these assumptions, a partial answer to the question of the shape of the individual delay function can be obtained indirectly from the data already presented. Specifically, the question posed here is whether fast rats have, on the average, a different delay function from slow rats, apart from the over-all difference in speed of running.

The different delay groups can be subdivided into fast, middle, and slow thirds, and the R-speed plotted separately for these subgroups. When this was done, it was clear by inspection that the curves were strikingly parallel and, indeed, no statistically significant interaction was found.

Strictly speaking, this outcome means only that the variances of the several delay groups were homogeneous. However, if one assumes that the fast rats in one group would also have been fast (relative to the group) rats had they been trained at another delay, then it can be inferred that the shape of the delay function is independent of individual differences in speed of running. This assumption seems reasonable since, in every experiment in which rats have been shifted from one reward condition to another, there is a clear tendency for the faster rats under one condition to continue to be the faster rats under the second. For example, when the five delay groups in Exper. 56C were shifted from 2 to 12 pellets, the correlations between the R-speeds under the two conditions were .92, .76, .84, .67, and .80 for the 0, 1, 3, 10, and 30 second delay groups respectively.

This analysis of the data therefore suggests that:

6. Individual differences affect the delay function as an additive parameter, i.e. fast and slow rats have, on the average, parallel functions relating speed to delay of reward.

AMOUNT OF REWARD

Several studies reported in the literature together tend to support the generalization that performance is a concave downward, increasing function of the amount of reward. Among them are the studies by Crespi (1944), Grindley (1929), Kling (1956), Metzer, Cotton, and Lewis (1957), Reynolds (1949), and Zeaman (1949). Analytically, the amount of reward is a complex variable that can be decomposed into a number of components such as the weight of the reward, its caloric value, the duration of the consummatory response, the visual size of the reward, and the number of units involved. For the present purposes, however, the focus is on the relationship between performance and the amount of reward as experimentally manipulated and not upon the possible mechanisms underlying this relationship.

As used here, amount of reward refers to the number of pellets

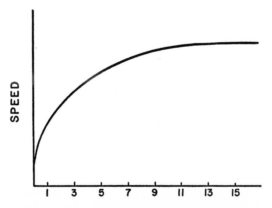

AMOUNT OF REWARD (NUMBER OF PELLETS)

Figure 11. Hypothetical curve showing the nature of the relationship between performance and the amount of reinforcement. This curve was based on the data in Table 5.

given at the end of the alley. Accordingly, groups differing in amount of reward differed in all the possible components of this variable mentioned above. They differed also in the time spent in the goal box since the conventional procedure was to remove a rat as soon as it had completed its allotted reward.

Speed as a function of amount of reward. No study run in the present apparatus included a sufficient number of groups receiving different amounts of reward to permit estimating this function. The function shown in Fig. 11 was based on the data given in Table 5. This function originates above zero at the level of per-

Table 5. R-speeds at the end of training for the constant amount groups in the six experiments in which different groups received different constant amounts of reward. Because the conditions differed in other significant ways between experiments, only within-column comparisons can be made.

			Experiment			
Amount	54B	55B	55E	56C	56D	Beier (1958)
1		.430			.502	.407
2				.510		
3		.453				
4	.516					
5			.403			
6		.447				
7	.598				.548	.611
8						
9			.576			
10						
11						
12		.465		.603		
13						.658

formance without reward. A single pellet has a very marked effect upon performance, leading to R-speeds falling almost halfway between the baseline level without reward and the maximum average speeds attained with larger rewards. At the upper end, it is difficult to obtain differences in speed among groups getting more than 10-pellet reward. The function shown in Fig. 11 summarizes these general observations.

In Fig. 12, the acquisition curves for the three constant-amount groups run by Beier (1958) are shown for the several response measures separately. The curves for the 1-pellet group do not show the nonmonotonicity found with the conditions of delayed reward, but instead show a somewhat slower relative rate of approach toward their asymptotes than the corresponding curves for the larger-amount groups. This finding could be interpreted as indicating that the rate at which habit is acquired is a function of the amount of reward. An alternative account, however, is that the larger amounts of reward facilitate the extinction of fear and thus

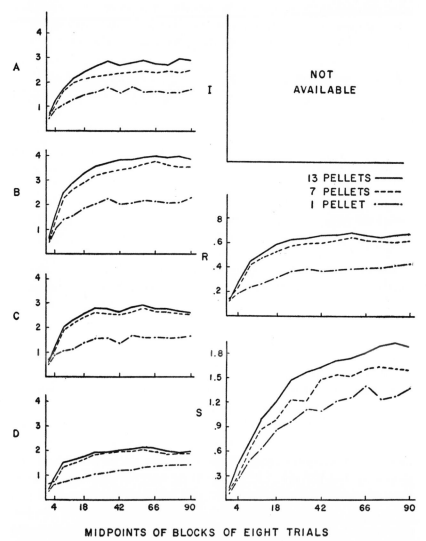

Figure 12. Performance curves of groups receiving 1-pellet, 7-pellet, or 13-pellet reward. (Data from Beier, 1958)

indirectly increase running speed. According to this interpretation the differences in relative rate of learning should not appear if the groups are first given a large number of unrewarded trials in the alley before the different amounts of reward are instituted. No study using this procedure has yet been run.

In summary of these data:

7. Response speed in all sections of the alley is a concave downward, increasing function of the amount of reward.

8. Groups given a large amount of reward reach an asymptote of speed in fewer trials than groups given a small reward.

Individual differences in the amount function. The three constant-amount groups run by Beier (1958) were broken down into fast, middle, and slow thirds according to the logic developed previously in connection with individual differences in the delay function. The three resulting functions appeared to be reasonably parallel and the interaction was not statistically reliable. Tentatively, then, it is concluded that:

9. Individual differences affect the amount function as an additive parameter, i.e. fast and slow rats have, on the average, parallel functions relating speed to amount of reward.

INTERACTIONS

The conventional design for showing that a variable affects performance is to hold all other known relevant variables constant so that any obtained differences in performance can be reasonably attributed to differences in the variable in question. Valid as this procedure is, one can always ask whether the findings were to some extent peculiar to the particular values at which the controlled variables were held constant. For this reason the indicated question, once a variable is known to affect performance, is whether it interacts with other known variables.

Delay and amount of reward. Following the 57 acquisition trials in Exper. 56C, the amount of reward was increased from 2 to 12 pellets. All subjects continued to receive their reward at the accustomed delay (0, 1, 3, 10, or 30 seconds) so that a new delay function could be estimated with the larger reward. As a control on possible changes not due to the shift in the amount of reward, half the subjects in the 3-second delay condition were continued with the 2-pellet reward.

Performance had become reasonably stable after 22 trials with the increased reward. The functions relating speed to delay of reward with a 12-pellet amount are shown in Fig. 13, together with the original 2-pellet functions.

As has already been noted with respect to this experiment, some performance curves had not attained their final levels by the end

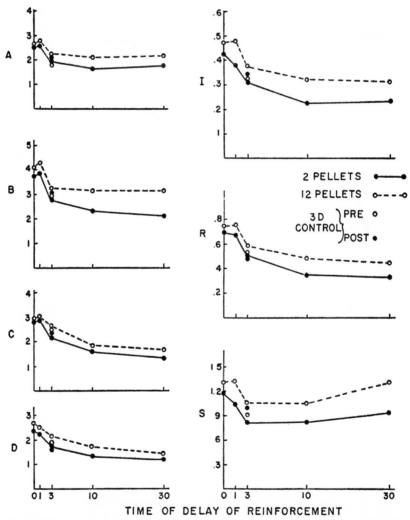

Figure 13. Performance as a function of delay of reward after 57 trials with 2-pellet reward and after an additional 22 trials with 12-pellet reward. One group at 3-second delay continued to receive 2-pellet reward as a control for the additional trials. (Exper. 56C)

of the original 57 trials, but the speeds in the last foot of the alley had become reasonably stable. Analysis of variance was therefore done using only *D*-speeds and the results are summarized in Table 6. It will be observed that the delay conditions produced a reliable

Table 6. Analyses of variance of Exper. 56C covering terminal *D*-speeds at 2 and 12 pellets for groups with 0, 1, 3, 10, or 30 seconds delay, including one control group at 3-second delay that was not shifted to 12 pellets.

Source	d.f.	m.s.	F
Between			
Hooded-albino	1	.010	
Delay	4	5.650	15.69 **
Delay x hooded-albino	4	.350	
Error	57	.360	
Within			
Shift (2 vs. 12 pellets)	1	2.810	4.46 *
Shift (3-sec.-control)	1		.007 (t^2)
Shift x hooded-albino	1	.130	
Shift x delay	4	.030	<1.00
3-sec. vs. 3-sec.-control	1		6.10 * (t^2)
Shift x delay x hooded-albino	4	.070	
Error	57	.063	

effect that was independent of the hood/albino breakdown. The change in the amount of reward significantly affected performance beyond any effect of the additional trials as indicated by the 3D-control group. Of major interest in the present context is the fact that the *F* for the interaction between delay and amount of reward was less than 1.0.

If the null hypothesis is accepted, so that delay and amount of reward are taken as interacting additively, then there could be a limiting function, parallel to the others, relating speed to delay of reward with zero amount. Operational meaning can be given to such a statement if the delay of no-reward is defined as the time a nonreinforced rat is detained in the empty goal box. However, since it has already been shown (pp. 42 ff.) that detention time does not appreciably affect performance without reward, this expectation is not confirmed. The indicated solution, then, is to use the nonindependence of delay and amount of reward at the point of nonreinforcement as grounds for disallowing noreinforcement in the statement of the interaction between them.

Accordingly, the data in this section may be summarized as follows:

10. For finite values of delay and nonzero values of amount, the delay and amount of reward interact additively in determining response speed.

Delay of reward and drive. Following the 57 acquisition trials in Exper. 55D, the drive level was reduced by changing the maintenance diet from 9 or 12 grams to 16 grams per day. (A month's rest and relearning intervened between these observations.) All subjects continued to receive a 2-pellet reward at their accustomed delay (0, 1, 3, 5, 10, or 30 seconds). The function relating speed to delay of reward at the lower drive level is shown in Fig. 14, together with the original function obtained under high drive.

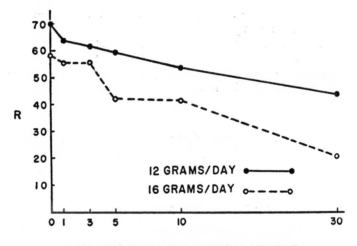

TIME OF DELAY OF REINFORCEMENT

Figure 14. Performance as a function of delay of reward after 57 trials on high drive and after an additional 24 trials on low drive. (Exper. 55D)

There is a slight indication that these functions diverge with increasing delays, which would suggest a behavioral form of additive interaction. However, the interaction is not statistically reliable. Since other studies (Ramond, 1954) reported in the literature have also failed to show a significant interaction between these variables, the most likely conclusion is that:

11. Drive interacts additively with the time of delay of reward in determining response speed.

Amount of reward and drive. Exper. 55B was designed as an incomplete factorial involving four levels of amount of reward (1, 3, 6, or 12 pellets) and four levels of drive (2, 12, 24, or 48 hours of deprivation). The procedures in this experiment differed appreciably from the conventional ones in order to accommodate the deprivation variable. The rats were fed a fat-concentrated diet every 48 hours and were run every other day.

Asymptotic speeds for the various groups are given in Table 7.

Table 7. Terminal *R*-speeds as a joint function of hours of deprivation and amount of reward. (Exper. 55B)

Number of hours of food deprivation:	Number of pellets reward:			
	1	3	6	12
2	.306			.382
12	.393	.419	.449	.445
24	.411			.388
48	.467	.486	.446	.534

Although there are several aberrant entries, the over-all picture is one of an additive interaction, and the statistical analysis did not reveal a significant interaction. Therefore, it is tentatively concluded that:

12. Drive interacts additively with the amount of reward in determining response speed.

DISCUSSION

The major data reported in this chapter show that reward acts to increase response speed above the baseline level that obtains without obvious reward, and that the terminal level of performance is higher the larger the amount of reward and the shorter the time of its delay. That is, under conditions of constant reward, speed is maximized by getting as much reward into the subject as quickly as possible. These variables may be thought of as determining the incentive value of the goal box via the immediate secondary reinforcement available upon entry into the goal box.

A more detailed analysis of the amount and delay variables cannot be made from the present data since the component variables may not always have operated independently. For example, differences in the amount of reward were confounded with a delay variable because it takes a longer time to eat more food. Thus, increasing the reward above 10 or 12 pellets may have had little further effect simply because it took the rats 20 to 30 seconds to eat this amount and any additional pellets were consumed after too long a delay to affect response speed. The conclusions must therefore be restricted to conditions of the type studied.

One aspect of this procedure requires special mention because of the increasing attention being given to so-called "competing" responses (see e.g. Cotton, 1953; Spence, 1956, p. 154). The most extreme proposal would be that a rat either runs at a fixed speed or does not run (see Pereboom and Crawford, 1958) and that all the variance observed in speed is accounted for by responses that are incompatible with running. Such a proposal might seem to question the procedure of recording only the time taken between two points in the alley without reference to what the rat actually did during that time. Simply as a matter of fact, only under the longest delays of reward were grossly incompatible responses (such as stopping and retracing) observed, and their incidence was very low even then. Furthermore, if the occurrence of incompatible responses is taken as evidence that the instrumental response tendency is relatively weak, then the resulting slow speed correctly represents this tendency. At least within a single procedure, nothing in the competing-response analysis necessarily denies a monotonic relationship between the incentive value of the goal event and performance.

That this relationship is linear, however, cannot be confidently asserted. The unit-of-measurement question is of special significance in interpreting the interactions between the amount and delay of reward and drive, because only on the assumption that response speed is a linear estimate of response tendency can the obtained additive interactions in performance be taken as indicating additive interactions among the relevant intervening variables. There is still very little evidence on the interactions which does not require the assumption that speed is an appropriate unit of measurement. Data obtained using conditions of correlated reinforcement suggest that incentive is best viewed as a multiplicative function of the amount and delay of reward. Thus the conclusions stated here may apply only to speed in conditions of constant reinforcement.

NOTE: ON THE EFFECT OF TIME IN THE GOAL BOX

In all the conditions described in this chapter, differences in reward were confounded with time in the goal box. Rats given a delayed reward had more time (not eating) in the goal box than those given their reward immediately, and rats given a large reward had more time (eating) in the goal box than those given a small reward. Of some concern is whether time in the goal box, per se, has an appreciable effect on performance.

As a partial test to determine this, Gonzalez (Exper. 58D) ran a group of rats that were detained in the goal box for 28 seconds after eating their reward. For comparison, another group received the same amount and delay of reward without the post-reward detention, and a third group spent the same total time in the goal box as the first group but the reward was given near the end rather than near the beginning of their stay. The performance curves for these three groups are shown in Fig. 15.

It will be seen that time spent in the goal box after reward had no appreciable effect on running speed, whereas time spent before reward (i.e. delay) had a clear and significant effect. This is con-

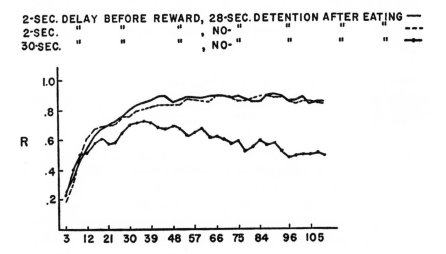

Figure 15. The effect of post-reward detention in the goal box compared with no detention and with pre-reward delay. (Exper. 58D)

sistent with the results obtained by Fehrer (1956). The suggestion
is, therefore, that the reported effects of delay and amount of reward did not result from the confounded variable of time in the
goal box.

Note: On the Use of More Than One Trial a Day

All the data reported so far were obtained on a one-trial-a-day
schedule. It is only slightly less efficient to run 100 rats one trial a
day than to run 10 rats 10 trials a day, although a single experiment takes considerably longer to run using the former procedure.
Widely distributed practice has several advantages over massed
practice for the type of research in this program.

It has already been noted that both the delay and amount of
reward are completely confounded with time in the goal box, but
that this aspect alone seems to make little difference at one trial
a day. However, with massed trials the reward conditions are necessarily also confounded with the intertrial interval, and this last
variable does have a significant effect on performance. For studies
of amount of reward, massed trials involve still further confound-
ing with drive level in that rats given a large reward on the first
trial of the day may have an appreciably different level of hunger
on the second trial than rats given a small reward.

Another source of complication in massed trials arises from the
possibility that traces from one trial will persist as significant components of the stimulus complex for a later trial. This means that
variation in the stimulus situation must be reckoned with. In a
similar vein, the effects of "warm-up" (see e.g. McGeoch and Irion,
1952, pp. 150 ff.) and "pre-feeding" (see e.g. Morgan and Fields,
1938) must also be included.

Nevertheless, some of the later research has been conducted with
massed training in order to increase the number of trials possible
within a reasonable period of time. To provide familiarity with
such a procedure, the performance of the constant reward group
in Exper. 57B has been broken down to show speed on the 4 trials
within each day separately. The acquisition curves [1] are shown in
the upper graph of Fig. 16. It will be noted that more trials (al-

1. In comparing the curves in Fig. 16, it should be borne in mind that a second
trial is necessarily given after a first trial, and hence when major changes (e.g.
acquisition and extinction) are taking place, the later trials have the advantage
of generalization from the earlier ones.

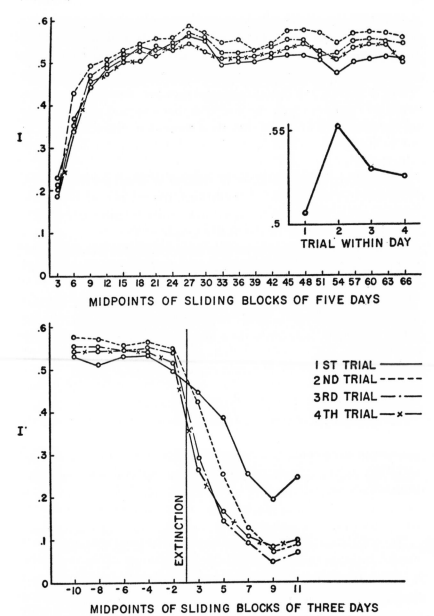

Figure 16. Acquisition (upper graph) and extinction (lower graph) with four trials a day, plotted for each trial-within-day separately. (Exper. 57B)

though fewer days) are required with 4 trials a day than with one trial a day for the curves to reach their limits and that speeds are consistently different on the different-numbered trials. This latter effect is shown separately in the inset where speed during the last 20 days is plotted as a function of trial number. Both of these statements are consistent with the assertion that a second trial is simply not the same as a first trial, having a somewhat different stimulus and being subject to unique effects of fatigue, warm-up, drive reduction, etc.

Although extinction will not be treated in detail until the chapter on changes in the reward conditions, the extinction curves for the same group have been broken down similarly into trials-within-day and are presented in the lower graph of Fig. 16. There is a clear interaction between reward-nonreward and trial-within-day, the first trial being the slowest when rats are being rewarded but the fastest when they are not being rewarded.

Massed trials therefore clearly introduce a number of additional complexities into the analysis of performance (see also Cotton and Lewis, 1957). Certainly these must ultimately be dealt with. The preference for widely distributed practice results from an attempt initially to keep the conditions as simple as possible.

Note: On Spontaneous Recovery

The rats in Exper. 55D were given 23 extinction trials followed by a 14-day rest during which only the regular maintenance schedule was followed. They were then returned to the alley for 8 additional nonreinforced trials. The purpose of this was twofold: Would spontaneous recovery occur after training and extinction with widely distributed practice, and, if so, would it be differential among groups that had been performing differently during acquisition because of differences in the time of delay of reward?

The suggested answer to both questions is affirmative. Fig. 17 shows the *D*-speeds for the 0, 3, and 30 second delay groups during the last trials of the first extinction, on the test for spontaneous recovery, and during the additional extinction trials. This pattern of results appeared in all groups and all response measures, but was particularly clear near the goal (where, as will be shown later, the extinction effect was maximal) for groups that were markedly different in acquisition performance.

One of the most familiar accounts of the phenomenon of spontaneous recovery follows Pavlov (1927) and later Hull (1943) in assuming that a part of the inhibition built up during nonreinforcement dissipates during a period of rest. Another promising observation (see Estes, 1955) is that tests for spontaneous recovery may involve a return to a stimulus complex that is more like the originally reinforced one and less like the one that prevailed during extinction. While both approaches may indeed be involved in spontaneous recovery following massed extinction, the evidence of spontaneous recovery following widely distributed practice is not easily interpreted in those terms.

It is possible to account for the present data in terms of the incentive variable by making an assumption about the relative contribution to incentive of the rewards on previous trials. This assumption may be stated verbally as follows: If several reward events have been encountered following instances of a response, the one most recently encountered will make the greatest relative contribution in determining incentive for the next trial, but the advantage of the more recent event diminishes over time. More loosely, one might say that the subject "expects" that what happened on the last trial will also happen on the next trial, but that

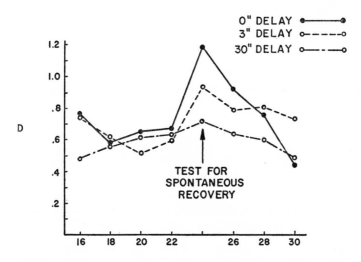

MIDPOINTS OF SLIDING BLOCKS OF THREE EXTINCTION TRIALS

Figure 17. Spontaneous recovery resulting from a 14-day rest after acquisition and extinction had been run at one trial a day. (Exper. 55D)

Incentive

the distinction between the last trial and previous trials fades over time. This analysis is closely similar to that proposed by Miller and Stevenson (1936), who related spontaneous recovery to the relative rate of forgetting as a function of the passage of time.

One mathematical expression of this assumption is shown graphically in the upper curve in Fig. 18. Two events are repre-

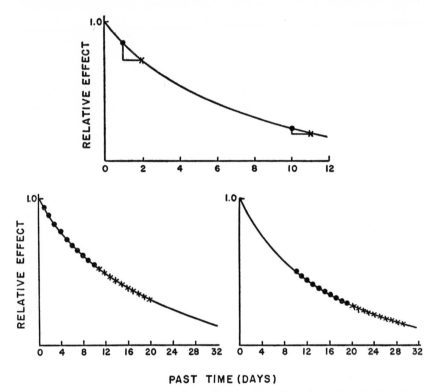

Figure 18. Graphic representation of the assumption that the relative effect of an event on incentive diminishes over time. In the lower graphs, this assumption is applied to the derivation of spontaneous recovery following widely distributed practice.

sented by a circle and an X, and it can be seen that the advantage of the circle event is greater one day after its occurrence than it is 10 days later.

This is applied to a test for spontaneous recovery in the lower curves in Fig. 18. In the left portion is shown a sequence of 10 reinforced trials (indicated by X's) followed in time by 10 nonreinforced trials as their relative effect would be determined without an increase in the intertrial interval. The nonreinforcements occupy the predominant positions and produce extinction-level performance. After a 10-day rest, as shown in the right portion of Fig. 18, however, the relative advantage of the nonreinforcements has lessened and the reinforced trials can again contribute appreciable incentive to respond. As the transition effect is lost, the 20 trials approach the status of 50 percent partial reinforcement.[2]

This hypothesis is not ad hoc to the phenomenon of spontaneous recovery. It correctly predicts the various distribution-of-trials effects during extinction, as e.g. that massing extinction trials hastens extinction especially following spaced acquisition (see Reynolds, 1945). Indeed, the hypothesis was actually developed to handle various sequential effects in conditions of varied reinforcement, and spontaneous recovery was an unexpected implication of it. It has not, however, been formally integrated into a comprehensive behavior theory and is therefore still only suggestive.

2. Actually to use such a weighting device, an additional rule is needed to determine how many of the events can contribute to the incentive. One such rule is to add arithmetically back through previous events until a sum of 1.0 is reached, events happening prior to that point being ineffective.

CHAPTER 4

Conditions of Varied Reinforcement

IN THE constant reward conditions discussed in the previous chapter, the amount and delay of reward were the same on all the trials for any one subject. This chapter is concerned with conditions in which the reward is varied from trial to trial according to some schedule predetermined by the experimenter. Only variations in amount and/or time of delay of reward will be considered, although the reward could also be varied in other dimensions, such as quality and unit.

In conditions of varied delay of reward, the amount of reward is held constant and the delay is determined from a probability distribution that can be plotted on coordinates such as are shown in the upper left quadrant of Fig. 19. The particular condition illustrated there is variation between two equally likely values of delay although, of course, more than two values can be used and they do not need to be equally likely. The empirical problem is to relate performance to the several parameters of this distribution, e.g. to the average delay, to the variance in delay, etc.

A comparable series of statements would describe conditions of varied amount of reward. Here the delay is constant while the amount is varied. A condition of varied amount of reward with two equally likely values is depicted in the upper right quadrant of Fig. 19.

Both the delay and the amount of reward can be varied simultaneously, in which case three polar possibilities emerge. In one, the delay and amount are uncorrelated with each other, i.e. the value of delay is selected independently of the value of amount. Combining the two conditions already mentioned, there would be four equally likely events as shown in the lower left quadrant of Fig. 19. More complex independent variations in delay and amount would simply generate a surface on the coordinates shown. The other two polar possibilities are for the delay and the amount of reward to be perfectly correlated with each other, either positively or negatively. In these extremes, only two events occur, as depicted in the lower right quadrant of Fig. 19.

The familiar condition of partial reinforcement can be described in these terms as an instance of simultaneously varied delay

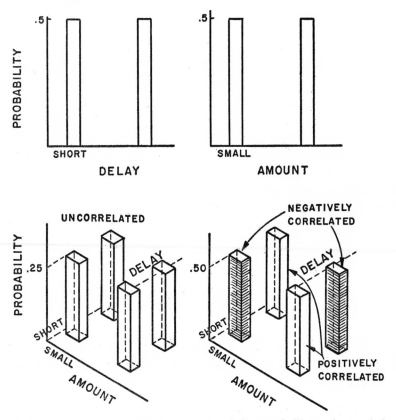

Figure 19. Coordinates for describing varied reward, illustrating varied delay with two equally likely values, varied amount with two equally likely values, and simultaneous variation of delay and amount where the values of delay and amount are uncorrelated, positively correlated, and negatively correlated.

and amount of reward with perfect positive correlation. That is, the larger (nonzero) amount in partial reinforcement always accompanies the shorter (noninfinite) delay. In general, any condition that includes occasional nonreinforcement involves a positive correlation between delay and amount because these dimensions of the reward are not independent at the point of nonreinforcement.

The probability distribution alone does not give a completely adequate description of varied reward conditions; it is important also to know the particular sequence in which the rewards are encountered by the subject. Were the reward on any trial for each subject determined by drawing at random from the selected probability distribution, then the sequential dependencies would be random because the reward on any trial would be independent of the rewards on the previous trials. The conventional procedure, however, is to use a sequence of rewards that conforms exactly to the specified probability distribution over relatively small blocks of trials, e.g. 5 out of every 10 trials are rewarded in a 50 percent partial reinforcement condition. This procedure, which has been used in all the present studies, necessarily introduces nonrandom sequential dependencies since the occurrence of one event slightly increases the proportion of the other event(s) on the remaining trials. Accordingly, a sufficiently talented subject could sometimes predict, at better than the over-all probability distribution, the reward on the ensuing trial from information about the rewards on the preceding trials.

It should be apparent from even this brief description that the variety of possible conditions of varied reinforcement is enormous. A convincing exercise is to imagine trying to predict performance on trial #101 knowing only that 500 pellets of reward have been given during the course of the preceding 100 trials. Because of the size of this area, the following data provide only a token description of it.

Varied Delay of Reward

One group of rats in Exper. 54A was rewarded after a 1-sec. delay on half the trials and after a 9-sec. delay on the remaining half. Two control groups were run concurrently, one of which had a constant delay at the mean of the values for the varied delay group (5-sec.) and the other at the shorter value (1-sec.). Performance curves for the three groups are shown in Fig. 20.

It will be seen that this condition of varied delay of reward led to a slower relative rate of learning than did constant delay and that performance ultimately surpassed that by the group with a constant delay at the mean of the values for the varied delay group and reached a level only slightly inferior to that by the group with a constant delay at the shorter of the values for the varied delay group. Analysis of variance of the terminal performance data yielded an over-all *F* of 11.62 which, with 2 and 20 d.f.,

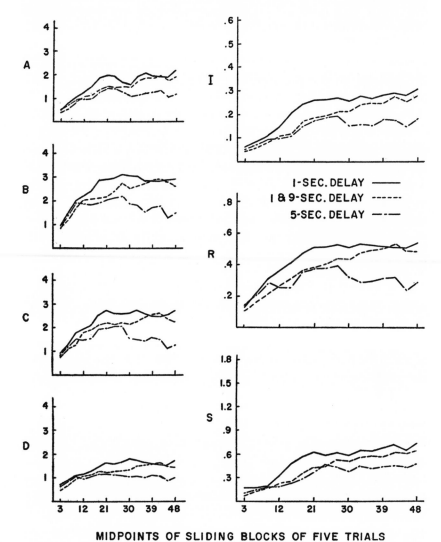

MIDPOINTS OF SLIDING BLOCKS OF FIVE TRIALS

Figure 20. Performance curves when the delay of reward was varied between two equally likely values compared with constant delay at the mean and preferred values. (Exper. 54A)

is significant at the .001 level. Subsequent t-tests showed that the varied delay group was superior to the constant delay group that had the same average delay (t = 3.345, p < .01).

Kincaid (Exper. 55A) ran three groups for 10 massed trials a day, using delays of 0 and 9 sec., 0 and 30 sec., and constant 0 sec. The differences among these groups at the end of training were very slight, terminal R-speeds being .759, .755, and .764 for the three groups respectively.

Fig. 21 represents an attempt to summarize the expected effect of varying the delay of reward between two equally likely values. The coordinates relate speed to the difference between the delays. The family of solid curves has the absolute length of the short delay as its parameter and was generated by the following reasoning: (a) when the difference between the delays is zero, the condition is one of constant delay of reward and hence each curve originates at a point determined by the function relating speed to delay of reward; (b) if the shorter of the two delays is very long, then giving an even longer delay on half of the trials should have no detrimental effect since both delays will be down on the flat portion of the delay function, and hence the family of solid curves is bounded on the bottom by a straight line of zero slope; (c) the data suggest that delaying the reward on half the trials has only a slightly detrimental effect on performance, and hence the family of solid curves is bounded on the top by a function presumably similar to the delay function in form but having appreciably less over-all drop; and (d) the intermediate functions can be inserted symmetrically.

The family of dashed curves of Fig. 21 has as its parameter the length of the average delay. The points on any of these functions refer to conditions that have the same average delay but with different variances (e.g. a 5-sec. average delay could be given with equal frequencies of 0 and 10 sec., 1 and 9 sec., etc.). These functions show that performance under varied delay is superior to performance under constant delay at the mean of the delays for a varied group. Inversely, they show that, given a designated average delay, performance will be better the larger the variance in delay and will be maximal when the short delay is zero.

The family of curves having the length of the longer delay as its parameter is not shown. These curves would rise in a manner similar to the dashed curves but more rapidly.

At its present stage of quantification, Fig. 21 can be used only to predict relative performance by groups falling along the same curve. We cannot yet make a prediction about two groups that differ in their smaller, larger, and average delays unless there is no overlap. For example, we cannot tell whether speed would be faster if delay were varied between 1 and 9 sec. than if it were varied between 2 and 4 sec. And, of course, the effects of variations in delay with more than two values and/or with unequal probabilities are not depicted at all.

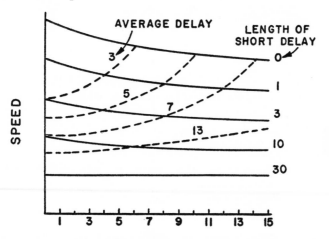

DIFFERENCE BETWEEN TWO EQUALLY LIKELY DELAYS

Figure 21. Estimated effect of varying the delay of reward between two equally likely values, showing speed as a function of the difference between the delays. Solid curves connect points with a common short delay and dashed curves connect points with a common average delay.

Notwithstanding the fairly small amount of data available on varied delay of reward, there are enough constraints (see also Crum et al., 1951; Peterson, 1956; and Wike and McNamara, 1957) acting in generating Fig. 21 to justify considerable confidence that it is a reasonably accurate representation. Its major implications may be stated verbally as follows:

13. When the delay of reward is varied irregularly between two equally likely values,

    a. among groups with the same shorter delay, average performance is higher the shorter the longer delay;

    b. among groups with the same longer delay, average performance is higher the shorter the shorter delay;

c. among groups with the same average delay, average performance is higher the larger the variance in delays.

VARIED AMOUNT OF REWARD

Beier (1958) gave three groups of rats an average of 7 pellets reward per trial. For one of these the reward was constant (7

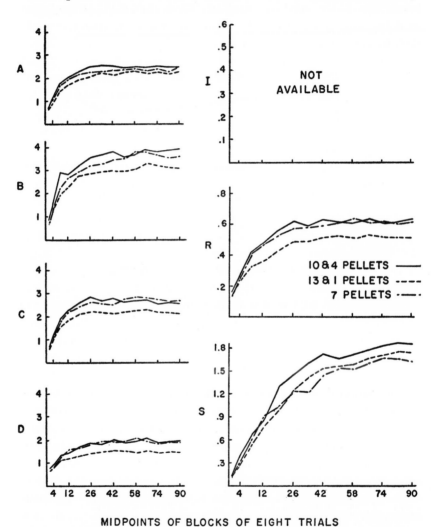

MIDPOINTS OF BLOCKS OF EIGHT TRIALS

Figure 22. Performance curves when the amount of reward was varied between two equally likely values for three groups getting the same average amount of reward but differing in the range of variation. (Data from Beier, 1958)

pellets), for one the amount of reward was varied irregularly between 10 and 4 pellets, and for the third the amount was varied between 13 and 1 pellets. Performance curves for these three groups are shown in Fig. 22.

Varied amount of reward tilted the gradient of speed of running toward the goal relative to that observed with constant reward. The 13-and-1-pellet group ran faster than the 7-pellet group near the start but slower near the goal. A similar pattern can be seen in the 10-and-4-pellet group except that it did not run slower than the 7-pellet group even in the last foot of the alley. On balance, the 10-and-4-pellet group ran slightly faster than the 7-pellet group, while the 13-and-1-pellet group ran appreciably (p < .05) slower.

Two other studies provide comparisons of the effect of varied amount of reward relative to that of constant reward at the mean amount. In Exper. 55E variation between 1 and 9 pellets produced almost the identical R-speed as a constant 5-pellet reward (.405 to .403). In Exper. 54B variation between 1 and 7 pellets produced slightly faster R-speed than constant 4-pellet reward (.538 to .516). In both studies the varied groups were appreciably slower than control groups getting constant rewards at the larger of the amounts for the varied groups, although only in Exper. 55E was this difference statistically reliable (t = 2.344, p < .05).

Fig. 23 represents an attempt to summarize the expected effect of varying the amount of reward between two equally likely values in much the same way that Fig. 21 dealt with varied delay of reward. The coordinates relate speed to the difference between the amounts. The family of solid curves has the absolute size of the smaller amount as its parameter and was generated by the following reasoning: (a) when the difference between the amounts is zero, the condition is one of constant amount of reward, and hence each curve originates at a point determined by the function relating speed to amount of reward; (b) if the smaller of the two amounts is very large, then giving an even larger amount on half of the trials should have no further beneficial effect on performance since both curves will be up on the flat portion of the amount function, and hence the family of solid curves is bounded on the top by a straight line of zero slope; (c) the data suggest that giving a small reward on half the trials reduces performance appreciably below what the larger reward alone would produce, and hence the family of solid curves is bounded on the bottom by a function presumably similar to the amount function in form but having a smaller over-all rise; and (d) the intermediate functions can be inserted symmetrically.

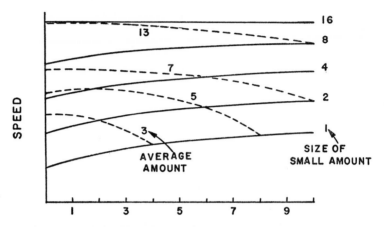

DIFFERENCE BETWEEN TWO EQUALLY LIKELY AMOUNTS

Figure 23. Estimated effect of varying the amount of reward between two equally likely values, showing speed as a function of the difference between the amounts. Solid curves connect points with a common small amount and dashed curves connect points with a common average amount.

The family of dashed curves in Fig. 23 has as its parameter the size of the average amount. The points on any one function refer to conditions that have the same average amount but with different variances. These functions show that performance under varied amount of reward may be superior to performance under constant amount at the mean of the amounts for the varied group—if the average amount and the variance in amount are both reasonably small. Otherwise, varied amount produces performance inferior to that produced by constant amount. Inversely, these functions show that, given a designated average amount, performance will be better the smaller the variance in amount if the average amount is large, but will be maximal with an intermediate degree of variance if the average amount is small.

The family of curves having the size of the larger amount as its parameter is not shown. These curves would fall monotonically and would not show the early rise seen in the dashed curves.

As with the summary graph for varied delay, Fig. 23 cannot be used for comparisons where the smaller, larger, and average amounts are all different and it does not deal with the more complex instances of varied amount. The graph includes enough constraints, however, to justify considerable confidence in it, although its generality is restricted by the fact that the relative effect of varied amount of reward depends partly on the distance from the goal. The major implications of the graph may be stated verbally as follows:

14. When the amount of reward is varied irregularly between two equally likely values,

   a. among groups with the same smaller amount, average performance is higher the larger the larger amount;

   b. among groups with the same larger amount, average performance is higher the larger the smaller amount;

   c. among groups with the same high average amount, average performance is higher the smaller the variance in amount;

   d. among groups with the same low average amount, average performance is highest with an intermediate degree of variance in amount.

Partial Reinforcement

Were it correct to view nonreinforcement as the limiting case of, and continuous with, other values of delay and amount of reward, then performance under partial reinforcement (see Jenkins and Stanley, 1950) could be deduced from the descriptive graphs for varied delay and varied amount of reward. If nonreinforcement is taken as an instance of infinite delay, the functions in Fig. 21 could be extrapolated to an infinite difference between the delays in varied delay conditions. This would give performance under partial reinforcement as a function of the delay of reward on the rewarded trials. Alternatively, if nonreinforcement is taken as an instance of zero amount, the family of solid curves in Fig. 23 could be expanded to include at the lower bound a function with a zero smaller amount. This would give performance under partial reinforcement as a function of the amount of reward on the rewarded trials.

Although such interpretations are tempting in their simplicity, and quite possibly even correct, it seems best to postpone asserting them. The analytical difficulty is that the previous descriptions were applied separately to varied delay or to varied amount, while partial reinforcement involves a simultaneous variation in

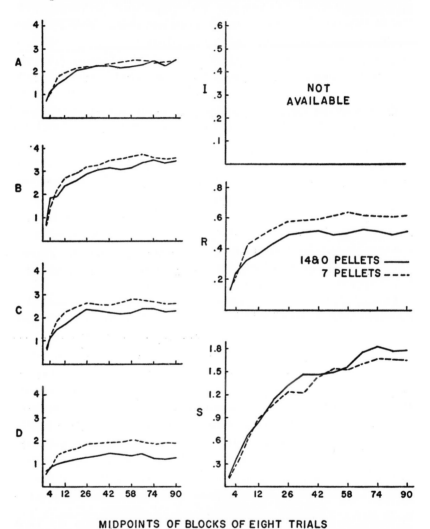

MIDPOINTS OF BLOCKS OF EIGHT TRIALS

Figure 24. Performance curves under partial reinforcement at one trial a day compared with constant reward with the same average amount. (Data from Beier, 1958)

both delay and amount. Presumably studies of other conditions of simultaneous variations in delay and amount will provide a larger context into which partial reinforcement can more confidently be placed.

Beier (1958) included a partial reward group (14 and 0 pellets) in her design as the limiting case of increasing the range of variation in amount of reward. The performance of this group is shown in Fig. 24 along with that of the constant 7-pellet group. Recalling the data from the other varied amount groups (Fig. 22) in this experiment, partial reward fits consistently into the picture: the gradient of speed of running was again tilted, and the over-all trend was for slower running with partial reward than with constant reward. Indeed, the 14-and-0-pellet group ran somewhat slower than the 13-and-1-pellet group.

Exper. 56A included a partial reward group running one trial a day and yielded comparable results. The 9-and-0-pellet group ran slower than the 9-and-1-pellet group (R-speeds $= .537$ and .580 respectively), and both of these were slower than the constant 9-pellet group (R-speed $= .620$). With widely distributed practice in our laboratory, therefore, partial reinforcement has acted like the limiting case of varied amount of reward [1] and produced speeds slower than continuous reward.

This is not the case with massed practice. Exper. 57B included a partial reinforcement group (4 and 0 pellets) as well as a continuous (4-pellet) reward group and was run at four massed trials a day. The I-speeds of these two groups are plotted in the upper graph of Fig. 25 and it will be seen that the partial reward group ultimately ran faster than the constant reward group. This finding was replicated in the same experiment by two groups that were given partial or continuous reward but were also given a mild electric shock at the goal. The I-speeds for these two groups are shown in the lower graph of Fig. 25. While speeds were slower under the shock condition, the superiority of partial reinforcement over continuous reinforcement was again evident.

1. Data inconsistent with this generalization were obtained in Exper. 56E, where rats were shifted after 50 trials with a 9-and-0-pellet amount to 9 and 1 pellets. R-speed slowed down during the additional 44 trials, but since no controls were available for aging and seasonal factors the result has been discounted.

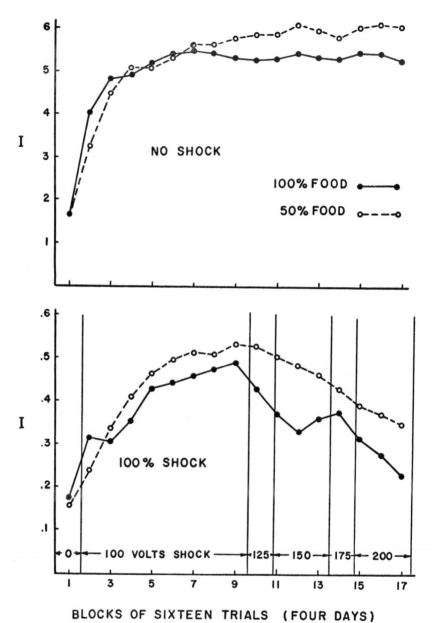

Figure 25. Performance under partial reinforcement with four massed trials a day. The upper graph is for groups without shock and the lower graph is for groups getting a mild electric shock (at the indicated intensities) every trial. (Exper. 57B)

Accordingly, whereas partially rewarded rats ran slower than continuously rewarded rats when the trials were widely distributed (Beier, 1958, and Exper. 56A), they ran faster when the trials were massed (Exper. 57B). The difference in performance may have been due to the fact that a small reward (4 pellets) was used in Exper. 57B, while larger rewards (14 and 9 pellets, respectively) were used by Beier and in Exper. 56A. The sequences were also different, the rats in Exper. 57B never getting a run of more than two unrewarded trials in succession. Most obviously, there was the difference in distribution of practice, although Weinstock (1954, 1958) has reported data showing that partially reinforced rats may run faster than continuously reinforced ones even with widely distributed practice.

Simply to mention some of the ways that massing the trials could affect performance under partial reinforcement: (a) partially rewarded subjects may have been under higher hunger drive on later trials of the day since they got fewer pellets on the early trials; (b) partially rewarded subjects may have had a higher drive produced by "frustration"[2] (see Brown and Farber, 1951; and Amsel and Roussel, 1952); (c) fast speeds may have been learned as a "superstition" (see Skinner, 1948); and (d) continuously rewarded subjects may have been inhibited because they were always running to a stimulus that included cues of the previous reward whereas the partially rewarded subjects were running to a variable stimulus that sometimes included traces of reward and sometimes did not (see Dember and Fowler, 1958).

It is quite possible that all these accounts will ultimately prove to be involved in a complete understanding of partial reward. The available data (see also Finger, 1942; Friedes, 1957; Hulse, 1958; Lewis, 1956; and Notterman, 1951) do not permit either the rejection or the establishment of any of them and this uncertainty is reflected in the following summary:

15. When the reward is omitted irregularly on half the trials,

a. in some circumstances (large reward, long sequences, widely distributed trials) partial reinforcement is inferior to other con-

---

2. Since the partially rewarded subjects ran faster on the first trial of the day as well as on the later trials, accounts (a) and (b) require either that the drive effects be conditionable (see e.g. Anderson, 1941) or the micromolar assumption that a specific speed of responding is learned.

ditions that involve the same average amount with a smaller range of variation in amount.

b. in some circumstances (small reward, short sequences, massed trials) partial reinforcement is superior to constant reward of the same amount.

TRANSITION AND SEQUENCE EFFECTS IN VARIED REINFORCEMENT

When the reward is varied between X and Y and speed is averaged across blocks of trials, any differences in performance attributable to prior reward are suppressed because trials following both X and Y events are pooled indiscriminately in the average. A transition effect would be indicated if speed following X trials differs systematically from speed following Y trials.

The existence of a transition effect can be deduced from two other effects already familiar in the available data. One of these may be called the change-of-reward effect since it refers to the fact that rats that are shifted to a particular condition of constant reward ultimately attain a performance level comparable to that shown by rats run under that condition from the beginning of training (see Chapter 9). For example, rats shifted from partial reinforcement to 100 per cent nonreinforcement (extinction) eventually slow down to the baseline level of performance without reward. Now, as far as the rat can tell, the reward received on any trial could be the first of a series of constant rewards at that level. Since the cumulated effect of a number of these reward events is to lead to the appropriate level of performance, the most reasonable assumption is that even one of them would tend to produce a small change in the indicated direction. The change-of-reward effect thus predicts that rats will run faster on trials after the larger or more immediate reward in varied conditions.

The other effect that implies a transition effect involves the concept of discrimination. Since X and Y are stimuli, they may produce traces which persist as cues for the next trial. If the likelihood of an X event is greater following Y trials than following X trials, then the traces of the prior reward are differentially reinforced and a discrimination should be formed (see e.g. Brunswick, 1939). The discrimination effect therefore predicts that rats will run faster on trials after the smaller or longer delayed reward in varied reward conditions.[3]

Since the change-of-reward and discrimination effects work in opposite directions, the over-all transition effect is not absolutely determinate. However, the amount of the discrimination effect can be varied relative to the change-of-reward effect since the former depends on the degree of massing of trials, the number of trials, and the differential in sequential dependencies. Thus, alternation between X and Y with highly massed trials should maximize the discrimination effect, and this condition has indeed been shown to lead to variable performance in which rats correctly predict the occurrence of the reward (Longenecker et al., 1952). At the other extreme, widely distributed practice with the sequential dependencies fully counterbalanced should minimize the discrimination effect relative to the change-of-reward effect.

Higher-order transition effects would be indicated if speed on trial N is differentially affected by the reward event on trial $N - 2$, $N - 3$, etc., with the rewards on the intervening trials counterbalanced. The change-of-reward effect should diminish continuously as the reward event is further removed from the trial in question. The discrimination effect should be weakened by the further decay of the traces of the reward event but might also be strengthened if there is an increase in the differential reinforcement.

The procedure of giving X to half the subjects and Y to the other half on any trial and then averaging across subjects suppresses any differences in performance attributable to the particular sequence in which the rewards are given. A specific sequence effect would be indicated if subjects that have had the same frequency of X and Y preceding trial N but have encountered them in a different sequence perform differently on trial N.

The existence of a specific sequence effect can be deduced from available data. Consider speed after 100 trials, 50 of which have been rewarded. Clearly, performance on trial #101 would be

3. This is true only in conditions where the reward frequencies are balanced within relatively small blocks of trials. Clearly, the sequence could be arranged so that X more frequently follows X than Y in which case the discrimination effect would work in the same direction as the change-of-reward effect. This is familiar in the context of repeated reversals and the general "learning-to-learn" area (see e.g. Harlow, 1949 and 1950, and also Restle, 1958).

low if the rewards had occurred on the first 50 trials, and would be high had the last 50 trials been continuously rewarded. Presumably performance would fall somewhere between these limits following sequences that are intermediate between the extremes.

In addition, an over-all sequence effect can be obtained by averaging across trials during which equal frequencies of X and Y events occur. That is, rather than looking at performance on the single trial after the frequencies have been equated, one might be interested in the average level of performance over all the trials. This effect, too, can be deduced from available data. If 50 rewarded trials are followed by 50 nonrewarded trials, the average performance across acquisition and extinction would certainly be lower than across 100 trials of an irregular partial reinforcement condition.

Table 8 has been prepared to illustrate the various comparisons that could be made between subjects running with different sequences to test for transition and sequence effects. Comparable comparisons can be made within a single rat's record if several of these sequences appear in the over-all sequence.

If the arguments presented above are accepted, then the existence of the various transition and sequence effects is already established. The important problem, therefore, is to determine how these effects are related to particular conditions of varied reward. The present researches were not designed primarily for this purpose, and hence the data do not permit any very systematic generalizations. They are presented here to illustrate the effects in the particular conditions used.

No tests have been made for specific sequence effects, but Beier (1958) included over-all sequence in the analysis of her data on varied amount of reward. Two (opposite) sequences were used: LSLSSSSLLSLLLLSS and SLSLLLLSSLSSSSLL, where L refers to the larger reward and S to the smaller. The former sequence led to slower average speeds, but the *F's* for sequence effects were 2.83 in *R*-speed and 3.04 for *D*-speed, which, with 1 and 62 d.f., fail to make the .05 level.

Beier has also provided a detailed analysis of transition effects in varied amount of reward, and her results are reproduced as Fig. 26. In the upper left corner, the first-order transition effect for the 10-and-4-pellet group is graphed over the major portion

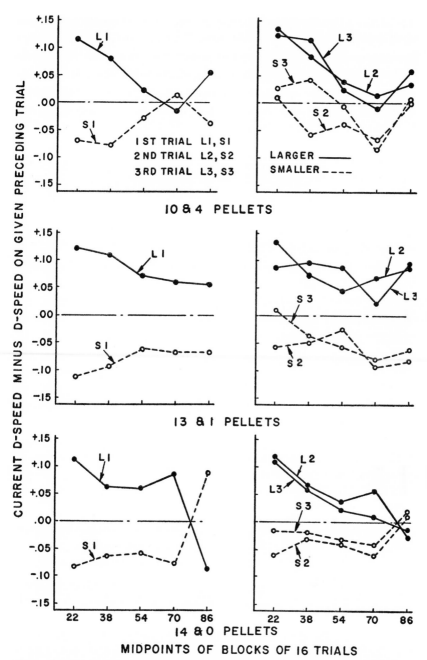

Figure 26. Transition effects with varied amount of reward and partial reinforcement at one trial a day. First-order effects are shown in the left graphs, second- and third-order effects in the right graphs. (Data from Beier, 1958)

of training by showing the change in speed following 10-pellet trials and 4-pellet trials separately. There was a clear tendency for the rats to speed up after the larger reward and to slow down after the smaller reward, especially during the first few blocks of trials analyzed. The convergence of the curves is statistically

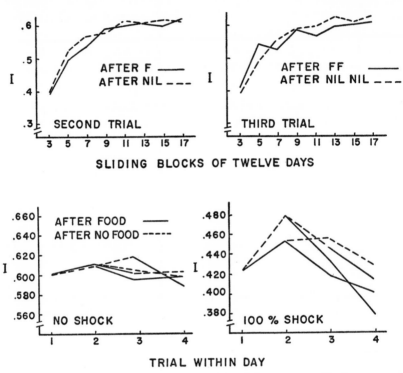

Figure 27. Transition effects under partial reinforcement with four massed trials a day. The upper graphs show second- and third-trial speeds separated according to whether the preceding trial(s) was reinforced or not. The lower left graph shows speed on all four trials for that group separated according to sequence of reward, and the lower right graph shows an analogous breakdown of speeds for a group given a mild electric shock every trial. (Exper. 57B)

significant and shows that the absolute transition effect becomes smaller, which, on the assumption that speed is a reasonably linear unit of measurement, indicates a reduction in the change-of-reward effect and/or an increase in the discrimination effect.

In the upper right corner, the second- and third-order transition effects for the same group are plotted in an analogous way. The remaining graphs show the various transition effects for the 13-and-1-pellet and 14-and-0-pellet (partial) groups. In general, a difference in reward on the first, second, or third preceding trial (intervening rewards counterbalanced) is reflected in differential performance. The crossing of the curves at the end of training for the partial reward group is statistically significant and indicates that the discrimination effect became dominant.

This was also seen in the partial reinforcement group of Exper. 57B where the rats were run four massed trials a day with reward given in one of the following orders on successive days: $++--$, $+--+$, $-++-$, $--++$. In the upper left graph of Fig. 27, the second-trial speeds are plotted separately depending on whether

Table 8. The six possible sequences in which two events (A and B) can be distributed among trials and the appropriate comparisons to determine the various transition and sequence effects. The sequence of events preceding the first trial shown must also be counterbalanced sufficiently to avoid differences in performance on the first trial.

		Trial			
Sequence	*1*	*2*	*3*	*4*	*5*
a	A	A	B	B	x
b	A	B	B	A	x
c	A	B	A	B	x
d	B	A	B	A	x
e	B	A	A	B	x
f	B	B	A	A	x

Transition effects:

    First order:

        Trial 2: [a + b + c] vs. [d + e + f]

        Trial 3: [a + e] vs. [b + f]

        Trial 4: [c + e] vs. [b + d]

    Second order:

        Trial 3: [(a + b) or (a + c)] vs. [(d + f) or (e + f)]

        Trial 4: [a + e] vs. [b + f]

    Third order:

        Trial 4: [a + c] vs. [d + f]

Sequence effects:

    Specific:

        Trial 3: [b + c] vs. [d + e]

        Trial 4: (a vs. c vs. e) and (b vs. d vs. f)

        Trial 5: a vs. b vs. c vs. d vs. e vs. f

    Over-all:

$$\sum_{2}^{5} \text{(trials): a vs. b vs. c vs. d vs. e vs. f}$$

the first trial was rewarded or not. In this case, the rats ran slightly faster on the second trial if the first trial was not rewarded even at the beginning of training, which could indicate a short-lived drive-type effect such as frustration (see Amsel and Roussel, 1952). In the upper right graph of Fig. 27, the third-trial speeds have been plotted separately depending on whether the first two trials were rewarded or not. (Days on which the first two trials were rewarded differently are not included.) The initial effect of cumulating two nonreinforcements was to lead to slower third-trial speeds than the cumulated effect of two reinforced trials, but the curves crossed as training continued indicating an eventual dominance of the discrimination effect.

The last 20 days for the partial reward group in Exper. 57B were used to prepare the lower left graph of Fig. 27. Here asymptotic speed on each trial-within-day is plotted in relation to the reward events on the prior trials. The first-trial speed was independent of the sequence of rewards on the previous day. The second-trial speed was virtually the same if the first trial was rewarded or not, indicating a close balance between the rate-of-change and the discrimination effects. The speeds separated on the third trial, speed being faster if the second trial was not rewarded, and fastest if both of the first two trials were not rewarded. The fourth-trial speeds were also somewhat faster if the third trial was not rewarded.

The lower right graph of Fig. 27 shows an analogous breakdown of the speeds of a partial reward group that also received shock on all trials. Shock served effectively to amplify the transition effects, and the results in general tend to replicate the predominance of the discrimination effect since speeds were generally faster following nonrewarded than rewarded trials.

While these transition effects appeared consistently in the data, they were small both absolutely and relative to the appropriate error variance. Thus, an analysis of variance (Table 9) of the third-trial speeds of Exper. 57B does not detect a significant effect of prior reward for either the no-shock or the shock conditions separately, the larger average effects with shock being balanced by an increase in the error variance. This heterogeneity of variance precluded making an analysis of the combined data.

The marginal statistical significance of these effects belies their importance. That one-trial effects could so consistently appear above the noise from other sources of between-rat and within-rat variance is strong testimony to their presence. Furthermore, they enable one to see, within a reward condition, many of the differences otherwise seen only by changing the conditions. For example, a number of experimenters (e.g. Humphreys, 1939) have noted an increase in speed during the early trials of extinction following partial reinforcement. The increase in speed following non-rewarded trials during training is typically averaged out, and the rise in a group mean curve could result simply from the fact that extinction is the first time all the rats are treated alike, thus making the transition effect manifest.

Table 9. Analysis of variance of the third-trial performance under partial reinforcement with and without shock, to show the effect of reward-nonreward on the first two trials. "Tests" refers to the five blocks of four days used in the analysis.

Source	d.f.	No shock		Shock	
		m.s.	F	m.s.	F
Rats	7	.3823		.2393	
Prior reward	3	.0054	1.35	.0100	1.00
First trial	1	.00086	.21	.00189	.19
Second trial	1	.00856	2.14	.01351	1.35
Interaction	1	.00663	1.66	.01463	1.46
Rats x prior reward	21	.0040		.0100	
Tests	4	.0090	2.00	.0973	3.58 *
Rats x tests	28	.0045		.0272	
Tests x prior reward	12	.0018	.72	.0069	1.05
Rats x tests x prior reward	84	.0025		.0066	

A large amount of additional data will be required before we can propose a completely satisfactory description of the various transition and sequence effects. Tentatively, however, we may conclude that:

16. When the reward is varied irregularly between two equally likely values, performance varies in accordance with the reward events recently encountered.

   a. In some circumstances (early in training, long sequences, widely distributed trials), speed is faster following the preferred reward event.

b. In some circumstances (late in training, short sequences, massed trials), speed is faster following the nonpreferred reward event.

DISCUSSION

When the reward varies from trial to trial, performance varies systematically in relation to the reward encountered on the previous trials. Average performance bears no simple relation to average reward, since it also depends on the variance of the distribution of rewards. When the reward is varied between two equally likely values, performance is different from that produced by a constant reward with the same mean value. Performance is consistently higher the wider the range of variation in the time of delay of reward. In contrast, wide variations in amount of reward lead to lower performance although, if the average amount of reward is small, some variation in amount may lead to faster speeds than constant amount.

These findings can be understood in terms of the assumption that incentive is related to the fractional anticipatory goal response (r_g) (see Spence, 1951a). Each amount of reward is assumed to evoke a particular amplitude of r_g which is then conditioned to the cues present at the time of its occurrence. When the reward is varied, each trial leads to an increment in the tendency of the r_g appropriate to the amount and delay actually encountered, and a decrement in the tendency of other r_g's conditioned on other trials.

In these terms, varied delay of reward involves a single r_g conditioned to two different ages of the traces of the stimuli present at the completion of the instrumental response. These tendencies will summate so that a long delay on part of the trials will reduce the conditioning at the short delay cues because they are reinforced on only part of the trials, but will partially make up this deficit by conditioning to a later age from which generalization can occur. On the other hand, varied amount of reward involves two different r_g's conditioned to the same trace age. These tendencies should compete, leading to a compromise between them so that a small reward on part of the trials not only reduces the conditioning of the larger r_g, because it is reinforced on only part of the trials, but also puts in a competing r_g which will average down the large one.

An important additional sentence was proposed by Beier (1958). Goal events, viewed as stimuli, should obey the laws of perception such as those of contrast and assimilation. Thus, the r_g evoked by a particular amount of reward may also depend upon what other amounts have been encountered recently in the situation.[4] Accordingly, variation between 10 and 2 pellets might involve r_g's comparable to those produced by 12 pellets and 1 pellet when received continuously.

Mathematical expression of these theoretical ideas could be proposed, but they would permit more degrees of freedom than the available data could effectively constrain. It seems prudent to leave the description of varied reward at pretty much an empirical level at the present time.

4. This proposition is not markedly different from the "elation" and "depression" effects noted by Crespi (1944) and Zeaman (1949) when amount of reward was changed (see also Schrier, 1958). The appeal of Beier's approach is that it uses laws that are not peculiar to affective stimuli and which can therefore be integrated with data from other areas. It is also interesting to note that changes in delay of reward have never been observed to produce elation and depression effects and such changes, while leading to a change in "value," do not involve contrasting r_g's.

CHAPTER 5

A Micromolar Theory

THE PURPOSE of this chapter is to describe the nature of a micromolar theory and to show how such a theory might deal with some of the situations reported in the preceding chapters. It must be recognized that the theory is still much more an approach or general attitude than it is a specific, formal set of postulates. Accordingly, while tentative, illustrative formalizations have been made later in this chapter, a general and informal discussion of the approach should provide an important introduction.

Any learning situation is assumed to have three aspects: (a) learning the stimuli to respond to, (b) learning the responses to make to those stimuli, and (c) learning the optimal way to make those responses. That is, the organism simultaneously acquires stimulus discriminations based on the qualitative and quantitative variations among the stimuli, and response differentiations based on the qualitative and quantitative variations among the responses.

The labels "quantitative" and "qualitative" are ambiguous. In the first place, it is often difficult to categorize definitively a variable as one or the other since some qualitative variations may be measurable and some quantitative variations may include differences in form. Furthermore, other dimensions, such as volume, tone, and expression, may also be identified. The terms are intended to convey the entire range of possible variations among stimuli and responses, "quantitative" referring to the intensity dimensions of stimuli and to the speed and vigor dimensions of responses, and "qualitative" including all other features of stimuli that can serve as a basis for discrimination and all other features of responses that can serve as a basis for differentiation.

The three aspects of each learning situation cannot be completely isolated, but some situations emphasize one almost to the exclusion of the others. In the conventional discrimination learning paradigm, for example, response differentiation is not relevant to measured preference. Similarly, trial-and-error learning emphasizes qualitative response selection, and research on correlated reinforcement concentrates on differentiating the way to make the response. Even in such situations, however, all three aspects are involved. In a stimulus discrimination problem, the subject must also learn what response to make (e.g. jumping, turning, approaching); in a maze, the subject must also learn that the choice points are the stimuli to which to respond, etc. In situations which emphasize one aspect, the other aspects are as simple and obvious as possible and, in any event, are not differential with respect to measured performance.

Some studies have differentially involved two of these aspects at the same time. A good example is found in the research on response-vs.-place learning (see e.g. Tolman, Ritchie, and Kalish, 1946, 1947; see also Blodgett and McCutchan, 1948; and Restle, 1957), in which rats are first run in the lower T of a +-maze with food on (say) the right and with a distinctive extra-maze cue (say, a light) over the correct goal box. Since a rat can learn the stimulus discrimination of approaching a light and the response differentiation of turning right, it would be expected to learn both in this situation. When a test trial is run from the opposite end, so that the response based on the stimulus discrimination and the response based on the response differentiation are made incompatible, performance will depend on the relative discriminability of the stimuli and responses. Two aspects are also involved in "successive" discrimination, where a rat is required to turn right when the maze is (say) white and left when it is black (see e.g. Lawrence, 1949).

No research has covered the simultaneous acquisition of all three aspects. As an example of such a design, suppose a rat enters a choice chamber containing four alleys, a pair of white and a pair of black alleys. The white and black pairs of alleys can be alternately on the right and left, and the speed at which the rat runs down the selected alley is recorded. One correct response could then be defined as "running fast down the left of the black alleys." In such a problem, the rat must learn to choose black over white, left over right, and fast over slow—i.e. all three aspects are differentially involved.

Such a design poses a number of novel complexities, primarily concerning the degree of interdependence in learning several aspects simultaneously. Thus, how is the difficulty of learning one aspect affected by the difficulty of the others? Similarly, how is the tendency to run slowly in black affected if the rat runs slowly and is not rewarded in the wrong black alley? If each of the three aspects starts at the 50-50 level, so that the probability of success is .125, how will learning compare with single-aspect learning having this initial probability, e.g. selection among eight spatially different alleys? It is precisely the complexity of such problems that favors first studying the simpler situations in detail. This brief description is intended merely to illustrate the master paradigm in terms of which any particular setting should be analyzed for its particular emphases.

The subject's problem is to learn the optimal way to make the right response to the right stimulus. The scientist's problem is to predict how well the subject will do this on the basis of three sorts of information. The first may be called the *subject conditions* since the information concerns the species of subject, his state of health, drive, wakefulness, and any other characteristics that are relevant to his response potentialities. The second concerns the *learning conditions,* including prior learning history, number and distribution of trials, and specification of the relevant aspects of the stimulus situation. Finally, there are the *performance conditions,* which identify the reward and punishment contingencies in the situation, i.e. the consequences of making each possible response in each possible way to each available stimulus.

A completely empirical approach to these problems would be to sample every possible combination of subject, learning, and performance conditions. However, there are an infinite number of them; a large book could be filled with systematic descriptions of the possible conditions using a single apparatus, a single species, a single drive, and a single reward. The alternative approach is to theorize, to attempt to formulate principles based upon a few observations that can be successfully generalized to a wide range of untried conditions. Since we can never hope to have sampled more than a relatively small number of the possible conditions, the need for some theoretical statements is taken to be self-evident. The type of theory favored here is a stimulus-response (S-R) micromolar theory.

What Is an S-R Theory?

The dependent variable in scientific psychology is behavior— the objective "doings" of the organism. Responses must be the ultimate referent of any behavior theory regardless of its structure. An S-R theory makes the most direct assumption in this regard, namely that responses are part of what the organism learns.

Typically, responses are not simply emitted; they occur to some stimulus configuration. If the evoking stimuli are freely available to the subject, then one can observe the rate at which the response occurs, but this in no wise alters the fact that the behavior takes place in some stimulus situations and not in others. An S-R theory assumes that the other part of what the subject learns is what stimuli to respond to.

These two parts are inseparably bound together. It is assumed that the organism does not learn responses independently of the stimuli to which he makes responses, and that he does not learn stimulus properties independently of the responses he makes to stimuli. Thus, the organism learns to talk only in the sense that he learns to make particular patterns of vocal responses when stimulated by specifiable physical objects, utterances by others, and feedback cues from his own prior responses. Similarly, the organism learns to discriminate tables from chairs only in the sense that to one configuration of stimuli he learns responses (labeling, sitting on) and to another he learns other responses.

An S-R theory assumes that learning constitutes a bond, or connection, between a stimulus and a response. Behavior is predicted on the basis of response tendencies, i.e. the strengths of these connections.

What Is a Micromolar Theory?

A micromolar theory extends the conventional S-R theory to include, in the definition of the response and therefore as a part of what gets learned, the quantitative dimensions of the response. This makes the response side of the S-R bond similar to the stimulus side in having both quantitative and qualitative dimensions conceived of as different events among which generalizations occur and discriminations are formed.

The extension has several significant implications. The most immediate is that the quantitative dimensions of the response cannot be viewed as measures, or indices, of response tendency. In the conventional S-R approach, it is assumed that the tendency to make a particular response to a particular stimulus can be measured by the speed and vigor of the response, e.g. the greater the rat's tendency to run down the alley, the faster it will run. But, according to a micromolar theory, response speed is itself part of what gets learned and the rat may run fast or slow depending upon the relative consequences of these different ways of responding.

The micromolar theory presented here has borrowed heavily from the Hull-Spence theory (see Logan, 1959). But many of the details and some of the variables and constructs have been revised to accommodate the modification of the definition of the response. The derivational procedures are distinctly more complicated in a micromolar theory.

Most generally, the micromolar approach suggests that stimulus differences provide a useful key to analyzing each aspect of the learning situation. Not only is discrimination learning based on the distinctiveness among external cues, but both quantitative and qualitative response differentiation are based on the discriminability of response-produced or feedback cues.

There are several ways these general ideas might be formalized. The approach taken here places the emphasis on the response side by identifying the various ways of responding as different responses with separate response tendencies. An alternative formalization placing the emphasis on the stimulus side would visualize the organism as responding or not on the basis of feedback cues of his current behavior. For example, a rat that is rewarded only if it takes over five seconds to run an alley could be viewed as discriminating between the rewarded cues of having waited five seconds and the nonrewarded ones of having waited less long. Indeed, one might propose a type of Gestalt approach in which learning is viewed as achieving that organization of the external and response-produced stimuli which provides the optimal pattern.

The present system includes many of the general ideas that

a stimulus-oriented micromolar approach might suggest. For example, the importance of response-produced stimuli in the learning of skillful ways of responding is reflected in the assumption of response generalization. It is quite likely that the stimulus-oriented and the response-oriented approaches would turn out to be isomorphic were they both developed into complete systems. The emphasis has been placed on the response side because this approach seemed somewhat simpler to conceptualize and implement at the present time.

THE CONSTRUCTS OF THE THEORY

Before turning from this broadest characterization of the approach to a detailed, illustrative set of assumptions, it may be useful to discuss briefly the major constructs in the theory. Most of them are already familiar parts of the S-R reinforcement approach as developed by Hull (1943, 1952), Spence (1956), and Miller (1959), but somewhat different interpretations are required by the micromolar assumption. There are five major constructs: habit, incentive, drive, effort, and inhibition. To be extremely informal for the moment, *habit* refers to how well the organism "knows" the response; *incentive,* to the consequences he "expects" for responding; *drive,* to how much he "wants" those consequences; *effort,* to how much work he "anticipates"; and *inhibition,* to how he "feels" at the moment. He will tend to respond to the extent that he knows how to respond and expects something he wants for responding; he will tend not to respond to the extent that it will require a lot of work and he feels tired or bored. The theory is an attempt to anchor these constructs to objective, empirical referents in the stimulus and antecedent conditions and to provide combination rules so that testable hypotheses can be deduced.

Habit (sHr). "Habit" is the major associative construct used by Hull and Spence to link stimulation to behavior. Because of the micromolar definition of the response, each quantitatively different way of responding is assumed to have a separate habit strength. Viewed across any response dimension, such as response speed, there is a habit profile composed of the habit strengths of the quantitatively different responses. Responses acquire habit either directly as a result of occurring and being rewarded or indirectly through generalization from the reinforcement of similar responses. Although response generalization is presumably related to stimulus generalization based on the similarity of response-produced cues, it will here be anchored directly to response similarity measured by differences in the quantitative dimensions of the response.

No simple way is yet known to trace the expected development of habit strength from these assumptions, because the habit profile across response speeds on the second trial depends upon the subject's speed on the first trial, since the direct increment to habit will accrue at that speed which occurred and was reinforced. The generalization of this habit to responses differing in speed permits faster and slower responses to occur and be rewarded or not according to the prevailing conditions of reinforcement. The changes in the habit profile over trials may therefore vary widely among different subjects.

This problem has been partially avoided simply by not dealing with the early phases of acquisition where the habit profile is changing. Thus, by concentrating on performance at and beyond the initial asymptote, it may be assumed that the habit profile will be flat at unity for all speed responses. While this assumption is adequate for the immediate purpose, it is only an approximation; whatever response has occurred most frequently will tend to have the strongest habit. The effects of this are particularly apparent when the conditions are changed so that performance should tend toward a different level.

No definite stand need be taken here on the reinforcement-contiguity issue. It is assumed that a rat is always reinforced after running down an alley, and since every trial is viewed as a reinforced one, there is no basis in this research for determining whether reinforcement is a necessary condition for building up habit.

Incentive (sINr). "Incentive" has been used by Hull and Spence to reflect the quantitative values of the reward as encountered by the subject, being generally higher the bigger the reward, the better its quality, the shorter its delay, and the greater its frequency. Incentive is here assumed to be specific to each S-R event, depending directly upon the reward following previous occurrences of that particular micromolar response to those stimuli, and indirectly on the reward received for similar events.

One aspect of incentive which is particularly important in analyzing the type of research reported here is the time between presentation of the stimulus and receipt of reward. The faster a rat runs down an alley, the sooner it gets to the end. It is this fact which, under conventional reward conditions, provides differential incentive value for running fast.

Incentive is presumably learned on the basis of prior experiences. Spence (1951a) has used the fractional anticipatory goal response (r_g–s_g) as the mechanism through which incentive is anchored to the reinforcement variables, and the present analysis makes frequent reference to this mechanism. However, a response-oriented micromolar approach requires that the sINr for each possible response be available before the organism starts to respond in order to act differentially and mediate selection of the optimal response. Incentive has therefore been anchored directly to the conditions of reinforcement, although this procedure is adequate only for estimating stable performance levels.

Drive (D). "Drive" is the only major construct that is not specific to particular S-R events. This follows the approach of Hull and Spence of summating the various drives present into a generalized drive state. Of special importance here is the question of whether the incentive value of a reward is affected by the (relevant) drive level at the time it is received; i.e. does a piece of food of a particular size produce the same incentive regardless of how hungry the subject is? At least over the fairly small range of drive levels used, it is assumed that the relation between sINr and the conditions of reinforcement is independent of the drive level.

Effort (sFr). This construct is new within the S-R reinforcement approach, although a similar variable has been used by Tolman (1955). "Effort" depends upon the work required by the response and reduces, in proportion to its amount, the likelihood of making the response.

Two conceptions might be proposed. In the one tentatively followed here, sFr is postulated as a direct function of work so that sFr is immediately given and functions mathematically as a threshold. That is, a response cannot occur unless the response tendency based on habit, incentive, and drive exceeds the effort required.

An alternative approach would view effort as learned on the

basis of past experiences: e.g. the subject must learn how much work it takes to run fast. This would account for instances where the learning curve temporarily overshoots its eventual asymptote. The "not-responding" mechanism used by Hull in treating conditioned inhibition might be adapted to this end. However, until the other variables that are changing during acquisition have been related to the number of trials, there is no clear basis for formalizing this idea.

Temporary inhibition (sTIr). It is assumed that the occurrence of a response to a stimulus sets up a tendency that opposes repeating that response to that stimulus regardless of whether the response was reinforced or not. The inhibition is temporary and diminishes over time. Half of this notion is familiar in Hull's theory as "reactive inhibition." The logic of the present theory, however, favors the inseparability of stimulus and response and therefore includes the idea of "stimulus satiation" (see e.g. Glanzer, 1953a and 1953b) as well as that of response fatigue (see Walker, 1958). When these are placed in opposition, as in recent work on alternation behavior (see Dember and Fowler, 1958), the tendency to avoid the same stimulus relative to the tendency to avoid the same response presumably depends on the discriminability of the stimuli and responses.

A major problem with sTIr in a micromolar theory is the question of whether it applies to quantitative variations in the response. That is, is there a temporary tendency opposing running at the same speed as on the previous trial? If so, then an additional source of trial-to-trial variability must be considered. A definite stand on this issue is not taken because an empirical test could not be made until the other sources of intra-subject variability have been more precisely specified.

Since most of the research reported here involved widely distributed practice, sTIr presumably was minimal. Accordingly, it is referred to subsequently only when dealing with discrepancies between the data obtained with massed and distributed trials.

Response measures. A micromolar theory makes predictions in terms of probability of response. Each response, defined with reference to its quantitative dimensions, has a response tendency based upon its habit, incentive, drive, effort, and temporary inhibition components. The momentary oscillation of these tendencies produces a probability distribution showing the likelihood of each response having the strongest tendency at the moment.

Conventional response measures, such as speed and amplitude, are therefore not typically useful as indices of response tendency. Predictions about these measures are made by determining the expected probability distribution of speeds or amplitudes and calculating the relevant parameters of this distribution for comparison with measured performance.

There are circumstances in which a micromolar theory predicts a monotonic relationship between the quantitative dimensions of the response and the several aspects of response tendency, such as drive or amount of reward, and for which a macromolar theory might be useful. These are situations in which increases in the observed quantitative dimension (a) are differentially reinforced and (b) require more effort. Response speed using the conventional procedure is a case in point, since faster speeds require more effort but get reward sooner. Rats are therefore expected to run faster under higher drive or to a larger reward. On the other hand, greater forces of a bar-pressing response require more work but do not typically gain added reward, and force is therefore not expected to show any simple relationship to the components of response tendency.

It should be observed that the precise relationship expected depends upon the particular terms function involved. For example, a one-second reduction in response time normally reduces by one second the time before the reward is received. It would be possible to let a one-second reduction in response time get the reward two seconds sooner. Such a procedure would be expected to yield a quantitatively different relationship between (say) drive and response speed although the function should still be a generally increasing one. Accordingly, a macromolar analysis for such situations would be restricted to a greater-than level of quantification.

An Illustrative Micromolar Model

It is a big move from a casual and informal description of a theory to a rigorous, formal statement of postulates. It has been necessary to take a tentative step in this direction in order to illustrate adequately the micromolar approach. The implications of the approach can best be understood in terms of mathematical representations of the assumptions and subsequent manipulations of these symbols.

Any research directed at a relatively small area of behavior can have theoretical significance only in the context provided by a reasonably general behavior theory. The present studies are primarily relevant to the incentive construct in the theory. But predicted performance depends upon all constructs in the theory and hence the interpretation of any obtained data must take the entire system into account. For example, whether delayed reward should be assumed to provide less incentive than immediate reward depends in part upon whether, elsewhere in the theory, delay has been assumed to have some effect such as frustration or counterconditioning.

The postulates given below cover a number of areas on which the present research has no direct bearing but which are needed as a context in which to embed the suggested theoretical ideas. The present approach leans heavily on the Hull-Spence approach not only for general orientation but also for content. Indeed, most of the postulates, while worded somewhat differently, could be traced to their origins in the works of Hull (e.g. 1943, 1952) and Spence (e.g. 1951b, 1956).

It is assumed that the ideas of Hull and Spence are sufficiently familiar to the reader, either through their own writings or through the various secondary sources (e.g. Hilgard, 1956; Koch, 1954; Logan, 1959) that there would be little to gain from actually explicating these background details. The present research program has suggested that the micromolar assumption can be followed as a general approach to behavior theory if an effort variable is accepted and if the incentive variable is made specific to each S-R event and is anchored so as to include the interval as well as the amount and delay of reinforcement. These postulates reflect a somewhat greater emphasis on the inseparability of S-R events and attempt to treat classical conditioning in the same way as instrumental conditioning without providing any original data in support of this position. An explicit assumption has been made about the removal of inhibition in order to handle various effects in relearning and discrimination learning. Otherwise the differences between this system and those of Hull and Spence are believed to be relatively unimportant.

THE POSTULATES

I. *Response definition.*

A. The overt response (R) of the organism is isomorphic with the hypothetical response (r) of the model described by the following postulates.

B. The model is concerned with the probability of occurrence of any member of an r class.

C. The r class may be composed of any aggregate of behaviors differing qualitatively and/or quantitatively, provided only that the determinants of excitatory potential are the same for all members of the class.

D. The several dimensions of the response (e.g. speed, amplitude) are independent, and derivations concerning each may be made separately.

II. *Stimulus reception.*

A. Stimulus trace amplitude.

1. The occurrence of any physical energy (S), acting upon a suitable receptor, initiates a stimulus trace (s), the amplitude of which begins at a maximum shortly after the onset of S and decays as a decreasing concave-upward function of time (t).

2. The termination of a stimulus (S′) initiates a stimulus trace (s′), the amplitude of which begins at a maximum shortly after the offset of the stimulus and decays as a decreasing concave-upward function of time (t).

3. At any constant value of t, the amplitude of s or s′ is an increasing, concave downward function of the intensity of S as measured in physical terms.

4. The similarity of any two stimulus traces which would otherwise be identical were their amplitudes equal is inversely related to the arithmetic difference between their amplitudes.

5. Each stimulus trace interacts with concomitant stimulus traces, yielding an effective stimulus trace (s̄).

6. A change in intensity of a stimulus sets up simultaneously the s of the new intensity and the s′ of the old, s̄ being the absolute difference between them.

B. Stimulus trace quality. The stimulus trace is also characterized by qualitative dimensions which are uniquely related to the nonintensity characteristics of the stimulus as measured in physical or psychophysical terms.

C. Proprioception. Each response of the intact organism provides characteristic stimulation.

III. *Primary motivation.*

A. There are five states of affairs which produce drive (D) (D varies from zero to unity):

1. Hunger (Df) is an S-shaped increasing function of the number of hours [1] (hf) of food deprivation. Df is a concave downward, decreasing function of the amount of food in a regular maintenance diet.

2. Thirst (Dw) is an S-shaped increasing function of the number of hours (hw) of water deprivation. Dw is a decreasing function of the amount of water (or other suitable liquid) given during regular maintenance.

3. Sex (Ds) is an S-shaped increasing function of the number of hours (hs) of sex deprivation.

4. Pain (Dp) is an S-shaped increasing function of the intensity of noxious stimulation (Sp).

5. Fear (De) is an increasing function of the amplitude of responses (re) innately attached to noxious, unusual, or sudden stimuli (Se).

B. When several drives are concomitantly present within the model, the total drive (D) is the behavioral summation of the separate drives, e.g. $D = Df + DW - DfDw$.

C. For each drive there is a characteristic drive stimulus (S_D) the intensity of which is directly related to the intensity of that drive present.

IV. *Secondary motivation.* The responses evoking De can be attached to originally neutral stimuli according to the principles of this system. When so elicited, fear is termed a secondary drive and varies with the amplitude of the fear-evoking responses.

V. *Primary reinforcement.*

A. For each primary drive there is an appropriate goal re-

---

1. The three deprivation drives are not a function simply of time but also of the conditions during that time. Hunger may depend on the amount of activity during the deprivation; thirst clearly depends on the amount of dry food eaten as well as on temperature and humidity; sex may depend on activity. Furthermore, there are specific hungers and preferences that are not yet reflected in the postulates.

sponse (R_G) evoked by goal stimuli (S_G). The occurrence of R_G is a primary reinforcing state of affairs, the amplitude of R_G determining the amount of primary reinforcement.

B. When fear is elicited as a secondary drive, the occurrence of the appropriate R_G is termed derived primary reinforcement.

VI. *Secondary reinforcement.* A fractional part (r_g) of R_G can be attached to originally neutral stimuli according to the principles of this system. The occurrence of r_g is a secondary reinforcing state of affairs, the amplitude of r_g determining the amount of secondary reinforcement.

VII. *Habit strength.*

A. The occurrence of a reinforcement immediately following a response produces an increment in the habit tendency (sHr) for that response to recur to the stimulus traces present during the response. The limit of sHr is unity.

B. The increment in sHr per reinforcement (N) is a constant fraction of the yet-to-be acquired sHr.

C. Habit is permanent and cannot be reduced.

VIII. *Inhibition.*

A. Formation.

1. The failure of occurrence of a reinforcement immediately following a response produces an increment in inhibitory tendency (sIr) between the stimuli present during the response and that response. The limit of sIr is sHr.

2. The increment in sIr per nonreinforcement (n) is a constant fraction of the yet-to-be-acquired sIr.

B. Removal.

1. The occurrence of a reinforcement immediately following a response produces a decrement in inhibitory tendency.

2. The decrement in sIr per reinforcement is a constant fraction of the sIr present.

IX. *Effective habit.* The effective habit strength (s$\bar{\text{H}}$r) is the arithmetical difference between the sHr and the sIr present.

X. *Unlearned response tendencies.* The organism is born with, or is predisposed to acquire through maturation, tendencies to respond (sUr) in a particular manner to a specifiable pattern of stimulation.

XI. *Incentive motivation.*

A. The occurrence of R_G or r_g immediately following a response produces incentive motivation (sINr) for repetition of that response to the coincident stimulus traces.

B. The sINr is computed sequentially as follows:

1. sJ′r is a decreasing concave-upward function of the time the reward is delayed after the response is complete.

2. sK′r is an increasing concave-downward function of the amount of reinforcement.

3. sKr is the product of sJ′r and sK′r.

4. The change in sKr on any trial is a constant fraction of the difference between its previous level and that appropriate to the delay and amount of reward encountered on that trial.

5. sJr is a decreasing concave-upward function of the response interval, i.e. in the time that response requires for completion.

6. sINr is the product of sKr and sJr.

7. The total motivation complex (sMr) is the product of D and sINr.

XII. *Generalization.*

A. Stimulus generalization. Any sHr, sIr, or sKr established between any stimulus and response generalizes to all similar stimuli. The amount of generalized s̲Hr, s̲Ir, or s̲Kr is a function of the amount at the original s and is a decreasing concave upward function of the difference between the original s and the generalized s̲.

B. Response generalization. Any sHr, sIr, or sKr established between a stimulus and any response generalizes to all similar responses. The amount of generalized sHr̲, sIr̲, or sKr̲ is a function of the amount available for the original r and is a decreasing concave upward function of the difference between the original r and the generalized r̲.

C. When several sHr's, sIr's, or sKr's generalize upon the same stimulus and/or the same response, the total of each is determined by the behavioral summation of the separate amounts.

XIII. *Excitatory potential.* The excitatory potential (sEr) for a stimulus to evoke a response is given by the product sH̄r and sMr.

XIV. *Effort.*

A. Effort (sFr) is a positively accelerated function of the work to be involved in the response.

B. sĒr is the arithmetic subtraction of sFr from sEr.

XV. *Oscillation.*

A. A number (sOr) is selected at random from a normal distribution having a constant mean and variance and a 5-unit range.

B. The value of sOr remains constant for a behavioral unit of time (BUT).

C. sĖr is the arithmetic subtraction of sOr from sĒr.

XVI. *Temporary inhibition.*

A. The occurrence of a response to a stimulus sets up a temporary inhibition (sTIr) of the tendency to repeat that response to that stimulus.

B. sTIr dissipates as a concave upward, decreasing function of the time since the previous occurrence of the response to the stimulus.

C. sĖr is the arithmetic subtraction of sTIr from sĖr.

XVII. *Competition of reaction potentials.*

A. When several incompatible responses are in competition the one with the largest sĖr will occur.

B. The probability of occurrence of any one response within an exhaustive domain can be approximated by raising all competing sĖr's to a power that is positively related to their raw sum and determining the proportion of the new sum commanded by the response.

An Illustrative Derivation

Although a micromolar theory seems well adapted for conditions of correlated reinforcement, it is not immediately obvious that such a theory can deal adequately with constant reward conditions. As these conditions do not involve an explicit correlation between the response dimensions and the reward, there would seem to be no basis for predicting differential effects such as are found with various amounts and delays of reward. The following derivations are intended not only to illustrate the actual mechanics of the theory but also to show that a micromolar approach can, at least in principle, be applied successfully to the kinds of constant reward conditions typically treated by a macromolar theory.

The condition selected for the major derivation is that for the *I*-speed of a group of rats receiving 2 pellets reward at a one-second delay on a 24-hour feeding cycle and a 12-gram diet. The specific functions used are not proposed as a general quantification of the model; they were selected only to give a reasonable and approximate representation of obtained data.

The amount of reward determines sK'r. Using the function

$$sK'r = .75(1 - 10^{-.1367W}) + .25, \qquad (1)$$

it obtains that 2 pellets yields an sK'r of .6. Since the amount of reward is independent of *I*-speed, this value of sK'r will apply to all response speeds. These considerations are shown graphically in the first row in Fig. 28.

The delay of reward determines sJ'r. Using the function

$$sJ'r = .6667(10^{-.0969D}) + .3333, \qquad (2)$$

it obtains that a delay of one second yields an sJ'r of .8667. Since delay is uncorrelated with *I*-speed, this value of sJ'r will apply to all response speeds. These considerations are shown in the first three graphs in the second row of Fig. 28.

In the fourth graph in that row, the values of sK'r and sJ'r have been multiplied to yield the sKr. This value, which is constant at .52 for all response speeds, may be thought of as the incentive produced by a goal box into which a 2-pellet reward is customarily dropped after a 1-sec. delay.

To complete determination of the incentive variable, we must determine the sJr based on the fact that faster speeds get the rat to the goal box sooner than slower speeds. Assuming that sJr depends on this response interval according to the function

$$sJr = I^{-.5}, \qquad (3)$$

and since response interval against speed is described by

$$I = R^{-1}, \qquad (4)$$

it obtains that sJr varies among the responses of different speeds according to the function

$$sJr = R^{.5}. \qquad (5)$$

These considerations are presented in the first three graphs in the third row of Fig. 28. The total incentive can then be represented by the equation

$$sINr = .52R^{.5}, \qquad (6)$$

as shown in the last graph in the third row of Fig. 28.

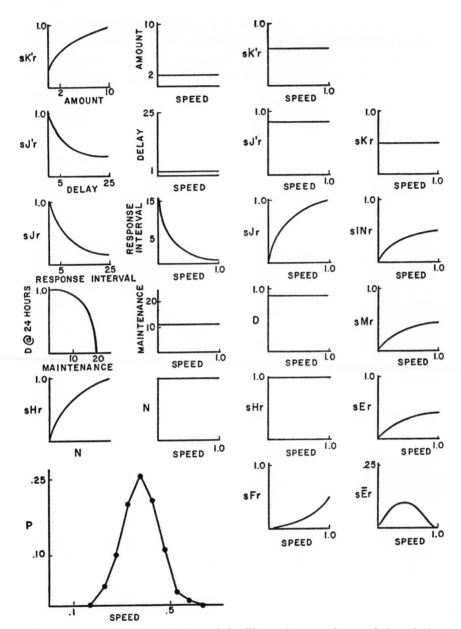

Figure 28. Graphic representation of the illustrative equations and the solution of the micromolar theory.

The drive level (D) produced by a daily 12-gram diet (M) is estimated from the function

$$D = (1 - M/20)^{.5}, \tag{7}$$

and yields a value of .9. The total motivation (sMr) is then the multiplication of D and sINr, yielding the equation

$$sMr = .468R^{.5}. \tag{8}$$

These considerations are shown graphically in the third row of Fig. 28.

The growth of habit is a concave downward, increasing function of the number of trials, but, as we have noted previously, the precise course of habit growth will depend on the speeds actually performed. For predicting asymptotic speed, however, we may take the slightly incorrect assumption that enough different speed responses will have occurred to raise sHr virtually to unity for all speed responses. Hence, the sEr values at asymptote are approximated by

$$sEr = .468R^{.5}. \tag{9}$$

Finally, taking the equation

$$sFr = .5R^2 \tag{10}$$

as a representation of the effort function, we can write the equation for sĒr as

$$s\bar{E}r = .468R^{.5} - .5R^2. \tag{11}$$

This function is shown in the lower right corner of Fig. 28 and gives the effective excitatory potential for each speed response.

A quick behavioral prediction can now be made because the speed that has the highest sĒr will be the most likely to occur and hence will be the expected modal response. Differentiating the sĒr equation and setting equal to zero:

$$\frac{d\,s\bar{E}r}{d\,R} = .234R^{-.5} - R,$$

$$R^{1.5} = .234,$$

$$(\text{modal})\ R = .38. \tag{12}$$

More detailed predictions can be made by transforming the sĒr function into a probability distribution. Briefly to describe how this is done: (a) select class intervals of speed for which probabilities are to be estimated; (b) integrate the sĒr function and evaluate the definite integral for the several class intervals involved (these areas are treated as relative indices of the excitatory potentials for those response classes); (c) determine the total area and thence the power approximation to oscillation; (d) raise the areas to the indicated power and standardize to sum to unity.

These steps have been illustrated numerically in Table 10, and

Table 10. Steps in the transformation of an sĒr equation into a probability distribution over response-class intervals.

Response class	$\int_0^R$	$\int_i^u$	$\left[\int_i^u\right]^P$	P
.00–.05	.00348	348		
.05–.10	.00969	621		
.10–.15	.01757	788		
.15–.20	.02656	899	7	.0038
.20–.25	.03640	984	55	.0302
.25–.30	.04677	1037	182	.0998
.30–.35	.05747	1070	373	.2045
.35–.40	.06828	1081	470	.2577
.40–.45	.07901	1073	397	.2177
.45–.50	.08946	1045	217	.1190
.50–.55	.09955	1009	97	.0532
.55–.60	.10902	947	23	.0126
.60–.65	.11774	872	3	.0016
.65–.70	.12558	784		
.70–.75	.13233	675		
.75–.80	.13790	557		
.80–.85	.14216	426		
.85–.90	.14489	273		
.90–.95	.14596	107		
.95–.957	.14599	3		

Condition: 2 pellets, 1″ delay, 12 gm/day. sĒr $= .468\ R^{.5} - .5\ R^2$
Maximum nonzero R: $R^{1.5} = .936$; $R = .957$
Total area: $.312\ (.957)^{1.5} - .1667\ (.957)^3 = .14599$
Power (P): $P = 150\ (.14599) + 1 = 22.8985$
Median R $= .3814$

the resulting probability distribution is plotted in the lower left graph of Fig. 28. The expected median response speed is .3814.

These same equations and operations have been used for the other values of delayed reward on which data were obtained in

Exper. 56C. The smooth curve in Fig. 29 represents the results of these computations, and the circles give the actually obtained data. It is clear that the present interpretation of the micromolar theory does successfully imply a concave-upward decreasing function relating *I*-speed to time of delay of reward, and that a reasonably good fit to the data can be obtained.

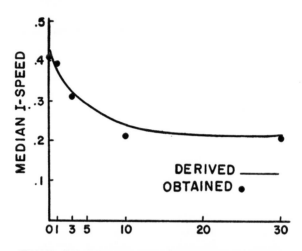

Figure 29. The function relating median *I*-speed to the time of delay of reinforcement as derived from the micromolar theory using the illustrative equations, and actually obtained speeds.

By referring back to Fig. 28, the reader can easily convince himself that differences in the amount of reward or in the drive level would have appropriate effects on predicted speed. Such differences would affect the constant in the sĒr equation (9), and predicted speed is a monotonic increasing function of the size of this constant.

Speed is not, however, a linear function of this constant, but instead is a root function of it. For this reason a multiplicative interaction between intervening variables may appear as an additive performance interaction between the relevant independent variables.

The use of this theory for the more complex correlated reinforcement conditions will be illustrated as the results obtained using those conditions are presented. In general, it can be anticipated that the theory predicts adjustment to conditions in which the amount and/or the delay of reward are correlated with the response speed, since the maximally reinforced way of responding will tend to have the highest sĒr and hence it will be the most likely to occur.

NOTE: ON THE EFFECT OF DRIVE ON INCENTIVE

In relating incentive to the reward conditions, an assumption must be made about whether the incentive value of a given reward is affected by the drive level present at the time it is given. It would seem that the subject must at least be hungry enough to eat if food is to produce incentive. Beyond this, a given quantity of food might have more (or less) incentive value the hungrier the subject is. One might argue that the hungry subject needs the food more and hence "values" it higher, or that a small amount of food is relatively inconsequential to a very hungry subject and hence has less incentive value.

This question cannot be answered directly by means of present techniques in the alley. However, evidence in studies of alternation behavior provides an indirect approach to the question. In an experiment by Fowler, rats escaping shock in the stem of a T-maze by turning either direction tended to alternate on the second trial if the shock on the first trial had been weak, but to repeat if the shock had been strong. Since these results were independent of the shock present on the second trial, they can be interpreted as indicating that alternation is independent of drive but inversely related to the amount of reinforcement.

If this interpretation of the shock data is accepted, and if it can be legitimately generalized to the hunger drive, then the alternation situation can be used to address the question of whether the incentive value of a given amount of food is affected by the level of hunger. If rats differing in hunger show different degrees of alternation, the differences could be interpreted as indicating a difference in the reinforcement provided by the food.

Following this reasoning, rats from several of the experiments in the alley were run in an alternation situation. The apparatus was a simple T-maze with a grey stem, a white arm, and a black arm. The rats were given a free choice trial with 5 pellets reward in the arm chosen and were then returned immediately to the start box for their second trial.

The various drive conditions and the percent of alternation are summarized in Table 11. Only very small differences in alterna-

Table 11. The effect of various conditions of hunger drive level on percent alternation in a T-maze.

Experiment	Drive	N	Percent alternation
58C	12 gm/day for 120 days, 10 gm/day for 3 days, 24-hr. deprivation	8	75
58C	12 gm/day for 100 days, 18 gm/day for 20 days, 20 gm/day for 3 days, 24-hr. deprivation	24	83
58D	12 gm/day for 120 days, 36-hr. deprivation	13	85
58D	12 gm/day for 120 days, 36-hr. deprivation and 20 gms. given 3 hrs. before test	13	77
57B	12 gm/day for 60 days, 6 gm/day for 1 day, 24-hr. deprivation	13	85
57B	12 gm/day for 60 days, 20 gm/day for 1 day, 10 gms. reward pellets given 2 hrs. before test	17	71

tion behavior resulted from the manipulations of the drive level. There was a slight tendency for low-drive animals to alternate least, particularly under conditions in which the animals became so satiated on the reward pellets that several refused to eat the pellets in the T-maze. The differences, however, are so small as to make reasonable the assumption that the incentive value of a particular reward is largely independent of the drive level.

Note: On the Power Approximation to Oscillation

The theory presented here has followed the approach developed by Hull in assuming that reaction potential is subject to oscillation from moment to moment and that, when several responses are in competition, the one with the highest potential at the moment will occur. This assumption, however, is not mathematically convenient for converting reaction potentials into probabilities and, when more than two responses must be considered, there is no straightforward solution at all.

The author has elsewhere (Logan, 1956) used one approximation to the solution of this problem. Basically, that procedure involved evaluating all possible pairs of responses and determining joint probabilities. The procedure used here is a simpler approximation.

Consider two responses, A and B, with reaction potentials of .60 and .40 respectively. Using the formal oscillation assumption, it is possible to derive the probability of A as a function of the size of the sigma of the oscillation distribution; generally, the larger the sigma of oscillation, the lower the probability of A.

If we use the formula

$$Pr[A] = E_A{}^P/(E_A{}^P + E_B{}^P),$$

then the probability of A will be seen to be an increasing function of the exponent P. If this formula is used, an increase in the value of P has the same effect as reducing the sigma of oscillation.

However, with a constant value of the sigma of oscillation, probability using the oscillation procedure depends only on the arithmetic difference between the competing excitatory potentials and not on their absolute size. That is, if the excitatory potentials were .80 and .60 rather than .60 and .40, the same probability of

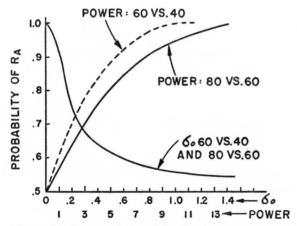

Figure 30. Percent choice of the dominant response as determined by the oscillation assumption and by the power approximation to it.

the stronger response would be expected. With the power procedure, this is not the case. Using the same power, a constant arithmetic difference produces a lower probability of A the higher the absolute values of the sEr's. Accordingly, an additional rule must be used to relate the appropriate power to the size of the competing reaction potentials.

These effects are shown graphically in Fig. 30. It will be seen that the mathematical consequences of the oscillation assumption can be represented by a power approximation containing two parts: (a) for any constant value of sEr, the appropriate power is inversely related to the indicated sigma of oscillation and (b) for any constant sigma of oscillation, the appropriate power is directly related to the absolute size of the competing sEr's. These rules can be equally well applied with any number of competing reaction potentials.

CHAPTER 6

The Problem of Response Definition

ALTHOUGH most psychologists seem to agree that behavior is the proper dependent variable in psychological research, no explicit definition of the response is generally accepted. Implicit notions about the response have been borrowed from the everyday vernacular, and relatively little attention has been paid to formalizing these or other ideas. This chapter will present some of the problems concerning the nature of the response that were encountered during the present research program.

The problem of defining the response is pragmatic and cannot be solved solely by logical analysis. Analysis can help to identify the various alternatives, but the choice among them is made on the basis of how successfully any definition works. Because the body of empirical knowledge in psychology is relatively small and expanding rapidly, any propositions made at the present time must be recognized as being very tentative.

At the most primitive empirical level there is no particular problem, since it is sufficient to describe the observations made and the relationships found. However, if one wants to formulate laws in order to generalize beyond the specific situation studied, then one must indicate how other responses should be viewed when applying the laws. Thus, it is not immediately obvious how observing rats running down an alley could enable us to make statements about other responses of the rat, much less about interesting aspects of human behavior. Generalizations can be made only in terms of some conception of responses that tells how the laws discovered in one situation can be interpreted for other situations.

The present approach assumes that responses that differ in any way whatsoever are different in the sense that they may be put into different response classes so that separate response tendencies can be calculated for them. They may not be different in the sense that a subject can differentiate between them, since the scientist (or his instruments) can typically make finer discriminations than the subject. The degree of difference in this second sense is reflected in the numerical value of response tendency: responses that are indiscriminable to the subject will, if separated by the scientist, have the same numerical strength.

The problem of response definition is the problem of specifying the rules according to which several distinguishable behaviors are aggregated into a single response class about which empirically true statements can be made. For example, the response class "bar-press" aggregates presses with the left paw, the right paw, the mouth, etc. An empirical law that asserts a relationship between some dimension of bar-presses and some independent variable assumes that that relationship is true regardless of which member of the response class any particular rat happens to display.

There is no "natural" classification scheme inherent in behavior. The everyday language contains a wide range of response concepts and conventions for talking about behavior. Borrowing from the vernacular is common in the early stages of a science, but explication and refinement of such notions must ultimately be achieved. For a methodological discussion of the problem of defining psychological terms, see Mandler and Kessen (1959).

It should also be pointed out that different scientists may use different aggregation rules. Presumably each is guided by some theoretical notions in formulating concepts relevant to his interests. It seems likely that some laws will use concepts at one level and others at another. A discussion of response definition in this sense can be found in Logan, Olmsted, Rosner, Schwartz, and Stevens (1955).

Although from the present point of view responses could be distinguished if they differ in any way whatsoever, there is no point in separating responses into different classes if the theory does not permit calculating numerically different values of response tendency for them. That is, the theory can predict which of two responses is more likely only if different values of response tendency can be calculated. Differences among responses that are not importantly related to response tendency can be suppressed.

This conception is consistent with what appears to be the most common basis of response aggregation, namely the conditions of reinforcement. Responses are separated if the environment, broadly conceived, distinguishes between them in administering rewards. If responses are differentially reinforced, then differential incentive may be developed, in which case there would be a difference in response tendency. The exception is when the responses are indistinguishable to the subject, in which case the generalization of incentive between the responses will be complete and no differentiation could be formed.

There are other components of response tendency which could provide a basis for separating responses. Differential punishment may produce differential negative incentive (see Chapter 10). Differences in work may produce differences in response tendency through the effort variable. The initial strength of the response may affect its likelihood of occurring sufficiently to realize its possible response tendency.

Furthermore, the response is here considered to be inherently inseparable from the stimulus for the responding organism and hence the stimulus must be included in the definition of the response—or better, in the definition of an S-R event. This inseparability is already reflected in most common response labels (e.g. press the bar, run the alley) since they include the relevant stimulus term as well as the response term. Thus, variables that are correlated with stimulus differences and that affect response tendency provide a basis for forming classes of S-R events.

Finally, responses that are separated in one stimulus complex can be separated in a similar stimulus complex in which there is no internal basis for distinction. For example, if presses with either paw are reinforced in one apparatus, they could nevertheless be distinguished if the rat were at other times rewarded only for right paw presses in another apparatus.

It is not implied that all members of a class actually have the same numerical value of response tendency, but only that they could have. Some members may not have occurred sufficiently often to realize their possible strength. Accordingly, the theory makes statements about some member of the class indiscriminately and not about all members of the class.

A scientist cannot be prevented from separating into classes responses in which he is interested even though the theory provides no basis for making differential predictions. In the same vein, a scientist might be interested in classes that aggregate responses for which differential response tendency could be calculated. For example, if a rat is given a choice between two bars, one of which is rewarded only if pressed with the right paw and the other only if pressed with the left paw, the bar chosen is clearly an interesting datum even though each bar involves two differentially reinforced classes of behavior. One of the exciting problems to be solved is how to make predictions in such situations.

With this background let us turn to three aspects of the problem of response definition that will be briefly discussed here. The first of these concerns the aggregation rule for qualitatively different behaviors. This aspect has been dealt with as the distinction between molar and molecular approaches and is included here primarily to provide a familiar reference for contrast with the other aspects. The second concerns the aggregation rule for quantitatively different behaviors and will be characterized by the distinction between a "macro" and a "micro" approach. Finally, there is the problem of the duration of the response. These three aspects address the aggregation problem along somewhat different dimensions, seeking to bound the response class in terms of kind, amount, and extent.

Molar vs. Molecular

This aspect of the response definition problem concerns the aggregation rule concerning qualitatively different responses (see e.g. Guthrie, 1935; Hull, 1943; Spence, 1956; Tolman, 1932). Any particular instance of behavior is a member of a number of progressively larger and more molar qualitative response classes. For example, a rat that makes a series of movements in a T-maze also "turns right," "approaches the goal," etc. The issue here, then, is at what level of molarity can the behavior be most usefully described.

The rules discussed above would permit any aggregation that preserves the reinforcement contingencies in the situation. Thus, if the reward is given independently of how the rat gets into the correct goal box of a T-maze, then the various ways of doing it can be classed together. Similarly, any response that gets the bar down in a bar-pressing situation can be considered to be a press if there is no clear differential in reward, work, or other determinant of response tendency. In the alley, we have not distinguished between direct running, sidling or backing down it, climbing along the top, etc., since the reward was contingent only upon the breaking of the photobeam and not upon what portion of the animal broke the beam or how it got into that position.

The complication that has been added to this aspect of the problem is that it has been involved in the question of "what is learned" (see e.g. Campbell, 1954; Kendler, 1952; Roseboom, 1958; and Smedslund, 1953). It must be emphasized that the rules for aggregating qualitatively different responses into classes do not specify how molar a response the subject actually learns. When the subject performs in some way and is rewarded, he has not necessarily also learned all the other behaviors that the experimenter is prepared equally to reward on other occasions. As an obvious example, a hungry rat that has learned to press a bar for food could not be expected also to have learned that pushing against a panel is equally rewarded, even though both might fall, under some conditions, into the class of responses that make the food magazine click.

Indeed, the question of what the subject actually learns cannot be answered empirically. It can be answered in the sense that a theory can state what it assumes the subject has learned and can gain support for this assumption (along with the rest of the theory) from confirmation of its implications. An alternative theory, however, may do equally well making a markedly different assumption about what is learned. The present approach assumes that the subject learns (i.e. the direct increment in habit accrues to) the very specific S-R event that occurred, but that there is generalization to similar S-R events. The problem is to specify the dimensions of similarity in some way that permits more than attractive after-the-fact descriptions. Very little attention has yet been given to this problem.

"MACRO" vs. "MICRO"

This aspect of the response definition problem concerns the treatment of quantitatively different behaviors. The micro approach that is favored here treats variations in speed and amplitude in a manner closely analogous to that described for qualitatively different behaviors. Responses that differ quantitatively are considered to be different responses, but they can be aggregated into classes according to the same rules given previously.

There is almost always some basis for separating quantitatively different behaviors. Speed is typically differentially reinforced since faster responses get the reward sooner. Variations in both speed and amplitude presumably involve differences in effort. Although quantitatively different responses are sufficiently similar that generalization among them typically assures that all of the various speeds and amplitudes will occur, there are cases where the subject persists in making a quantitatively inefficient response even though a better, but untried, response is available.

The alternative macro approach treats quantitative differences among responses as a measure, or index, of response strength. Such an approach is exemplified in Hull's theory, in which the response is defined primarily by its qualitative properties and is assumed to increase in speed and amplitude as it increases in probability.

If speed and amplitude were consistently viewed as response measures for all situations, then a strong appeal for this approach could be made on the grounds of simplicity. Hull (1943) and Spence (1956), however, have restricted their use of the approach to conditions of uncorrelated reinforcement assuming, as Skinner (1950) has effectively argued, that speed and amplitude cannot be used as measures of response strength if they are specifically trained by correlated reinforcement. Actually, there is no reason in principle why speed and amplitude cannot be used as response measures in all situations. In the next chapter, an equilibrium model is described that deals with conditions of correlated reinforcement using the conventional macro approach. If successful, this approach would seem to have the advantage of derivational simplicity.

On the other hand, a micro approach has several logical advantages. It avoids the questionable distinction between qualitative and quantitative dimensions of the response since both are treated in the same manner. It makes the response side of the S-R bond similar to the stimulus side in having a number of dimensions along which generalization occurs and discriminations are formed. Furthermore, since it will be shown that the equilibrium model does not work, the micro approach offers the greater hope of providing a theory that is general enough to deal with the various conditions within simple instrumental conditioning.

THE DURATION OF THE RESPONSE

Any recorded instrumental response can be viewed as a behavior chain composed of a sequence of movements which, in combination, complete an act. One aspect of the response definition problem concerns the number of movements along such a chain [1] that may be aggregated. The qualitative and quantitative characterization of each link must be retained in aggregating them into chains. The maximum appropriate chain length is presumably that over which the reward is determined. Thus, when a rat is required to run down an alley for food, the response begins with the onset of the stimulus (i.e. the opening of the start door) and ends when the requisite chain has been completed.

This procedure is sufficient to determine whether a specified chain did indeed occur. If, however, one wants to do more than make an all-or-none identification, i.e. to assign a score to the performance, then a more detailed interpretation is necessary, since differentially reinforced chains should not be given the same score. Suppose, for example, that a rat is required to run slowly in the first half of an alley and rapidly in the second half. Clearly, any number of sequences could take the same total time, yet only some of them are rewarded. One should not aggregate, for scoring purposes, links that have different correlations with the reward even though it is their joint performance that determines the reward.

THE INDEPENDENCE OF THE RESPONSE
DIMENSIONS

The breakdown of the response into the several types of dimensions discussed here is admittedly artificial. One advantage of treating all differences among behaviors according to the same rules is that there is no need to be concerned about the nature

---

1. The sequence in which the links are performed is considered to be an aspect of the qualitative dimensions, i.e. different sequences are qualitatively different responses that may be aggregated if differential response tendencies cannot be computed.

of the differences. However, brief attention should be paid to two issues that belong in the context of independence among the response dimensions.

One of the issues is whether the quantitative dimensions of the response (speed and amplitude) are independent of each other. Certainly they are not independent at zero, since one cannot measure the speed of a response of "no-amplitude." Beyond this, however, at least a degree of independence is assumed to the extent that the dimensions can be separated by simultaneous differential reinforcement. Only if the dimensions are at least partially independent can one group learn to make a slow, weak response while another group is learning a slow, vigorous response. However, a correlation may be induced between speed and amplitude by appropriate reward conditions.

The second issue concerns whether the quantitative and qualitative dimensions of the response are independent. This question must be considered because of the fact (Ferster and Skinner, 1957; Wilson and Keller, 1953) that animals in a bar-pressing situation that are required to take a long time between responses in order to get reward perform pacing responses that consume time. Similar observations, reported in a later chapter, are that rats given more reward when they ran slowly typically performed rituals that competed with running. It could therefore be argued that the rats learned responses that were qualitatively as well as quantitatively different from those observed under conventional conditions of constant or varied reward.

It is but a small extension of this argument to assert that *all* quantitative differences among responses involve qualitative differences. A sufficiently sensitive observer could identify a great many dimensions of topography, form, continuity, and quality of behavior and would probably be able to find differences in some of them whenever quantitative differences appeared. If one accepts this analysis a micro approach is necessarily favored, because, if quantitative differences also involve qualitative differences, and if qualitative differences are treated as separate responses, quantitative differences must also be separate responses.

Indeed, it should be further recognized that, particularly with slow responses, time may be spent in many ways and hence there are many possible qualitative differences among responses that are quantitatively identical. It is this fact that presumably accounts for the tendency for subjects to learn topographically unique responses when required to respond slowly. If the reward is contingent only upon the response satisfying some restricted quantitative dimension, so that any of a variety of qualitative characteristics are permissible, then a large response class is involved. In such a case, the members of the rewarded class that are most similar to nonrewarded classes will be differentially weakened by a generalized extinction effect so that the more distinctive responses will become dominant. This tendency could presumably be reduced by also imposing restrictions on the qualitative characteristics of the response, which would, however, reduce the size of the response class and make the learning more difficult because of response generalization.

A second reaction to the tendency for rats to learn rituals under conditions of correlated reinforcement is the macromolar one. From this point of view, the response (say) of stopping and turning around on the way to the goal is a member of the same qualitative response class as running directly to the goal under conventional conditions of uncorrelated reinforcement, and hence the fact that it takes time to turn around correctly indicates a weaker response tendency. However, it could be argued that turning around in the alley should be classed as a different response from running directly to the goal when only slow responses are rewarded because the two ways of behaving are differentially reinforced. This argument inverts the actual condition because reward is not differentially contingent on turning around; there are a number of other equally successful ways of responding. However, the presumption would be that the rat learns that he has to turn around in the alley rather than that he has to take time somehow.

As was mentioned previously, the question of what is learned cannot be answered empirically. It might be possible to test any specific version of this macromolar assumption, depending on how it was implemented. Thus, it might be concluded that the distribution of speeds should be bimodal since the rat would either turn around or run directly to the goal, in which case the unimodal distributions presented in Chapter 8 would be relevant. Similarly, one might think that the rats would develop very stereotyped rituals, whereas highly practiced subjects show fairly large variance in the topography of the response but very small variance in its quantitative dimension. In any event, these and the other observations reported in Chapter 8 are consistent with the micromolar theory in which it is assumed that the subject learns a particular speed of responding.

A third reaction to the problem of ritualistic behavior induced when a subject is required to respond slowly is macromolecular. Behaviors that are qualitatively different would always be viewed as different responses, but it would be held that quantitative variations are possible among behaviors that are qualitatively the same. Quantitative variations would be used as indices of response tendency only if there were no qualitative differences. Thus, just as one would not say that the tendency to run down an eight-foot alley is weaker than the tendency to run down a four-foot alley simply because it takes more time to run down the longer alley, turning around in the alley would be recognized as a different response from running directly to the goal and the times cannot be taken as reflecting relative response tendencies.

It should be noted that implementing this approach would be exceedingly difficult and would require techniques that differ from the conventional ones along the lines proposed by Spence (1956). One would have to specify how to determine qualitative identity on absolute grounds. Typical learning curves could not be interpreted as indicating the growing strength of the response because instrumental behavior early in training is almost always topographically different from what it is late in training. Functions relating response tendency to such variables as amount of reward would have to be modified appreciably, because an animal getting a large reward behaves differently from an animal getting a small reward. In general, complex problems would arise in separating qualitative response generalization from response strength.

By way of summary, it should be noted that all the approaches have assumed that the slow responses observed under correlated reward are different responses from the fast ones observed under uncorrelated reward. The micromolar approach treats all such quantitative variations as different responses; the macromolar approach calls them different only when the reward is correlated with them; and the macromolecular approach calls them different although other quantitative variations are not treated as different responses. It is probable that a more sophisticated conception of the response will become necessary as these various approaches are developed.

Another approach, to be developed in some detail in the next chapter, does not consider a slow response to be different from a fast one even though it may be topographically distinct. Rather, the macromolar assumption that speed is an index of the strength of the molar response of completing the alley is held consistently.

DISCUSSION

The purpose of this chapter has been to call attention to several aspects of the problem of response definition rather than to provide even a tentative general formulation. The aspects discussed were encountered in the present research program, and many of the problems that are involved in a generally adequate definition of the response have not been included. We have not considered the effect of progressively correlating reward with some qualitative characteristic of the response, e.g. more reward for better form. Similarly, reward might be progressively correlated with sequence of links in a chain, e.g. more reward the fewer the errors in a multiple T-maze. The nature of the response in selective and discrimination learning (see Spence, 1952) must also be considered, and other aspects of the problem will undoubtedly be encountered in these contexts.

The three issues discussed in this chapter share with almost every issue that divides learning theories the feature of treating a continuum as a dichotomy. An extreme position is the elemental, molecular approach, which decomposes behavior into separate and distinct components. The opposite position is the Gestalt, molar approach, which holds that large chunks of behavior are inherently indivisible. Observed behavior typically occupies an intermediate ground, and a theorist, starting from either end, must immediately supplement his general position with "fudge" factors that will enable him to handle the data. The present approach starts at the elemental level and considers all features of all aspects of the behavior as defining unique responses. Larger aggregates must then be built up by generalization among the elements—which is saying that they are really not entirely unique. It may be possible to start equally well at the molar level and decompose by discrimination—which is saying that the elements are not entirely inseparable. Accordingly, no attempt has been made in this book to disprove any alternative approaches to the data.

NOTE: ON HULL'S SCALING PROCEDURE

Performance in the alley has been described in terms of response speed, which was computed as the simple reciprocal of the time required to run the alley or portions thereof. There is, of course, no guarantee that this unit of measurement is the best one to use in the sense that the laws expressed in terms of it will provide the simplest description of the results. The problem of selecting a unit of measurement is perhaps the most challenging one facing those interested in quantitative laws and theories of any general scope.[2]

To illustrate this problem, consider the following question: how are differences in reward reflected in performance at different distances from the goal? Specifically, suppose one group of rats is given a large reward and another group is given a small reward, and we wish to determine whether these groups differ more near the goal than they do further back in the alley. Such a question can be answered only in relation to the unit of measurement used. We could begin with a selected unit and answer the question in terms of it; or conversely, we could begin with an assumed answer, and derive a unit that will fit. Clearly, as Bergmann and Spence (1941) have pointed out, the ultimate decision depends upon which unit provides, over a variety of problems, the simplest laws.

Hull (1947) proposed that the sigma of the oscillation distribution (within-rat trial-to-trial variability in performance) might provide a useful unit of measurement and described a procedure, based on the Thurstone (1927; see Guilford, 1936, pp. 217 ff.) scaling methods, for translating observed performance into this unit. Briefly, the procedure requires determining the proportion

2. This problem appears in the micromolar theory as the question of how best to distribute quantitatively different responses along the abscissa of the graphs.

of the subjects that ran faster on trial i than they did on trial j. The separation between the two trials is then estimated as the abscissa of the normal probability integral corresponding to this proportion. After this is done for all combinations of trials taken two at a time, the several estimates of each separation are averaged and then scores are assigned by starting at zero on the first trial and cumulating the successive separations.

The data selected for scaling came from a group of eleven rats that had run 57 trials in the alley without reward and were then run an additional 22 trials with a reward of 12 pellets. The last 5 trials without reward determined the zero point, and speeds in the start, middle foot, and last foot of the alley were scaled over the remaining 22 trials. Although Hull used Thurstone's Case III, which includes an estimate of the variances and an appropriate modification of the separations, the computationally simpler Case V was used for the present data. Despite this short cut, and the small number of cases from which the proportions were estimated, the results are surprisingly clear.

In the first three graphs of Fig. 31, the three scaled speeds are plotted separately. The dashed curves along with each are the original speed scores transformed so as to force them to start at zero and have the same over-all mean as the scaled speeds. The close congruence of the scaled speeds with the linear transformation of the raw speeds is perfectly clear. This result was not unexpected since Hull derived scaled speed as an estimate of excitatory potential and assumed that raw speed is a linear estimate of this variable. To a linear approximation within a segment of the alley, then, raw speed and scaled speed would seem to yield the same answer.

In the fourth graph of Fig. 31, the three scaled speeds are plotted on the same coordinates. There are two points to be made with respect to this graph. First, in terms of scaled speeds, the increase in performance following the introduction of reward appears fastest at the start of the alley so that, early in the reward training, performance far from the goal is superior to performance near to the goal. This is quite the opposite of what would be expected from a theory that assumes that the effect of the reward must work backward from the goal.

The second, and for our purposes more important, point is

that performance ultimately appears as a decreasing function of distance from the goal. This is emphasized in the last graph of Fig. 31, where performance over the last five trials is plotted against distance from the goal in terms of scaled speeds and raw speeds. Whereas speed of running increases to a maximum near the mid-

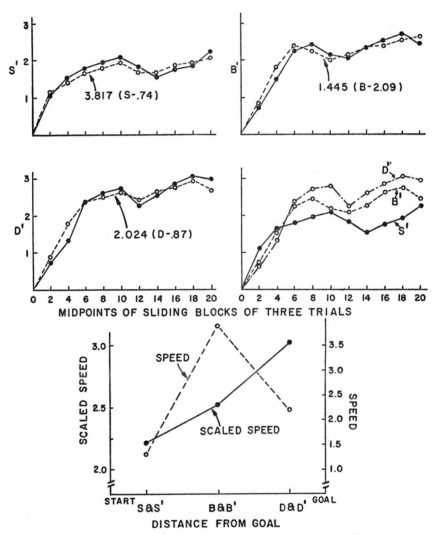

Figure 31. Scaled speeds in the start (S′), middle (B′), and last (D′) foot of the alley, compared with linear transformations of the raw speeds and with each other. (Exper. 56C)

dle of the alley and then decreases, scaled speed shows a monotonically increasing function as the goal is approached. The latter picture, of course, is more consistent with Hull's conception of the goal gradient (Hull, 1939).

On balance, scaled speeds offer promise of providing a simpler, more consistent picture of performance in the alley than do the raw speeds reported here. Computationally, because of the linear relationship between scaled speed and raw speed, it may be possible to obtain a single estimate of this function for the several segments of the alley and then to transform the raw speeds directly without repeatedly using the laborious scaling procedure. Whether these possibilities will be fulfilled remains to be determined from future research.

NOTE: ON THE CORRELATIONS AMONG RESPONSE MEASURES

The alley used for the present research provides seven measures of performance on each trial, but in some of the studies only one or several of them were recorded. For this reason, as well as because of a general interest in the question of whether each of these measures reflects basically the same information, intercorrelations among them were run using the 94 subjects in Expers. 54A, 54B, 55E, and 56D. A terminal score for each of the seven measures was estimated for each subject, and the intercorrelations indicate the extent to which subjects that were fast on one measure tended also to be fast on the other measures. The matrix of these intercorrelations is shown in Table 12.

Table 12. Intercorrelations among individual differences in speed under conditions of uncorrelated reinforcement for starting speed (S), speed in first foot (A), second foot (B), third foot (C), fourth and final foot (D), all four feet of the alley (R), and starting plus all four feet of the alley (I).

	S	A	B	C	D	R
A	.63					
B	.64	.92				
C	.56	.82	.91			
D	.43	.64	.74	.70		
R	.50	.71	.74	.74	.96	
I	.83	.86	.91	.80	.57	.74

Although further stability might have been gained from adding more subjects, the major conclusions seem clear enough. First, it will be noted that starting speed (the first column) generally shows the lowest correlations with the other measures (see also Kobrick, 1956). That is to say, fast starters are not necessarily fast runners. Second, the highest correlations tend to occur among adjacent segments of the alley (the major diagonal). In other words, speed in one segment is more highly correlated with speed in the next segment than it is with speed in segments further removed. Finally, and in general, while the correlations are sufficiently high that the same general conclusions would be expected in all measures, they are at the same time sufficiently low to warrant reporting the separate measures when available.

CHAPTER 7

The Equilibrium Model for Correlated Reinforcement

CORRELATED reinforcement conditions are ones in which some quantitative dimension of the response is differentially reinforced. Using speed and amplitude as the major quantitative dimensions of the response and amount, delay, and frequency as the major dimensions of the reward, there are six possible types of simple conditions of correlated reinforcement—any one of the three reward dimensions varying systematically with either of the response dimensions. We shall use correlation between response speed and delay of reward as a primary reference illustration.

All instrumental learning situations involve a special case of correlated reinforcement, since the behavior must meet certain speed and amplitude criteria in order even to be considered a response. Thus there is always differential reinforcement between responses above and below these criteria. The concept of uncorrelated reinforcement refers to conditions in which the differential reinforcement of speed and amplitude is a more or less incidental consequence of the fact that the experimenter must be able to identify reliably the occurrence of some response.

Accordingly, we shall say that delay is uncorrelated with speed when the reward is given at a predetermined time after the rat gets to the end of the alley, even though if the rat took longer to get there than the experimenter were willing to wait it would not be rewarded and the delay would effectively be infinite. To correlate delay of reward with speed, the apparatus must be so wired that the length of time the rat takes to get to the goal box determines how long it must wait before the reward is delivered.

Within the constraints of apparatus design, any single-valued function can be used to relate delay of reward to response speed. It may be generally increasing, so that faster responses get a longer delay; decreasing, so that faster responses get a shorter delay;

or nonmonotonic, so that intermediate speeds get a longer (or shorter) delay than extremely fast or slow speeds. Within these broad classes the particular function can vary considerably. For example, if the delay is reduced one second for each second reduction in response time then faster responses get the reward with a shorter delay; but if the delay is reduced two seconds for each second reduction in response time, there is an even greater penalty for running slowly.

A variety of more complex conditions can be devised, but since there is little more to be said about them yet, only a few need be mentioned as illustrative. Delay may be correlated with speed in links of the response chain, e.g. only speed in the third segment of the alley determines the delay. Several links may be involved and these may have opposite correlations, e.g. minimum delay is attained by running slowly in the first segments and rapidly in the last. Delay may be determined by cumulative performance over trials so that speeds on preceding trials are also important, e.g. delay is the difference between response time on this trial and that on the previous trial. Delay may be correlated with a trial lag, e.g. speed on this trial determines delay on the next trial. The reader can probably supply a number of additional possibilities.

One other type of condition should be mentioned. The reward does not have to be constant for identical response speeds; i.e. the delay of reward may vary from one trial to another on which the speed is the same. Thus, the conditions can be set up in such a way that each individual speed receives a distribution of delays such as one of those described in Chapter 4. Furthermore, the distributions can be different for different speeds, e.g. slow speeds might be given a relatively constant delay whereas fast speeds have widely varied delays of reinforcement.

Another level of complexity in correlated reinforcement is the simultaneous correlation of two dimensions of the reward with the same dimension of the response. In all the cases just described the amount of reward was constant, but it too can be correlated with speed so that the rat's performance determines both amount and delay of reward. In such conditions, the effects will be complementary if the same speeds that minimize delay also maximize amount; they will be antagonistic if delay favors one speed and amount favors another.

A still more complex level can be attained by bringing in a second response dimension, so that both speed and amplitude affect the reward received. Simply to mention some of the possible combinations: speed and amplitude may jointly determine delay; speed may determine delay, and amplitude determine amount (or vice versa); and speed and amplitude may jointly determine both delay and amount.

These examples by no means exhaust the possible conditions of correlated reinforcement, but should suffice to characterize the type of conditions being considered. They also point out the extremely restricted range of conditions thus far studied in the laboratory.

INTRODUCTION TO THE MODEL

In conditions of correlated reinforcement the subject controls some dimension of the reward; i.e. the amount, delay, or frequency of reward depends upon his speed of running. Accordingly, reward and performance are mutually interdependent under such conditions, since speed on one trial determines the reward on that trial and that reward in turn affects speed on the next trial.

One can adhere to the conventional type of S-R analysis and still deal with conditions of correlated reinforcement by using an *equilibrium* analysis. The prediction is that performance should stabilize at a level which produces just the level of reward which is appropriate to just that level of performance. To illustrate the logic of this solution, let us consider a condition in which only slow responses (say, those which take over 5 seconds) are rewarded.

The condition is, at first, the same as fixed reward, since the subject initially responds slowly and therefore gets the reward on each trial. When, however, speed increases to above the cutoff the response is nonreinforced and should begin to extinguish. Accordingly, performance cannot stabilize at either a very slow or a very fast level: a very slow average speed produces 100 percent reinforcement that should lead to faster responding; a very fast average speed produces 0 percent reinforcement that should lead to extinction toward slower responding. The equilibrium solution determines the intermediate level of average speed which produces that frequency of reinforcement which will balance the reinforcement and extinction effects so as to maintain that performance level.

Such an analysis makes predictions that seem reasonable at a low level of quantitative specificity. Suppose, for example, that the 5-second cutoff in the previous example were increased to 10 seconds. The equilibrium model predicts that the subject would then run more slowly but would achieve a less perfect solution because it would require more unreinforced responses to maintain the larger extinction effect necessary to keep performance down to the lower level. However, it might be expected that adjustment to conditions of correlated reinforcement, while imperfect, is better than the equilibrium model would predict. The purpose here is to develop the model sufficiently to permit quantitative predictions so that deviations can be detected.

THE CONDITION

One of the conditions of correlated reinforcement on which data will later be presented is called "controlled interval of reinforcement." The interval of reinforcement is the time between the occurrence of the stimulus and the receipt of the reward which, in the present studies, refers to the time between the opening of the start door and the delivery of the food. The interval of reinforcement can be controlled by the experimenter, hence the subject has nothing to gain from running faster than the prevailing interval.

For the immediate purposes, it should be noted that the procedure of controlling the interval of reinforcement involves a correlation between response speed and the delay of reinforcement. With a 10-second controlled interval, if the rat runs in 1 second, the delay will be 9 seconds; if it runs in 2 seconds, the delay will be 8 seconds; etc. It is therefore a condition of negatively [1] correlated delay of reinforcement, the delay being shorter for slower responses. This condition will be used to illustrate the equilibrium model.

THE INCENTIVE FUNCTION

The incentive function shows how performance depends upon reward. It describes the relationship obtained between the rele-

1. "Negative" correlation is used to refer to conditions in which the preferred event is given for slow responses; "positive" correlation is used when fast responses maximize reward or minimize punishment.

vant dimension of the response and the reward when the latter is controlled as an independent variable.

In this case, the correlation is between response speed and the delay of reinforcement, and the appropriate incentive function therefore shows speed as a function of delay of reward. This function was estimated in a previous chapter (see p. 46). In general, speed is slower the longer the delay of reinforcement.

THE TERMS FUNCTION

The terms function shows how reward depends upon performance. It describes the particular condition of correlated reinforcement being used and shows how the relevant dimension of the reward is affected by the level of the relevant response dimension.

In this case, the interval of reinforcement is controlled at (say) 10 seconds and the terms function describes the fact that the delay of reinforcement increases as speed increases. As previously mentioned, this function would be linear if delay were plotted against response time; i.e. each second reduction in response time adds a second to the delay. Plotted against speed this function is curvilinear.

THE EQUILIBRIUM SOLUTION

The incentive and terms functions together determine the equilibrium level of performance. This can be seen with the help of Fig. 32. If the rat runs slowly, say at R1, then the terms function shows that it will receive a short delay, D1. Since the incentive function shows that a D1 delay produces a response speed faster than R1, the effect would be to lead to faster running. If, on the other hand, the rat runs fast, say at R2, then the terms function shows that it will receive a long delay, D2. Since the incentive function shows that a D2 delay produces a response speed slower than R2, the effect would be to lead to slower running. There is only one speed, R0, which receives just that delay, D0, which provides incentive for that same speed. It therefore represents a stable equilibrium [2] for this particular condition.

There are several biases in this simplest solution. One con-

2. Because the change in the speed of running is gradual, we need not consider the problem of whether any particular condition would lead to an "exploding" solution.

cerns the fact that correlated reinforcement involves trial-to-trial variation in reward because of the trial-to-trial variation in performance. That is, when reward depends upon some quantitative dimension of the response, any variance in that dimension will necessarily produce variance in reward. The exact degree of the variation in reward depends jointly upon the subject's oscillation in response and the particular terms function being used. For any one terms function, the greater the subject's oscillation, the greater the variance in reward. On the other hand, if the terms function is relatively steep around the point of equilibrium, then the reward will not vary greatly. For example, consider a condition in which more reward is given for faster speeds up to a 3-second response time, but with no further increase in reward for still faster speeds. If the subject should then attain a level such that it never takes more than 3 seconds, it will always receive the same reward even though its speed varies from trial to trial above this value.

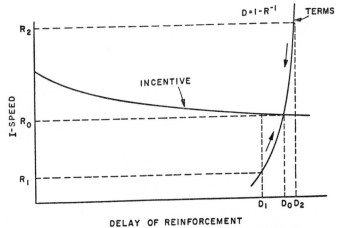

Figure 32. The equilibrium solution for a condition of controlled interval of reinforcement in which the time of delay of reinforcement is negatively correlated with speed.

Accordingly, the incentive function should have been based on varied reward using an uncorrelated variation in reward corresponding to that which the correlated condition will produce. It would be extremely difficult to determine this precise function. However, since varied delay of reward typically produces faster speeds than fixed delay at the mean of the delays involved (see Chapter 4), one need only bear in mind that the prediction slightly underestimates the complete solution that takes variation in reward into account.

THE EFFECT OF INDIVIDUAL DIFFERENCES

A second source of bias in testing the equilibrium model arises if the performances of subjects who have different incentive functions are averaged. This bias is shown graphically in Fig. 33, where

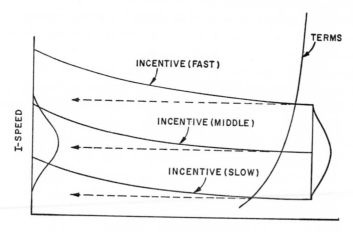

DELAY OF REINFORCEMENT

Figure 33. The effect of negatively correlated delay of reinforcement on between-subject differences. According to the equilibrium model, the normal distribution obtained with uncorrelated reinforcement (shown vertically on the right) is both contracted and distorted (as shown along the ordinate).

individual differences in the function relating speed to delay of reward are taken as being additive. The incentive functions for a fast, median, and slow rat represent the family of individual functions which are presumably distributed more or less normally. Each rat is expected to reach equilibrium at the intersection of the terms function with his individual incentive function, faster rats being in equilibrium at faster speeds and appropriately longer delays.

However, the between-subject variance should be reduced by this particular condition of correlated reinforcement. By projecting the individual equilibria upon the ordinate, one can see that the fast rats are slowed down and the slow rats are speeded up. Accompanying this contraction in variance is a distortion in the distribution due to the fact that the slow rats are speeded more than the fast rats are slowed, and as a result, the mean of the individual equilibria exceeds the equilibrium solution using only the mean incentive function. Again, then, the prediction underestimates the complete solution in this case.

The precise effect of individual differences depends upon the slope of the terms function as it slices through the family of individual incentive functions. The steeper the terms function, the less the expected contraction in individual differences in performance; conversely, it should be possible to reduce greatly the between-subject variance by using a terms function that is almost horizontal. It should also be noticed that the distortion results from the curvilinearity of the terms and incentive functions; were these both linear, fast rats would be slowed down as much as slow rats are speeded up. Contrariwise, if the terms function accelerates sharply around the point of intersection with the mean incentive function, then the distortion would be increased.

Finally, individual differences should have the opposite effect with positively correlated delay of reward (i.e. shorter delay for faster responses). In such conditions, fast rats are speeded up and slow rats slowed down, and the between-subject variance should be increased.

PROCEDURES FOR TESTING THE EQUILIBRIUM MODEL

Three procedures have been used to test the equilibrium model for conditions of correlated reinforcement. Each has possible artifacts which must be considered when interpreting the results.

Estimation of the incentive function. The most elegant and straightforward test is to obtain an empirical estimate of the relevant incentive function by running the necessary groups with uncorrelated reinforcement. Presumably we can then determine the equilibrium for any terms function and compare this prediction with obtained performance.

The two sources of bias in this procedure have already been noted, the one resulting from the fact that varied reward is involved in correlated reinforcement, and the other arising from the expected distortion in the between-subject differences. For conditions of negatively correlated reinforcement, however, both biases lead performance to be faster than predicted. It will be seen that a micromolar analysis expects performance typically to be slower than predicted, and deviations in this direction cannot be attributed to the biases in this procedure.

Despite the seeming elegance of the procedure, apparently no statistical test is exactly appropriate for evaluating deviations from prediction, because the data are constrained to fall on the terms function, and the deviations from prediction should be measured along that curve rather than vertically by simple subtraction. Analysis of results from this procedure will therefore be somewhat circuitous.

Switch to correlated reinforcement. The problem of individual differences can be avoided by switching subjects from constant reward to correlated reward. For example, a rat may be trained with (say) a controlled 4-second delay of reward until its performance stabilizes at (say) 2 seconds (so that average interval is 6 seconds), and then shifted to a 6-second controlled interval of reinforcement. Each rat then serves as its own control since the equilibrium model predicts that it will continue at the same level of performance. From a micromolar point of view, there is now a better solution available, since running slower should take less effort and result in a shorter delay of reward.

This procedure, however, assumes that a rat shifted to correlated reinforcement will eventually perform as if it had been trained originally under that condition. This is itself an empirical question. Accordingly, while a change in performance would indicate an inadequacy in the equilibrium model, no-change might not be definitive.

Matched-control procedure. The most definitive procedure is to assign to each experimental subject receiving correlated reinforcement a matched-control subject. The matched-control rat is given the same amount and delay of reward achieved by its experimental mate, uncorrelated with its performance. The test may be conceptualized with reference again to Fig. 32. The performance of the experimental rat is constrained to fall somewhere on the terms function since whatever it does, that function determines what it will get. The performance of the control rat must fall along the incentive function since whatever it gets will determine what it will do according to that function. If the equilibrium solution is correct, then the experimental rat will perform at the intersection of the functions and the performance of its control mate therefore will also be at that point. If, however, the experimental rat deviates from prediction, along the terms function, its mate will be driven along the incentive function, producing a difference in their performances.

Thus, the procedure permits testing the solution without estimating the parameters of the incentive function or making an exact prediction about where performance should stabilize. It assumes, however, either that the subjects are well matched or that individual differences in the incentive function are indeed additive. This is illustrated in Fig. 34, where converging individual in-

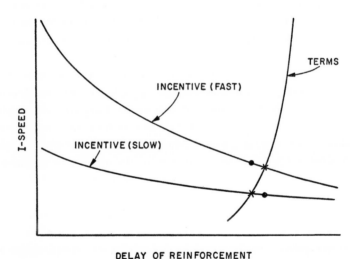

DELAY OF REINFORCEMENT

Figure 34. The effect of a poor matching of experimental (shown by X's) and control (shown by O's) subjects when the matched-control procedure is used.

centive functions have been assumed. Expected performances by two experimental rats, one fast and one slow, are shown by X's. If a fast control rat is matched to the slow experimental one, and vice versa, the control performances are shown by circles. It can be seen that the mean of the experimental rats is below that of the matched controls, producing an artifactual difference.

The matching in the subsequent studies was done after sufficient trials to avoid radically poor matches, and since the evidence suggests that individual differences are approximately additive, this complication is believed not to be very critical in interpreting the present results.

However, the matched-control procedure may sometimes involve another complication that *is* critical: the reward may actually be correlated for the control subjects as well as the experimental ones. Consider a condition in which reward is given to the experimental rat only if it runs slowly. The control rat will then receive partial reinforcement and, as was suggested in Chapter 4, the reward may actually follow slow responses and lead to superstitious slow running. Indeed, because the reward is pegged to the performance of another rat, the sequences are very likely to permit this effect. Thus both the experimental and control rats will run slowly at first, will be rewarded, and both will tend to speed up. Then as the experimental rat runs too fast and is nonreinforced, the control rat should also tend to slow down and be running slowly when reward is again earned by the experimental mate. Only if the experimental and control rats get out of phase in their speeds of running will this correlation be avoided—although it may then be reversed so that the control rat is on the opposite correlation rather than on uncorrelated reinforcement. This problem must be borne in mind in interpreting the results of the several studies that used this procedure.

GENERALIZING THE EQUILIBRIUM MODEL TO OTHER CONDITIONS

The type of equilibrium solution described in this chapter can be generalized to all the various possible conditions of correlated reinforcement. One may use another reward dimension (such as amount of reward), another response (such as bar-pressing), or another dimension of the response (such as amplitude) and solve by placing the terms function involved against the relevant incentive function.

A three-dimensional analysis can be made when several reward dimensions are correlated simultaneously with the response. Suppose, for example, that both the amount and delay of reward were correlated with speed. The incentive function would then be a surface depicting speed as a joint function of amount and delay, and equilibrium would obtain when the terms function intersected that surface.

The analysis of more complex conditions may introduce new problems of estimation. Solutions to several of these, such as dealing with discontinuous terms functions or extreme variations in reward, will be proposed in the next chapter in the context of particular conditions. There seems to be no limit, in principle, to the type of correlated condition to which the model can be applied. Because it can be used within conventional macromolar theories to provide predictions over a wide range of conditions from a relatively few estimated incentive functions, it deserves to be seriously tested. Only the consistent failure of this model would justify adopting the more complicated micromolar approach.

CHAPTER 8

Conditions of Correlated Reinforcement

MOST of the following studies of conditions of correlated reinforcement were designed to test the equilibrium model in the belief that the success or failure of that model would determine whether it would be fruitful to explore the more complex micromolar approach. Conditions of negatively correlated reinforcement provide the clearest test of the equilibrium model and were therefore studied most extensively. As a result of this orientation, most of the systematic questions about correlated reinforcement yet remain to be answered.

The best procedures for demonstrating the rat's adaptiveness to conditions of correlated reinforcement have only gradually become known. For example, rats require several hundred trials to "solve" some problems. Since the early studies were run for only the 60 to 80 trials that are typically adequate for uncorrelated reward conditions, the generality of those data is certainly limited. Nevertheless, all the available results will be mentioned, at least briefly, in order to provide as complete a picture as possible of the effects of the various conditions.

There is very little historical precedence for the importance that has here been attached to conditions of correlated reinforcement. Few textbooks or other secondary sources even mention this type of condition, undoubtedly a reflection of the relative paucity of empirical data in the area.

Skinner (1938, Ch. 8) seems to have been the first to study these conditions in any detail, although early studies by Anderson (1932) and Wendt (1936) involved temporal discriminations. Skinner showed that rats could be trained to hold a bar down for several seconds if only such prolonged presses were reinforced. He also showed that the force a rat exerts on a bar depends importantly on the force required to activate the feeding mechanism. Subsequently Hays and Woodbury (see Hull, 1943, p. 304, and 1952,

p. 209), Arnold (1945), and Weiss (1958) have extended this research and have shown that the distribution of forces tends to converge upon the minimum force that is adequate to produce reward. Recently Notterman (1959) has described an apparatus with which the amount of reward can be made proportional to the time integral of the force the rat exerts on a bar.

The differential reinforcement of rate of response in a bar-pressing or key-pecking situation is closely related to the present interest in the correlation of reward with response speed. Skinner mentioned this type of condition in 1938, and Ferster and he (1957, Ch. 9) have provided fairly extensive data on the effects of differentially reinforcing either high or low rates of pecking by pigeons. Several associated studies (Anger, 1956; Conrad, Sidman, and Herrnstein, 1958; Sidman, 1956; and Wilson and Keller, 1953) concern selective reinforcement of spaced responses in the free-responding situation. These data show clearly that the rate of responding is affected by the relative reinforcement of different inter-response times, the subjects showing distinct but typically far from perfect adjustment to the temporal requirements of the conditions.

The above studies were all done in the bar-pressing or key-pecking situation, typically using the free-responding procedure. They were not designed to test the equilibrium model presented in the previous chapter, although the results, taken in conjunction with other studies in those apparatuses, probably indicate better adjustment than the equilibrium model would predict. The reward in the studies was given in an all-or-none fashion, and the several kinds and degrees of differential reinforcement have not been considered. In a similar vein, the response has previously been dichotomized rather than viewed as a continuum with which reward may be correlated in any of a variety of ways.

The following studies do not extend our knowledge of correlated reinforcement very far. They do, however, generalize previous findings to include the type of situation and procedures used here and illustrate the great wealth of possibilities in conditions of correlated reinforcement.

NEGATIVELY CORRELATED DELAY OF REINFORCEMENT

In conditions of negatively correlated delay of reward, the time of delay of reward is shorter if the response is made slowly. Considering only how quickly the reward can be obtained, some conditions of this type might not be expected to favor running slowly. These are ones in which the increase in response time that would be required to shorten the delay is greater than the decrease in delay achieved by running slowly. The first two conditions to be described involve an exact balance between these two times; i.e. each second reduction in response time increases the time of delay of reward by one second.

Controlled latency of reinforcement. The latency of reinforcement is defined as the time between the beginning of the response (in this case, breaking the first photobeam) and the delivery of the reward. Mathematically, the latency of reinforcement is equal to the delay of reinforcement plus the response time. The latency of reinforcement can be controlled in the sense that the minimum latency can be specified. For example, if the latency of reward is set at 10 seconds, then the rat cannot get the food in less than 10 seconds no matter how fast it runs, but the latency of reward will equal response time if the rat takes over 10 seconds in the alley.

The equilibrium solution for this condition is the same as that given in the preceding chapter for interval-controlled conditions. In this case, the relevant response measure is R-speed, since the delay of reward depends only on running time and not on starting time. Fig. 35 shows how the equilibrium model can be used to generate a predicted function relating R-speed to controlled latency of reinforcement.

The incentive function used in Fig. 35 is an approximate fit to the data obtained from the several delay-controlled conditions in Exper. 55D (see Fig. 8). As a part of that experiment, five groups of rats were run with the latency of reinforcement controlled at 2, 4, 6, 10, or 20 seconds. Terminal performance under these conditions is compared with the equilibrium prediction in Fig. 35. R-

Table 13. Analysis of variance showing the effect of controlling the latency of reinforcement at 2, 4, 6, 10, or 20 seconds for both hooded and albino rats. (Exper. 55D)

Source	d.f.	m.s.	F
Latency of reinforcement	4	.1403	8.20 **
Hood-albino	1	.3367	19.69 **
Latency x hood-albino	4	.0348	2.04
Error	40	.0171	

speed was slower the longer the latency of reinforcement, and although the albinos conformed reasonably well to prediction, the hoods ran appreciably slower than predicted. Analysis of variance (see Table 13) showed that the latency of reinforcement was a significant independent variable and that the speeds of the hoods and albinos were reliably different.

A second study of controlled latency of reinforcement was designed to test the equilibrium model again with hooded rats. Only hooded rats were used in Exper. 56B, the experimental condition being 13-sec. controlled latency of reinforcement. A single control group was run with a constant 12-sec. delay of reinforcement to provide some estimate of the incentive function around the point of expected equilibrium. The performance curves for the two groups are not shown graphically. The rats with controlled latency

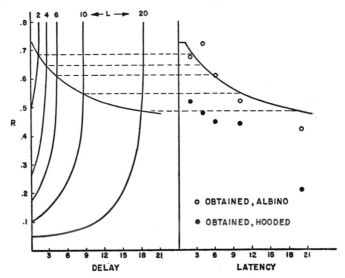

Figure 35. Graphic representation of successive solutions of the equilibrium model, the resulting predicted function relating *R*-speed to controlled latency of reinforcement, and data obtained under these conditions. (Exper. 55D)

of reinforcement did not learn to run slowly, and their performance was comparable to that of the rats with controlled delay of reward (.489 and .476 respectively). These results are perfectly consistent with the equilibrium model.

A 4-sec. latency-controlled condition using both hoods and albinos, was included in Exper. 56C, which provided a second estimate of the incentive function. The performance of the latency-controlled group conformed closely to the prediction of the equilibrium model (predicted = .550; obtained = .565). Furthermore, when half of the rats in this condition were shifted from a 2-pellet to a 12-pellet reward, an appropriate change in performance occurred (predicted = .650; obtained = .631).

There was virtually no difference between the speeds of the hoods and albinos under the latency-controlled condition of Exper. 56C (*R*-speeds were .57 and .56 for hoods and albinos respectively). Since the hood-albino distinction has not been a significant source of variance in any study except the latency-controlled condition of Exper. 55D and since that difference was not replicated in Exper. 56C, it probably was a chance deviation because of the small number of rats involved. Alternatively, it may represent an as-yet-unknown effect of the severe deprivation conditions on which the hooded rats in Exper. 55D were maintained.

In general, then, the several studies of latency-controlled conditions suggest that:

17. Performance is a concave upward, decreasing function of the latency of reinforcement.

18. At least for a limited number of distributed trials with a small reward, performance under latency-controlled conditions can be correctly predicted by an equilibrium model using an incentive function based on uncorrelated delay of reward.

At first thought, the second conclusion would seem to be inconsistent with a micromolar theory since rats have nothing to gain from running fast when the latency of reinforcement is controlled. However, in terms of the postulates presented in Chapter 5, any reduction in delay (and hence increase in sJ'r) is accompanied by a corresponding increase in response interval (and hence decrease in sJr).[1] To calculate the incentive profile under these conditions would therefore require a quantitative comparison of the effect of a second in the goal box with the effect of a second in the alley. Although the relative quantification that would permit this comparison is not yet available, it is clear that latency-

1. It might also be noted that, because the rat's speed varies somewhat from trial to trial, average speed must be well above the controlled latency value if the rat is to avoid occasionally taking longer than necessary to get the food.

controlled conditions do not give very great advantage to slow responses. Hence, the micromolar theory need not be embarrassed by the fact that slow responses did not quickly become dominant when the latency of reinforcement was controlled.

Controlled interval of reinforcement. The interval of reinforcement is the time between the presentation of the stimulus (in this case, the opening of the start door) and the delivery of the reward. Interval-controlled conditions differ from latency-controlled conditions only in that the rat does not have to leave the start box in order to get the reward timer started. At an intuitive level, it might be expected that a rat would be more likely to delay starting than to slow down after having got under way. The equilibrium solution for interval-controlled conditions was given in the preceding chapter. The appropriate response measure is the response interval because the delay of reward depends upon speed over the entire length of the alley.

A 5-sec. interval-controlled condition was included as a part of Exper. 56C. The performance of this group conformed reasonably well to prediction both during the initial learning with a 2-pellet reward (predicted = .330; obtained = .378) and after half the rats had been shifted to a 12-pellet reward (predicted = .400; obtained = .423).

However, subsequent research using other conditions has suggested that the equilibrium model is most likely to fail after a large number of massed trials with a large reward. Exper. 59D was designed to study controlled interval of reinforcement with this procedure. A 5-sec. interval-controlled condition was used again, but the rats were run 4 trials a day with a 10-pellet reward. Each experimental rat had a matched-control rat for which the reward was delayed for the time its experimental mate had spent in the goal box on the corresponding trial (i.e. 5 seconds minus *I*-time).

The rats were run for 500 trials, and their *I*-speed curves are plotted in Fig. 36. The speed of the experimental group rose to a high level and then gradually declined slightly. In contrast, the control group continued to run at a very fast speed, the decline usually occurring when the reward is delayed, presumably being counteracted by the decrease in this delay that resulted from the declining speed of the experimental group. Accordingly, it may be concluded that:

19. When the interval of reinforcement is controlled, rats do not learn, within a reasonable number of trials, to run as slowly as the interval is set, but they do run somewhat slower than control rats receiving the same delay of reward.

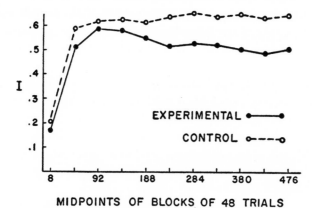

MIDPOINTS OF BLOCKS OF 48 TRIALS

Figure 36. Performance when the interval of reinforcement was controlled at 5 seconds compared with matched-control performance. (Exper. 59D)

Discontinuously correlated delay of reinforcement. In discontinuously correlated delay of reinforcement, a cutoff speed is selected and the delay depends only on whether the rat runs faster or slower than the cutoff. That is, the delay is x seconds if speed is above the cutoff and y seconds if it is below, with x being larger than y in negatively correlated conditions. For example, the rats in one group in Exper. 56C were given reward immediately on those trials when running time between the first and last photobeams was 3 or more seconds and were given reward after a 10-sec. delay if they ran the alley in less than 3 seconds.

(For convenience of identification, this condition will be symbolized by $2A,0D < .33R < 2A,10D$. This symbol is read as follows: a 2-pellet amount is given at a 0-sec. delay if R-speed is less than .33, and a 2-pellet amount is given at a 10-sec. delay if R-speed is greater than .33. Analogous symbols will be used to identify the reward conditions that obtain on either side of the indicated cutoff, e.g. $2A,0D < .2I < 12A,30D$ would represent an immediate 2-pellet reward if I-speed exceeds .2 and a 30-sec. delayed 12-pellet reward otherwise.)

The equilibrium model can be applied to this type of condition by correcting the incentive and terms functions on the basis of the fact that performance (and hence reward) will vary from trial to trial. If the coordinates are changed to show the relationship between average delay and average speed, then the corrected func-. tions intersect and an equilibrium can be determined. Consider first the terms function. If the rat were to run, on the average, precisely at the cutoff, then the average delay would be 5 seconds, composed of half 0-sec. and half 10-sec. delays. The higher the average speed, the larger the proportion of long delays, and therefore the longer the average delay. Inversely, slower average speeds lead to shorter average delays. The originally discontinuous terms function can thus be made continuous, the slope of the function bridging the discontinuity depending on the amount of trial-to-trial variability in speed.

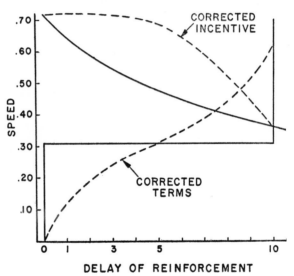

Figure 37. Graphic representation of the equilibrium solution for a condition of discontinuously correlated delay of reward. See text for a description of how the corrected functions were obtained.

The incentive function is corrected in an analogous manner. For the average delay to be 0 seconds, there can be no variance in delay and the original incentive function is correct at that point. Since the delay cannot exceed 10 seconds in this condition, an average 10-sec. delay would involve no variance and is also correctly given by the original incentive function. An average delay of 5 seconds under this condition must entail equally likely variation between 0-sec. and 10-sec. delays, and performance when the delay of reward is varied in this way was shown in Chapter 4 to be only slightly inferior to continuous 0-sec. delay. A reasonable approximation to the corrected incentive function can be generated from these points.

These considerations are shown graphically in Fig. 37. The intersection of the corrected terms and corrected incentive functions identifies the equilibrium speed. This figure is approximate since the corrected terms function was based on an estimate of the trial-to-trial variance and the corrected incentive function was based on previous studies of varied delay of reward. Although an exact prediction therefore cannot be made, the indicated equilibrium is in the vicinity of .5 R-speed and hence appreciably above the cutoff.

The condition of discontinuously correlated delay of reinforcement was studied in Exper. 56C. The results of this test, which was run with a small reward and widely distributed practice, were reasonably consistent with the equilibrium prediction since terminal R-speed was .515.

A second test of this type of condition was run in Exper. 57D, with four massed trials a day and with the matched-control procedure. The cutoff speed was based on I-speed rather than on R-speed, and one experimental group was given a small reward and a second was given a large reward.

The I-speed of the small reward (1A,0D < .2I < 1A,10D) group is shown in Fig. 38, together with that of its matched-control group. The slight difference that appeared near the end of training is neither strikingly large nor statistically reliable.

In sharp contrast, the performance of the large reward (12A,0D < .2I < 12A,10D) group differed markedly from that of its matched-control group. Comparison is made in Fig. 39 for all available response measures and it can be seen that the groups differed in speed in all sections of the alley. Statistical test of the I-speeds yielded a t of 6.76 which, with 5 d.f., is significant beyond the .01 level.

Not only did the rats in the 12-pellet experimental group run slower than the matched-control rats but they were even somewhat slower than the rats in the 1-pellet experimental group. That is, speed was inversely related to the amount of reward when the delay of reward was negatively correlated with speed. The difference

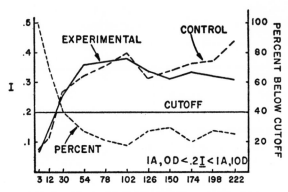

MIDPOINTS OF BLOCKS OF TWENTY-FOUR TRIALS

Figure 38. Performance when a small reward (1 pellet) was given immediately if *I*-speed was less than .2 (over 5 sec.) and was delayed for 10 sec. if *I*-speed was greater than .2, compared with matched-control performance. (Exper. 57D)

can be seen in Fig. 40 where the distributions of *I*-speeds for the two groups are plotted. The upper graph shows that the 1-pellet condition did not produce a clear modal speed and that there was no noticeable change between the next-to-last and last ten days of training. The lower graph shows that the 12-pellet group was converging on a distinct modal speed and that the variance around this mode was decreasing somewhat between the next-to-last and last ten days of training. It should be noted that this mode is somewhat above the cutoff speed and hence does not represent a very "good" solution for the condition.

The results clearly fail to confirm the prediction of the equilibrium model and thereby lend support to the micromolar approach. When the different speeds are viewed as different responses, then separate sEr's are calculated. The differential delay of reward produces sEr's for slow responses that can compete more or less successfully with the sEr's for fast responses. Fast responses, on the other hand, receive appreciable reward and entail shorter response intervals, so that their sEr's can compete, more or less successfully, with the sEr's for slow responses. Presumably, the greater the differential in delay, the more the difference in sEr would favor slow responses, and hence the more they would dominate.

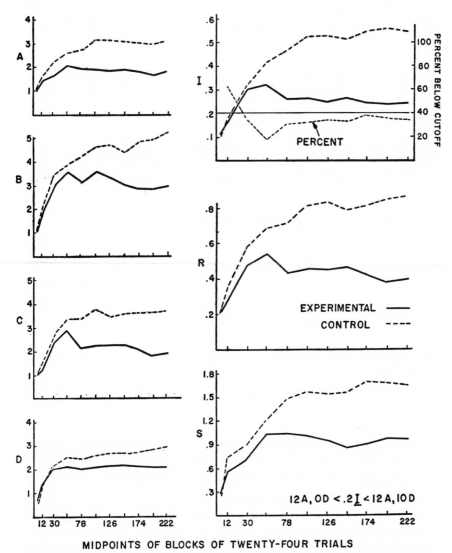

MIDPOINTS OF BLOCKS OF TWENTY-FOUR TRIALS

Figure 39. Performance when a large reward (12 pellets) was given immediately if *I*-speed was less than .2 (over 5 sec.) and was delayed for 10 sec. if *I*-speed was greater than .2, compared with matched-control performance. (Exper. 57D)

Following this reasoning, and using a few additional constraints, Bower (1959) was able to generate a graph to describe the expected effects of discontinuously correlated delay of reward. Fig. 41 is a comparable graph and was constructed as follows: (a) if the cutoff

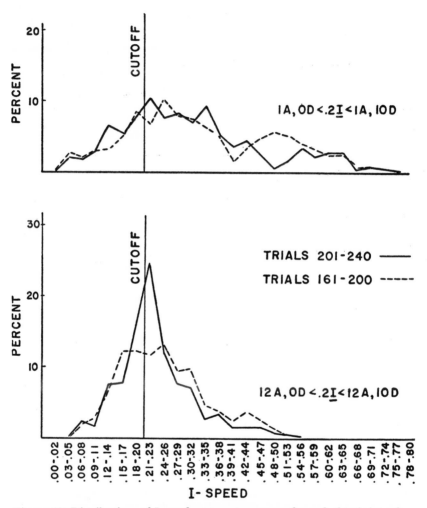

Figure 40. Distributions of I-speeds at two stages near the end of training when the reward was given immediately if I-speed was less than .2 (over 5 sec.) and was delayed 10 sec. if I-speed was greater than .2. The upper graph refers to a group given a small reward and the lower graph to a group given a large reward. (Exper. 57D)

is very short, so that the rat cannot run fast enough to encounter the delay, the condition is effectively uncorrelated reward with no delay and hence all curves originate at this point; (b) if the cutoff is very long, so that the rat will never run slowly enough to encounter the immediate reward, the condition is effectively uncorrelated reward at the appropriate delay and hence the curves should be arrayed according to the function relating speed to delay of reward (e.g. Fig. 8); (c) for any designated delay for speeds above the cutoff, the longer the cutoff the less the relative advantage of running slowly because the delay is reduced at the expense of an increase in the response interval; (d) for any designated cutoff, the longer the delay for speeds above the cutoff, the greater the relative advantage of running slowly; and (e) regardless of the differential in delay, running too far below the cutoff is disadvantageous since it increases the response interval without reducing the delay.

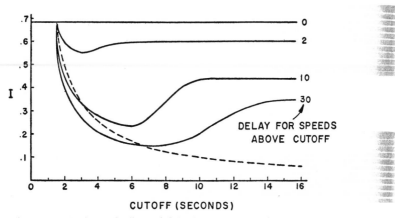

Figure 41. Estimated effect of delaying the reward if *I*-speed exceeds a designated cutoff, showing average terminal *I*-speed as a function of the length of the cutoff. The solid curves differ in the length of the delay imposed on fast responses; the dashed curve represents performance at the cutoff. (After Bower, 1959)

Bower ran several experiments that confirmed the major implications of Fig. 41. He found that terminal average speed was a decreasing function of the delay imposed on speeds above the cutoff and was a nonmonotonic (decreasing, then increasing) function of the length of the cutoff. In general, the longer the delay for fast speeds, the longer the cutoff could be and still induce the rats to run slowly.

An important implication of these data for a micromolar analysis is that the result of the competition between the sEr's of responses of different speed may be a compromise speed intermediate between them. The description given above would imply a bimodal distribution of speeds, the rat either running below the cutoff and hence minimizing delay (sJ'r), or running very fast and hence minimizing response interval (sJr). The occurrence of a single distinct mode slightly above the cutoff at a speed that does not maximize either sJ'r or sJr suggests an unfortunate compromise [2] between two "better" solutions.

The data in this section have a second important implication for the content of the micromolar theory—the indication that the delay and the amount of reward interact multiplicatively in determining reaction potential. Since the differential in delay was the same for the 12-pellet group as for the 1-pellet group in Exper. 57D, but the former showed the more distinct preference for slow responses, the detrimental effect of delayed reward is apparently greater the larger the reward.

All the conditions used have given immediate reward for slow responses whereas, of course, differential delay can be provided using two nonzero values. With this limitation, the results of this section indicate that:

20. When the delay of reward is negatively correlated discontinuously with response speed, so that the reward is given immediately if speed is below a cutoff and is delayed if speed is above that cutoff,

a. rats may learn to run slowly and hence deviate from the prediction of the equilibrium model.

b. speed is a decreasing function of the delay imposed on speeds above the cutoff, but the modal speed does not fall very far below the cutoff even with very long delays.

c. speed is a nonmonotonic function of the length of the

2. This compromise might have resulted from the use of a relatively long behavior chain which aggregated a large number of separate, uncompromising choices. More detailed analyses of this and other responses are needed to specify the most appropriate kind of compromise formula.

cutoff, decreasing with longer cutoffs until the cutoff gets long relative to the delay for speeds above the cutoff, after which speed increases with further increases in the cutoff.

21. The tendency to minimize delay by running slowly is greater with a large than with a small reward.

NEGATIVELY CORRELATED AMOUNT OF REINFORCEMENT

In conditions of negatively correlated amount of reward, a larger reward is given when speed is slow than when speed is fast. If pellets are used as the unit of amount, then the terms function takes discrete steps at each change in amount and continuously correlated conditions need not be considered.

Negatively correlated amount of reward necessarily involves a conflict about which no a priori statements can be made. The rat can either run fast and get a small reward quickly or run slowly and get a larger reward later. Presumably, if the differential in amount is small and the response time necessary to get the larger reward is long, then the rat may well take the smaller reward more quickly. This problem appeared in negatively correlated delay of reward, but in that context there was some basis for evaluating whether the added response time "paid off" since the gain was also in a time dimension. In the present context no guidepost is available.[3]

Discontinuously correlated amount of reinforcement. Fig. 42 illustrates the equilibrium solution for a condition in which 10 pellets are given if *I*-speed is less than .2 (5 seconds), and 2 pellets are given otherwise. The functions have been corrected in a manner analogous to that used with discontinuously correlated delay to show the relation between average speed and average amount. The corrected incentive function reflects the fact that widely varied amount of reward leads to a slower average speed than constant reward with the same mean value (see Chapter 4).

This condition (10A,0D < .2*I* < 2A,0D) was run in Exper.

3. Another lack of symmetry arises in comparing the learning of correlated delay as a function of the constant amount used, with learning of correlated amount as a function of the constant delay used. Delaying the reward in conditions of correlated amount would not only reduce the differential incentive (on the multiplicative assumption) but would also delay "information" about the adequacy of the response.

59C. The matched-control procedure was used to test the equilibrium model, as the functions shown in Fig. 42 are only approximate and no exact predictions could be made. There is a possible ambiguity in determining how the controls should be matched on the time dimensions of the reward. The experimental rats always get reward without delay and hence the control rats could be given the same amount without delay. However, one might argue that the experimental rats would have a longer interval of reinforcement if they ran slowly and that the controls should not get the reward any sooner than the experimentals. Accordingly, the controls were matched on delay of reinforcement until it was

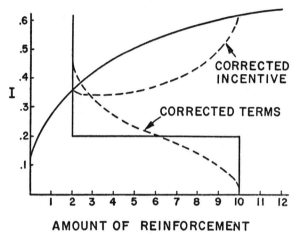

AMOUNT OF REINFORCEMENT

Figure 42. Graphic representation of the equilibrium solution for a condition of discontinuously correlated amount of reward. See text for a description of how the corrected functions were obtained.

apparent that the difference would occur on that basis (140 trials), and they were then shifted so as to be matched on interval of reinforcement. This meant that a varied delay was now imposed on the controls in such a way that longer delays tended to be correlated with the larger amount, which might have attenuated the effect of the delay. In any event, the results, which are shown in Fig. 43, were perfectly clear.

The speed of the experimental group passed the original *.2I* cutoff so quickly that its effect was hardly apparent. However, when the cutoff was raised to insure that the differential in reward

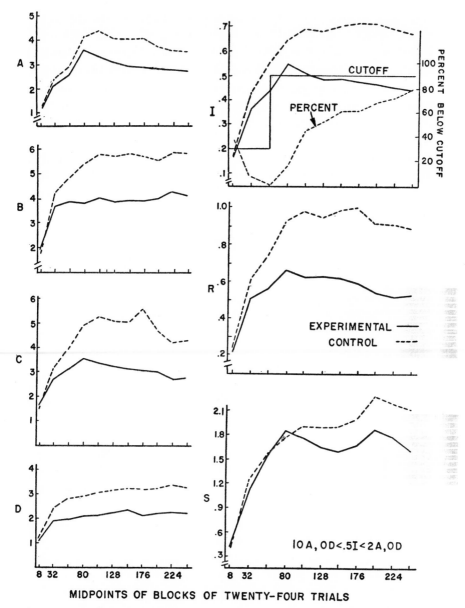

Figure 43. Performance when a large reward (10 pellets) was given if *I*-speed was less than .5 (over 2 sec.) and a small reward (2 pellets) was given if *I*-speed was greater than .5, compared with matched-control performance. (The cutoff had been set at .2 for the first 68 trials.) (Exper. 59C)

was encountered, speed decreased appropriately and the difference
between the experimental and control groups appeared. When the
cutoff was dropped back to *.2I*, the speed of the experimental
group decreased toward that cutoff, and hence the difference between the experimental and control groups was further accentu-
ated (see Chapter 9). Accordingly,

22. When the amount of reward is negatively correlated discontinuously with response speed, so that a large reward is given
if speed is below a cutoff and a small reward is given if speed is
above that cutoff, rats may learn to run slowly and hence deviate
from the prediction of the equilibrium model.

NEGATIVELY CORRELATED DELAY AND AMOUNT OF REINFORCEMENT

When both the delay and the amount of reward are negatively
correlated with response speed, their effects combine to increase
the differential incentive for running slowly. The only case of this
kind studied so far has involved nonreinforcement, i.e. the rat is
rewarded only if speed is less than the designated cutoff. Since
these conditions maximize the differential reinforcement for
running slowly, they are the most efficient for producing this way
of responding. But from a theoretical point of view, they are the
least interesting. In the previous conditions, the rat had a perfectly acceptable alternative to running slowly, since the reward
given for fast responses was itself sufficient to maintain those fast
responses were it not for the greater reward given slow responses.
In the present condition, experimental extinction will insure
that speed stays close enough to the cutoff to warrant at least occasional reward.

Case of nonreinforcement. Fig. 44 illustrates the equilibrium
solution for a condition in which the reward is given only if
R-speed is less than .33 (3 seconds). The functions are analytically
"corrected" in that they relate average speed and average reward
(in terms of percent reinforcement in order to avoid the problem
of averaging 0 and ∞ delays). The terms function shows that the
percent reinforcement decreases as average speed increases, while
the incentive function shows that average speed increases as percent reinforcement increases.[4] Equilibrium is attained at that

4. The possibility that this incentive function is nonmonotonic (see Chapter 4)
would not materially alter the logic of the solution.

average speed which produces a sufficient frequency of reinforcement to maintain that level of performance. Although the functions used in Fig. 44 are approximate, it is clear that the expected equilibrium speed is well above the cutoff speed.

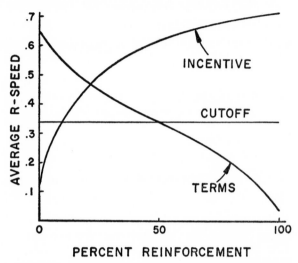

Figure 44. Graphic representation of the equilibrium solution for a condition in which reward is given only if *R*-speed is less than .33 (over 3 sec.). See text for a description of these functions.

This particular condition (2A,0D < .33*R* < 0A, ∞ D) was run as a part of Exper. 56C. After 80 trials on a one-a-day schedule, the rats were running rapidly as predicted by the equilibrium model. However, there was a gradual decrease in speed with continued training, and when half the rats were given 6 trials a day, their speed clearly dropped toward the cutoff. Ultimate adjustment was therefore better than predicted by the equilibrium model.

A more extensive test of the equilibrium model for these conditions was run in Exper. 57D. A 5-sec. response interval was used as the cutoff, and 4 massed trials a day were run. One experimental group was given a single pellet if *I*-speed was less than .2, and a second experimental group was given 12 pellets for slow responses. Rats in both groups were not rewarded if *I*-speed exceeded .2. A matched-control rat was given the same amount and frequency of reward as was earned by its experimental mate.

The *I*-speed curve under the 1A,0D < .2*I* < 0A,∞D condition is shown in Fig. 45 together with the curve of the matched-control group. The terminal average speed of the experimental group was very near the cutoff, and the difference between the experimental and control groups is clearly inconsistent with the equilibrium model.

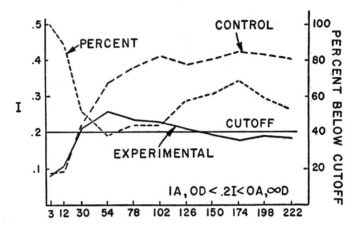

Figure 45. Performance when a small reward (1 pellet) was given immediately if *I*-speed was less than .2 (over 5 sec.) and was withheld altogether if *I*-speed was greater than .2, compared with matched-control performance. (Exper. 57D)

An even more striking difference occurred in the 12A,0D < .2*I* < 0A,∞D condition, the data for which are broken down to give all available response measures in Fig. 46. As with correlated delay of reward, the larger amount of reward produced more skillful adjustment to this type of problem. In this particular case, most of the difference between the experimental and control groups occurred in the start and early segments of the alley, both groups running fast near the goal.

The *I*-speed distributions for both experimental groups are shown in Fig. 47. The larger reward condition produced the more distinct mode, which in this condition fell slightly below the cutoff. It should also be noted that, whereas average *I*-speed was not changing appreciably during the last 20 days of training, performance of the 12-pellet group was nevertheless improving in

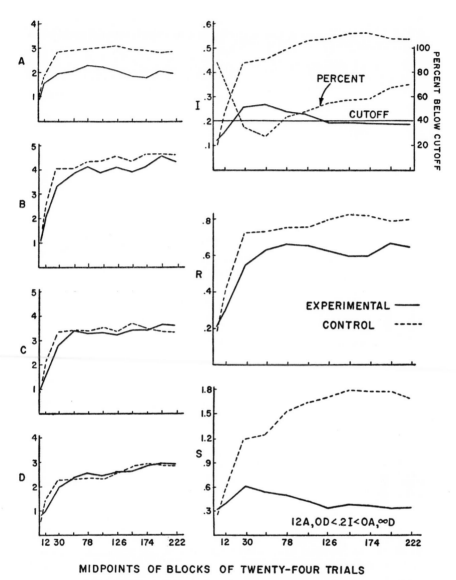

MIDPOINTS OF BLOCKS OF TWENTY-FOUR TRIALS

Figure 46. Performance when a large reward (12 pellets) was given immediately if *I*-speed was less than .2 (over 5 sec.) and was withheld altogether if *I*-speed was greater than .2, compared with matched-control performance. (Exper. 57D)

that both unnecessarily slow as well as unsuccessfully fast responses were being reduced in frequency.

All the cases thus far presented in which the equilibrium model clearly failed were run with massed trials. The earlier experiments with widely distributed practice did not include particularly de-

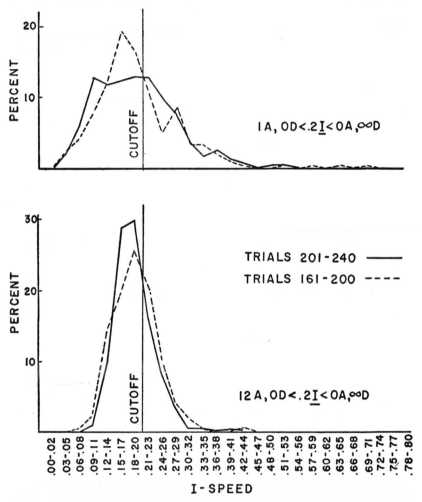

Figure 47. Distributions of *I*-speeds at two stages near the end of training when reward was given immediately if *I*-speed was less than .2 and was withheld altogether if *I*-speed was greater than 2. The upper graph refers to a group given a small reward (1 pellet) and the lower graph to a group given a large reward (12 pellets). (Exper. 57D)

manding conditions and were not run for the large number of trials that is apparently necessary. Exper. 58E was designed to test the $12A,0D < .2I < 0A,\infty D$ condition at a one-trial-a-day schedule. The data were grossly similar to those obtained with this condition using massed training, except that the difference between the experimental and control groups was not confined to the start but was fairly evenly distributed across the entire runway.

Because, as will be shown later, rats running more than one trial a day in this condition run slower on later trials of the day, the appropriate comparison of Expers. 57D and 58E should use only first-trial speeds. This comparison is made in Fig. 48. Since the

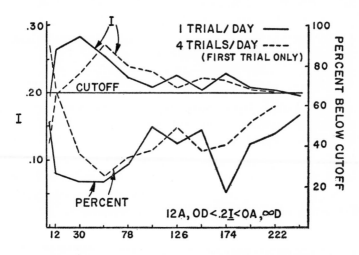

MIDPOINTS OF BLOCKS OF TWENTY-FOUR TRIALS

Figure 48. Performance when a large reward (12 pellets) was given if *I*-speed was less than .2 (over 5 sec.), comparing all trials of a group getting one trial a day with the first trials of a group getting 4 trials a day. (Expers. 57D and 58E)

initial rate of change (per trial) is faster with distributed practice, the speed of the rats [5] in the 58E experiment temporarily overshot

5. One rat was eliminated from the account of Exper. 58E because of the early death of its control mate, and because its data were quantitatively deviant (terminal *I*-speed was .240 compared with .200 for the other three rats, which difference, though small, made a difference in percent reinforcement of 13 for the one rat and 57 for the others). This rat had such a high operant level that it rarely had a "trial," but it was continuing to improve at the end of the experiment and, it is believed, would ultimately have shown adequate adjustment to the condition.

the cutoff further, but otherwise performance at one trial a day was closely comparable to first-trial performance with massed practice.

The data reported in this section can be summarized as follows:

23. If reward is given only when speed is below an arbitrary cutoff,

   a. rats will learn to run slowly and hence deviate from the prediction of the equilibrium model;

   b. rats can learn to run slowly with widely distributed practice;

   c. the extent to which speed converges upon a distinct mode just below the cutoff is an increasing function of the amount of reward;

   d. the particular pattern of solution varies among rats, depending partly upon the distribution of practice.

DISCUSSION

The data in this chapter have shown that the speed at which a rat runs down an alley depends not simply on the amount and delay of reward received in the goal box but also on the particular correlation that obtains between reward and response speed. Accordingly, the equilibrium model is not a generally useful device for dealing with the various conditions of correlated reinforcement, and the micromolar approach currently seems to be much more promising. All the results are consistent with the conception that behaviors differing in speed should be treated as different responses.

When the quantitative dimensions of a response are adjusted so as to maximize reward, the performance may be called skillful. The acquisition of such skills in rats is a gradual and continuous process in which different response speeds occur, are rewarded according to the prevailing conditions of reinforcement, and are strengthened or weakened accordingly.

As in any instrumental situation, the optimal response must occur and be rewarded if it is to become dominant. If average performance at any stage of practice deviates markedly from the currently optimal level, then adjustment will be slow not only because a large change must occur but also because only a few of the trials provide positive strengthening of the optimal response. Indeed, if the optimal response is outside the range of maintained behavior, the rat will fail to adjust. The effects of correlated reinforcement are therefore certain to appear only if the nonoptimal reward (on that drive level and training schedule) maintains a distribution of speeds which includes some of the more highly rewarded responses.

If the condition is one in which the nonoptimal reward is sufficient to maintain a performance level that does not occasionally include speeds below the cutoff, then the rat may not show very good adjustment to the condition. If the rats were first trained to the high and reasonably stable level produced by the poorer reward condition alone and were then shifted to the correlated condition, they would not adjust simply because they would never encounter the differential in reward. Indeed, even when these conditions are employed from the beginning of training, there is an element of risk that they will not take effect. If the training schedule and pattern of rewards pull performance across the cutoff very rapidly, then the slower responses will not have realized their full potentiality of habit and incentive. The result is the possibility that slow responses will not actually become dominant under a reward condition in which they would be dominant had they been practiced sufficiently. In such a case, either something must be done temporarily to force the occurrence of the slow responses or the cutoff must be raised to the point where the differential in reinforcement will be encountered.

Continuous correlations avoid this difficulty since any variance in performance at any level will insure some differential reinforcement.[6] However, such conditions spread out the total differential in reward over a wide range of performance and hence do not provide the sharp differentiation of a discontinuous function, when a small change in performance may produce a large change in reward.

The basic principle of a micromolar theory is that the likelihood of any response speed depends upon the relative incentive for

6. The differential reinforcement may not be equal at all performance levels with continuously correlated reinforcement. In 5-sec. interval-controlled conditions, for example, variation in speed between 3 and 4 seconds varies the reward between 2 and 1 seconds, while variation in speed between 4 and 5 seconds varies the reward between 1 and 0 seconds. The latter variation is in the more effective range of the delay function.

responding at that speed. Incentive, in turn, depends upon the amount, delay, frequency, and interval of reinforcement. The effect of the first three of these independent variables on perform-ance is generally recognized on the basis of data such as those pre-sented in the preceding chapters. The fact that rats learn to select response speeds that maximize these dimensions of the reward is particularly convincing evidence that their effects act directly on incentive motivation rather than on some habit or inhibition variable.

The interval of reinforcement has not previously been identified as an explicit determinant of incentive.[7] It was introduced into the micromolar theory to account for the fact that rats do run fast when the other dimensions of the reward are not correlated with response speed. Additional evidence for the inclusion of this vari-able was seen in those conditions which required rats to run slowly in order to get reward, since the rats tended to eliminate unneces-sarily long responses even though they were equally successful insofar as the other dimensions of the reward were concerned. Accordingly, the principle of maximization of reward must in-clude the interval as well as the amount, delay, and frequency of reinforcement.

The greater the differential in reinforcement among different response speeds, the more the rat can gain from responding skill-fully. The degree of differential reinforcement depends not only on the terms function of the correlated dimension of the reward but also on the level of the uncorrelated dimensions. Thus, delay-ing the reward for fast responses is less effective than withholding the reward altogether and, since the several dimensions interact multiplicatively, the effect depends also on the amount of reward. If the conditions are compelling, in the sense that large differences in reinforcement are involved, then all rats converge on virtually the identical modal response speed, and their trial-to-trial vari-ability is markedly reduced from that found in uncorrelated condi-tions.

However, a response class that is defined solely by a quantitative characteristic over a behavior chain includes a number of alterna-

7. The interval of reinforcement differs from within-chain delay of reinforcement in that the former includes the time required by the response itself while the latter refers to the time required by subsequent responses in the chain.

tive solutions, and the particular one that becomes dominant may vary appreciably among rats. Indeed, an experienced rat may show a number of different patterns. The predominant pattern under any condition can typically be predicted from the pattern produced by the poorer reward event.

For example, extinction with massed practice shows up first in the start and early segments of the alley. In conditions of correlated reinforcement in which the rat is not rewarded when it runs too fast, the use of massed trials produces slow starting speeds as the initial effect of nonreinforcement. Therefore, because the rat is most likely to have started slowly on those trials on which it gets rewarded, this type of solution becomes predominant. Although most rats on most trials wait in the start box and then run rapidly to the goal, there are observable differences in how they spend the waiting time. And within each animal, there is a clear tendency for running speed to be faster the longer the starting time (as indicated by tetrachoric correlations of $-.64$, $-.40$, $-.40$, and $-.30$ between S-speed and R-speed for the experimental rats in the $12A,0D < .2I < 0A,\infty D$ condition of Exper. 57D, compared with $-.04$, $.04$, $.04$, and $.64$ for the matched-control rats).

The effect of extinction with widely distributed practice appears predominantly near the goal rather than at the start of the alley, and the same condition of correlated reinforcement which leads to the "wait-and-run" solution with massed trials leads to slower responding throughout the alley with distributed trials. Similarly, delaying rather than omitting the reward leads to more widespread decrements in speed and hence in a different type of solution.

Variance in the qualitative aspects of behavior is permitted because the definition of the reinforced response class includes a variety of solutions. Presumably, the homogeneity of these aspects of the response could be increased by further refining the conditions so as to vary reinforcement also in terms of such features.

NOTE: ON THE TRANSITION EFFECT IN NEGATIVELY CORRELATED REINFORCEMENT

Under most conditions of correlated reinforcement, the reward varies from trial to trial as a result of behavioral oscillation in the response dimensions upon which the reward depends. Behavioral variability is not under the experimenter's control and therefore he cannot predetermine the particular sequence of rewards that the subject will encounter. Nevertheless, we can make an after-the-fact analysis of the data for transition effects in order to see whether performance varies systematically with the recent history of successes and failures.

Toward this end, the speeds on each of the four trials a day of the $12A,0D < .2I < 0A,\infty D$ group of Exper. 57D were separated according to whether the previous trials of that day had been rewarded or not. The results of this analysis are shown in the upper left graph of Fig. 49. There was an over-all tendency for the rats to run slower on successive trials of the day, as shown in the upper right graph, but there was little consistent separation depending on whether the preceding trial had been reinforced or not. There is a discernible tendency, however, for the slowest speeds to occur on later trials of the day if the earlier trials had not been rewarded. Although the transition effects on speed are absolutely small, they produce a sizeable effect upon the percentage of rewarded trials, as shown in the middle graphs. This effect on reward affects the control group's speed, as shown in the lower graphs, there being a particularly large increase in speed between the first and second trials, presumably because of the appreciably lower frequency of reinforcement on the first trials and a general, though small, tendency for speed to be faster following nonreward.

Similar transition effects were produced by the same reward conditions in Exper. 58E in which the training was given at one trial a day. Again the accumulated effect of several nonreinforcements was to lead to the slowest speeds (average I-speed $= .189$ after 3 or 4 failures, percent reinforcement $= 57$), while several successive rewarded trials led to the fastest speeds (average I-speed $= .208$ after 3 or 4 successes, percent reinforcement $= 45$). Although these effects fail to reach conventional levels of significance ($F = 3.85$, d.f. $= 3$ and 6), their existence will be further supported when the data on changes in the reward conditions are presented. Accordingly, it is tentatively concluded that:

24. The performance of rats for whom the reward is negatively correlated with response speed is largely independent of whether the immediately preceding trial was rewarded or not, but speed decreases after a number of consecutive nonreinforcements.

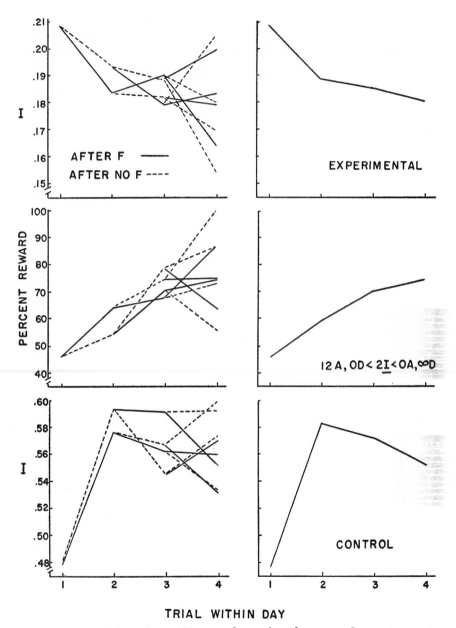

Figure 49. Transition effects with massed practice when reward was given only if *I*-speed was less than .2 (over 5 sec.). (Exper. 57D)

Note: On the Use of Positively
Correlated Reinforcement

All the conditions described in this chapter involve negatively correlated reward in which maximum reward is given for slow responses. Such conditions can be imposed from the beginning of training, because the rat initially responds slowly and hence encounters the optimal reward conditions. To use positively correlated reward, in which reward is given only for fast responses, it is necessary to start with a reasonably low criterion speed that the rat can attain without reward, and to raise the criterion in stages as the rat's speed increases.

This procedure of using graded criteria might be referred to as "shaping" a quantitative characteristic of the response by successive approximations (Skinner, 1938, p. 339). In contrast with the familiar techniques of shaping the qualitative features of a response, graded criteria can be described by explicit and objective rules. There are two major aspects of this procedure.

One concerns the relation of the criterion to the rat's current level of performance. The effect of the two extremes of the relation can be specified in advance. If, on the one hand, the criterion is kept so low that the rat always succeeds, then the condition is effectively uncorrelated reinforcement and performance will attain the level appropriate to the amount and delay of reward. If, on the other hand, the criterion is kept so high that the rat never succeeds, then perfomance will remain at the low baseline level. There is no evidence yet available to determine the relative effect of the various intermediate conditions.

The second aspect of the procedure of using graded criteria concerns the number of trials over which the criterion remains fixed. The procedure used in the present research was to change the criterion after each small block of trials. Alternatively, it might be better to keep the same criterion in force until the rat attains a specified level of success, and then to shift it. Again, there are no conclusive data available on the relative effect of these procedures.

The reason procedural questions seem to be particularly important is that positively correlated reward is consistent with any "hypothesis" that might become dominant. Suppose, for example, that a rat is run four trials a day and is rewarded on the two fastest trials. From studies of uncorrelated conditions, it is known that reward will most likely be earned on the second and third trials, since the rat typically runs slower on the first and last trials under such a schedule (see Fig. 16). Accordingly, the condition of rewarding the fastest half of the trials may also differentially reward trials-within-day and, as a result, further amplify the within-day gradient of speed of running. Indeed any discrimination that happens to develop will continue to gain strength because the rat will run faster in the presumed "positive" stimulus situation than in the "negative" one, and will therefore be differentially reinforced in a manner consistent with that discrimination.

Because of the uncertainty about these matters, the several studies of positively correlated reinforcement that are reported in this note were run as exploratory research in an effort to gain some preliminary evidence on these conditions. The procedures are probably not the most efficient for demonstrating the possible effects of positively correlated reinforcement.

In Exper. 58B two groups of rats were run six trials a day. Each individual rat was daily assigned a criterion speed based on its performance the previous day. The criterion for each rat in one group was selected so that the expected average frequency of reward was .33. By setting the criterion intermediate between the second and third shortest times on the previous day, if the same speeds occurred the rat would be rewarded on two of the six trials that day. The actual frequency of reinforcement might be higher or lower than .33 but, since the criterion followed the rat's speed each day, the frequency of reward could not deviate very far from .33 for very many days.

The criterion for the second experimental group in Exper. 58B was set at a more liberal level, designed to average a .67 frequency of reward. A matched-control rat was rewarded on the trials corresponding to those on which the experimental mate attained reward.

Performance curves under these conditions are shown in Fig. 50. In both cases, the experimental rats attained a higher level of performance than their matched controls. The differences, however, are not large either absolutely or relative to the appropriate error variance.

A second study of positively correlated reward used a different

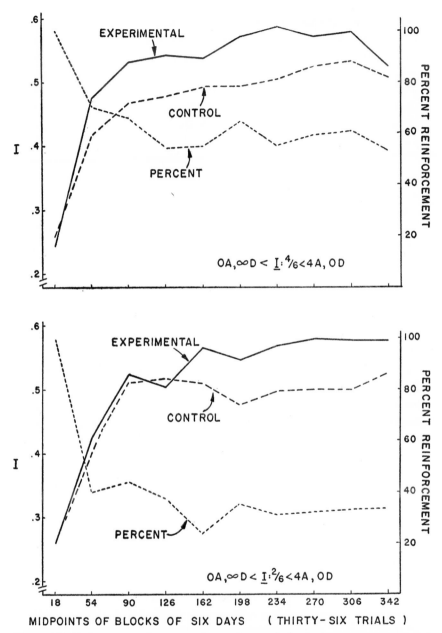

Figure 50. Performance when reward was given only for fast responses, compared with that of matched controls. The criterion was graded so that reward would be given on 4 of the 6 trials each day for the group shown in the upper graph, and on 2 of the 6 trials for the group shown in the lower graph. (Exper. 58B)

procedure for grading the criteria. In Exper. 59B, the criterion was the same for all experimental rats on any trial, and was advanced through preselected stages more gradually than in the preceding experiment. However, even after 350 trials there was no indication that the performance of the experimental rats was in any way different from that of their matched controls.

NOTE: ON THE EFFECT OF CHANGING THE AMOUNT OF REINFORCEMENT IN CONDITIONS OF NEGATIVELY CORRELATED DELAY OF REINFORCEMENT

It has been shown that a small reward produces unstable adjustment to conditions in which the reward is delayed or withheld if response speed exceeds a cutoff. One can ask whether the condition is learned as well with a small reward as with a large reward, the learning not being demonstrated in performance because the differential reinforcement is not sufficiently motivating. This is, of course, analogous to the "latent learning" question except that the initial training is with a small reward instead of no reward.

To answer this question, the rats in Exper. 57D that had been trained with a 1-pellet amount were shifted to a 12-pellet amount. The matched-control rats were carried along, continuing to receive the same amount and delay as their experimental mates. The *I*-speed curves immediately preceding and following this change in amount of reward are shown in the upper graph of Fig. 51, the left graph showing the group for which the reward was delayed and the right graph showing the group for which the reward was withheld.

The results in both cases are perfectly clear: increasing the amount of reward led to an increase in speed and hence to poorer performance on the problem as defined. With the delayed group, it is possible that speed was drawn so far above the cutoff that the effects of the correlation could no longer be felt. If so, the rats would never optimally readjust. The rats for which the reward was withheld showed not only the tendency to speed up as a result of the increased amount of reward but also the transition effect, leading them to slow down after several successive failures. Since the increased amount was actually encountered only when the rats ran slowly, the effect of the change was probably delayed but there was a gradual relearning to run slowly.

The lower graph of Fig. 51 shows data obtained by Bower (1959) on the effect of reducing the amount of reward without changing the delay conditions in which reward was given immediately if *I*-speed was less than .25 (4 seconds) and was delayed 30 sec. if *I*-speed was greater than .25. This reduction in amount of reward produced a very large drop in speed to well below the level previously observed when a small reward was used in conditions of negatively correlated delay of reward (see Figs. 38 and 40). Train-

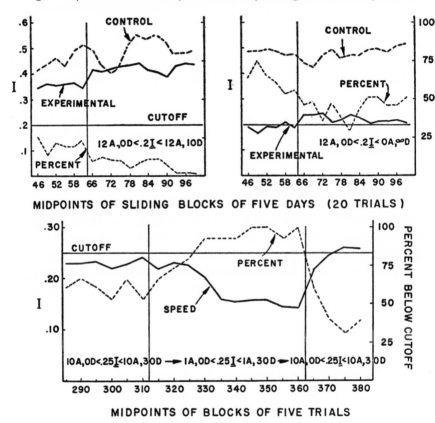

Figure 51. The effects of changing the amount of reward in conditions of negatively correlated reinforcement. The upper graphs show the results of increasing the amount of reward (from 1 to 12 pellets) when the reward was delayed (left graph) or withheld (right graph) if *I*-speed was greater than .2 (less than 5 sec.). (Exper. 57D) The lower graph shows the results of both a decrease and an increase in amount of reward (from 10 pellets to 1, and back) when the reward was delayed if *I*-speed was greater than .25 (less than 4 sec.). (Data from Bower, 1959)

ing was not continued long enough to see whether performance would have recovered to a level near the cutoff, the reward instead being returned to the original large amount. Speed quickly increased, actually overshooting the original stable level with that same amount.

It is therefore clear that adjustment to conditions of negatively correlated reward is specific to the prevailing amount of reward and is disrupted by changes in the amount. Empirically, then,

25. When the amount of reward is changed after the rat has learned to run slowly under conditions of negatively correlated reinforcement,

    a. an increase leads to an increase in speed that is temporary unless the change is so great that the correlation of reward with performance is no longer encountered.

    b. a decrease leads to a decrease in speed, and a subsequent increase in the amount leads to an overshooting of the original performance level.

Note: On the Effect of Changing Drive in Negatively Correlated Reinforcement

Rats that have learned to run slowly in order to get food might react to an increase in the hunger drive by running more slowly than usual in order to be more certain of getting the reward. However, the usual effect of increasing the drive level in uncorrelated reward conditions is to increase speed. Furthermore, if drive and reward have similar motivational effects, it might be expected that increasing hunger would increase speed since it was shown that increasing the amount of reward increased speed.

The rats in Exper. 56C that had been temporarily shifted to massed trials and had learned to run slowly in the $2A,0D < .33R < 0A, \infty D$ condition were subsequently tested at one trial a day with drive reduced to 3-hour deprivation and also with drive increased to 48-hour deprivation. Under the regular 24-hour deprivation condition, R-speed was .328 and reward percentage was 46. When the deprivation was increased to 48 hours, R-speed increased to .425 and reward percentage dropped to 33. Under the 3-hour deprivation condition, R-speed decreased to .270 and reward percentage rose to 86. Clearly, then, changes in drive in negatively correlated reward conditions affect speed in the same direction (although not necessarily with the same magnitude) as in uncorrelated reward conditions.

Though the effect of an increase in drive is to lead to poorer adjustment to negatively correlated reward, it does not follow that performance would ultimately be inferior. It was seen in the context of the amount of reward that larger rewards led to better learning but that increases in amount led to a temporary impairment. By analogy, it might be expected that rats would adjust better under high drive if sufficient practice were given at that drive level.

To test for this possibility, four rats that had been trained by Bower (1959) under a $10A,0D < .17I < 0A,\infty D$ condition with a 14-gram maintenance diet were continued under the same reward condition, with two receiving 10 gm/day and the other two, 16 gm/day. The rats were tested once a day and, as the differential maintenance diet took effect, the performance of the high- and low-drive rats separated, with the high-drive rats running faster and rarely getting reward.

These data are shown in the upper graphs of Fig. 52, the first point in each graph showing performance under the original drive and the next three points showing performance at one trial a day. The rats were then shifted to four trials a day for the remaining six points in order to give a large number of trials within a reasonable period of time. It will be observed that the high-drive rats did tend to relearn the problem although they did not attain as high a percentage of success as the low-drive rats. As can be seen in the lower graph of Fig. 52, however, the high-drive rats showed better adjustment if performance is scored in terms of deviation from cutoff. That is to say, the high-drive rats showed a distinct convergence on the cutoff speed, whereas the low-drive rats showed a somewhat larger variance around a modal speed appreciably below the cutoff. Because of the difference in modes, the difference in variance cannot be interpreted without some assumption concerning the unit of measurement.

More extensive research is required of drive effects in these conditions, especially using differences in drive from the beginning of training so that the change problem can be avoided. Conrad, Sidman, and Herrnstein (1958) found little effect of deprivation on spaced responding in a bar-pressing situation although the frequency of long interresponse times increased under very low drive. If drive level acts upon the internal timing mechanism, then changing the drive is analogous to changing the cutoff (see Chapter 9), and the prevailing drive would partially determine the difficulty of the discrimination. Accordingly, the length of the cutoff and

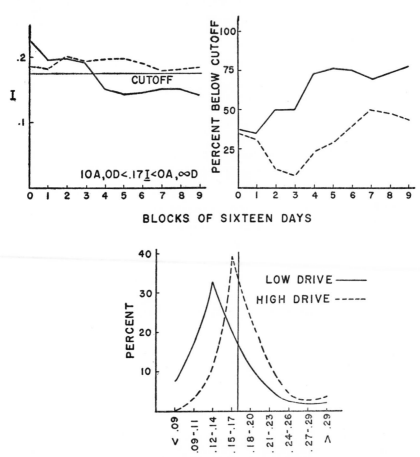

Figure 52. The effect of changing the maintenance diet from 14 gm/day to 16 gm/day (low drive) or 10 gm/day (high drive) on performance when reward was given only if *I*-speed was less than .17 (over 6 sec.). (Exper. 59E)

the amount of reward may interact importantly with the degree of drive in determining adjustment to conditions of negatively correlated reward.

In any event, the present data suggest that:

26. Adjustment to conditions of negatively correlated reward is better under high drive in the sense of producing a sharp convergence on the cutoff, but low drive produces slower speeds and greater frequency of reward.

27. After training on a condition of negatively correlated reward, increasing the drive leads to an increase in speed and decreasing the drive leads to a decrease in speed.

Note: On the Possibility of "Inhibition" in Negatively Correlated Reinforcement

When a rat has learned to run slowly under conditions of negatively correlated reward, it might be assumed that the running response is being actively inhibited until the appropriate temporal cues appear. Such an analysis could underlie the equilibrium model and is similar to the Pavlovian (1927) concept of "inhibition of delay." One incidental observation is consistent with this approach.

The rats in Exper. 58E that were running one trial a day under the $12A, 0D < .2I < 0A, \infty D$ condition were moved after about six months from small individual cages with a solid, slant front door to somewhat larger individual cages with a hardware-cloth, straight front door (to permit adequate cleaning and sterilization of the original cages). The change produced a marked increase in speed (from about .207 to .263), it taking 10 days before any rat got rewarded and 20 days before speeds were again at the pre-change level.

This finding could be analogous to "disinhibition." Following such reasoning, after the rats had readjusted to the condition and were performing at a reasonably stable level, a three-week rest was introduced in an attempt to obtain a form of "spontaneous recovery." However, in this case, there was no change in response speed, the rats running very slightly slower after the rest than on the last pre-rest training day.

The effects of a variety of such extraneous stimulus changes must be studied before a decision can be made as to whether an inhibition construct should be invoked in such conditions. If the evidence is positive, it would perhaps favor the stimulus-oriented type of micromolar approach.

One of the most well-known principles of behavior is the tendency for a response that was learned in one stimulus complex to occur in similar stimulus complexes. The comparable statement from a micromolar point of view is that the whole response-tendency profile acquired in one situation should generalize to similar situations. Thus, a rat that is first trained with correlated reinforcement to run slowly in one alley should, if given an opportunity to run in another alley, have a discernible tendency to run in the same way even if the conditions in the new alley do not maximally reward that response.

Simply to confirm this expectation, the four rats in Exper. 59E that had learned to run slowly on a $10A,0D < .17I < 0A,\infty D$ condition in the white alley were run in the black alley to a constant 10-pellet reward. Speeds were unusually slow on the first two trials in the new alley, but by the third trial, performance had settled into the pattern previously learned in the other alley. Speeds then began to increase, gradually but consistently, toward the level appropriate to the constant reward conditions. Although this increase took much longer than would have obtained had the rats not been first trained to run slowly in the other alley, it nevertheless occurred in fewer trials than are required to adjust to constant reward in the same alley (see Chapter 9).

This result clearly indicates that:

28. Rats trained under correlated reinforcement to respond in a particular way in one situation tend to respond in the same way in a similar situation.

CHAPTER 9

Changes in the Conditions of Reinforcement

AFTER training under any one of the conditions of reinforcement described in the previous chapters, the conditions can be changed to any other. The number of potential changes is therefore even larger than the number of possible original conditions. The present chapter concerns the effect on performance of a few of these changes in the conditions of reinforcement.

There is sometimes a problem in deciding when a change from one condition to another can properly be said to have occurred, because a number of different conditions partially overlap. The reward on any particular trial could be an instance of constant reinforcement, an instance of varied reinforcement that includes that reward, or an instance of correlated reinforcement in which the terms provide that reward for the observed performance. Because of the overlap, a number of trials are required in order to characterize the prevailing conditions.

For example, consider a condition in which reward is given only when the rat runs slowly. If the conditions are changed so that the reward is uncorrelated with speed, it may take several trials before the rat first runs fast enough to encounter the changed part of the reward conditions. This problem is not peculiar to conditions of correlated reinforcement; it occurs in any situation in which exposure to the change depends upon the subject's performance. A rat that is given all free trials in a T-maze first with reward only in the right arm might never reverse after a larger reward is put in the left arm. One can hardly expect performance to change unless the subject encounters the new conditions.

Nevertheless, the approach followed in this chapter is to identify the prevailing conditions by the experimenter's intentions and not necessarily by the subject's experiences. Accordingly, a change in the conditions of reinforcement will here refer to a change in the setting of the apparatus.

FROM CONSTANT REINFORCEMENT

It was seen in Chapter 3 that, in conditions of constant reward, speed is an increasing function of the amount of reward and a decreasing function of the time of delay of reward. When such conditions are changed there is typically no question that the change will be encountered, since any new reward must indicate some change in the conditions.

Extinction as a function of delay of reward. The constant reward groups in Exper. 55D, for which the reward had been delayed for 0, 1, 3, 5, 10, or 30 seconds, were extinguished after an intervening period during which the drive level was lowered by increasing the maintenance diet. The performance curves of three of these groups during the extinction trials are shown in Fig. 53. The curves for the other groups are comparable to the ones shown.

The curves start at different points because of the different reward conditions during acquisition, but there is no consistent evidence that the time of delay of reward affected the relative rate of extinction. This same conclusion was indicated during the extinction phase of Exper. 54A (see upper graph of Fig. 56).

However, this conclusion may apply only when the extinction procedure is to remove the rat within 3 to 5 seconds after it gets to the end of the alley. With this procedure, the rats for which the reward had been delayed during acquisition are removed from the goal box before their accustomed time of reward. There remains the possibility that resistance to extinction is affected by the relation between the delay of reward during acquisition and the detention time during extinction.

It should be noticed that speed in the start and first segment of the alley decreased relatively little during extinction. When extinction trials are given on a one-a-day schedule, the clearly visible effects of nonreinforcement appear predominantly near the goal, where the rats often stop and occasionally retrace back toward the start box. This pattern of behavior contrasts sharply with that produced by massed extinction trials since, with the latter schedule, the rats are slow to leave the start box but then usually run continuously to the goal.

Extinction as a function of amount of reward. Beier (1958) has provided data on the extinction performance of groups that re-

ceived different amounts of reward during acquisition. These data
are reproduced in Fig. 54. The curves cross each other, with the
group that had received the largest reward during acquisition
running slowest midway during the extinction trials. Relative rate
of extinction was therefore directly related to the amount of re-

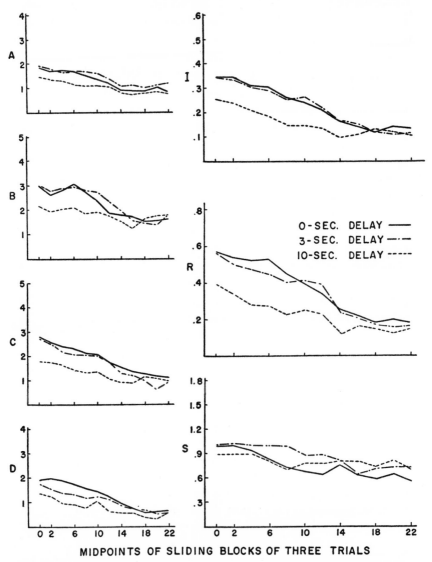

MIDPOINTS OF SLIDING BLOCKS OF THREE TRIALS

Figure 53. Performance during extinction of groups with different delays
of reinforcement during acquisition. (Exper. 55D)

ward (see Reynolds, 1950, for contrasting results in another situation). A smaller effect in the same direction was seen in Exper. 55E comparing groups that had been trained with 9 or 5 pellets reward (see also Hulse, 1958).

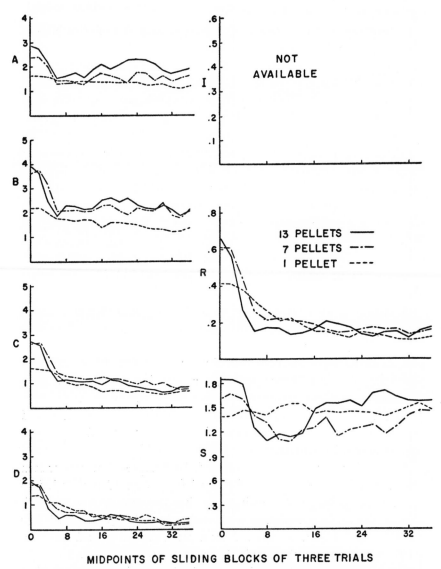

MIDPOINTS OF SLIDING BLOCKS OF THREE TRIALS

Figure 54. Performance during extinction of groups with different amounts of reinforcement during acquisition. (Data from Beier, 1958)

Beier suggested that this result may reflect, at least in part, a contrast effect such as she proposed in interpreting the effect of varied amount of reward. That is to say, zero reward contrasts most sharply with a history of continuous large rewards, and the goal response to nonreinforcement would therefore be weakest following such a condition.

Relearning and re-extinction. When reward is reinstituted following extinction, relearning occurs. This was the case in Expers. 54A and 55E, and it can be seen in Fig. 55 that speed had regained a high level within 12 to 15 trials. While appreciably faster than the rate of original learning by these groups, it does not differ very markedly from the rate of original learning after extensive adaptation to the apparatus without reward (see Fig. 31).

Of more importance, the speed differences that were produced by the reward conditions in original learning reappeared when the groups were retrained with the same reward. This occurred both in Exper. 54A, where the original difference had been based on the time of delay of reward, and in Exper. 55E, where the original difference had been based on the amount of reward. The result is consistent with the assumption that different habit profiles were built up during original learning and persisted into the relearning phase.

A second extinction was run in both experiments, but because original learning was apparently not complete the second extinction started at a somewhat different level, and it is therefore difficult to make a comparison that does not involve an assumption about the unit of measurement. There was, however, a suggestion that the second extinction took place more slowly than the first. Such a result is not unreasonable if acquisition, extinction, and relearning are viewed as together forming one possible sequence of partial reinforcement.

Increase in the amount of reward. In Chapter 3 it was shown that increasing the amount of reward from 2 to 12 pellets led to an increase in speed of running and that the change was approximately the same for groups with different delays of reward (see Fig. 13). The increase in speed took place smoothly and continuously and was complete within 10 to 12 trials.

No statements can be made as to whether performance overshot the level produced by 12 pellets from the beginning of training, since there were no control groups. In this case, an overshoot could hardly have been expected on incentive grounds because the new reward was near the upper limit of the incentive function. That is, even if the rats overreacted to 12 pellets because of contrast with 2 pellets, there would not be an observable effect on performance because an even larger reward does not produce faster speeds.

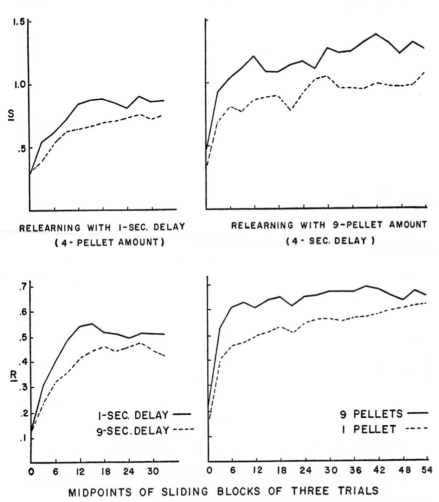

Figure 55. Relearning under the same reward conditions by groups that had received different reward conditions during original learning. The curves on the left show groups originally differing in delay of reward and, on the right, groups originally differing in amount of reward. (Expers. 54A and 55E)

Change to negatively correlated reinforcement. Initial training with a constant, uncorrelated reward could make it more difficult for the rat to adapt to conditions of negatively correlated reward. If the new conditions include appreciable reward for fast speeds, then slow responses may not occur and the rat will never optimally adjust to the change. However, if fast speeds are nonreinforced, slow speeds will result from extinction and, since the new conditions will be encountered, readjustment should occur.

Trapold (Exper. 58C) obtained data on this question by shifting rats from a constant 9-pellet reward to a $10A,0D < .2I < 0A,\infty D$ condition. Speed dropped from a high initial level to the cutoff in 174 trials; adjustment occurred about as rapidly as if the rats had been trained initially under the correlated condition.

Summary. The results of the several studies in which the reward conditions were changed after initial training under conditions of constant reward may be summarized as follows:

29. Relative rate of extinction is independent of the delay of reward during acquisition when the rats are removed immediately from the goal box on extinction trials.

30. Relative rate of extinction is faster the larger the amount of reward during acquisition.

31. A second learning after extinction is faster than original learning. Differences produced by reward in original learning reappear early in relearning even though the reward conditions during relearning are the same.

32. Increasing the amount of reward produces a rapid but continuous increase in performance.

33. Rats adjust to a condition of negatively correlated reward as quickly after pretraining with uncorrelated reward as they do if the correlated condition is used from the beginning of training.

From Varied Reinforcement

It was seen in Chapter 4 that the performance level maintained under conditions of varied reward depends not simply on the average reward received but also on the range of variation in reward. In general, speed is faster the wider the range of variation in delay of reward and the smaller the range of variation in amount of reward.

When the reward is changed following training with varied

reward, the new and old conditions may overlap. For example, if the delay of reward is first varied between 1 and 9 seconds and is then changed to variation between 1 and 5 seconds, the reward on half the trials is identical in the two conditions. This would also be true if the conditions were changed to constant 1-sec. delay, but this condition would involve a greater change on the other half of the trials. It seems reasonable to expect that the resistance to change in the reward conditions will be greater the greater the overlap of identical events and the more similar the nonidentical events.

Extinction as a function of varied delay of reward. The upper graph of Fig. 56 compares extinction following varied delay of reward (1 and 9 seconds) with extinction after constant delay when acquisition and extinction were run on a one-trial-a-day schedule. In this case, the relative rate of extinction of the varied delay group was comparable to that of the constant delay groups.

The lower graph of Fig. 56 compares extinction for two varied delay and one constant delay groups when both acquisition and extinction were run on a ten-trials-a-day schedule. Again, small variation in delay of reward (0 and 9 seconds) did not affect resistance to extinction relative to the constant delay group. However, more widely varied delay of reward (0 and 30 seconds) did reduce the rate of extinction.

Extinction as a function of varied amount of reward. Fig. 57 reproduces data obtained by Beier (1958) in her study of the effect of the range of variation in amount of reward. These data can be compared with those in Fig. 54 for the constant reward groups in her study. Consistent with the earlier results of Expers. 55E and 56A, the relative rate of extinction was reduced by varying the amount of reward. Beier's data show clearly that resistance to extinction is greater the wider the range of variation in amount of reward, the curves crossing midway during the extinction trials.

Extinction as a function of partial reinforcement. Beier's experiment, run at one trial a day, showed that partial reinforcement produced greater resistance to extinction than conditions with less widely varied amount of reward. Two comparisons of partial and continuous reinforcement on a four-trials-a-day schedule were made in Exper. 57B. The familiar partial reinforcement effect (see Capaldi, 1958; Katz, 1957; Kendler et al., 1957; Sheffield,

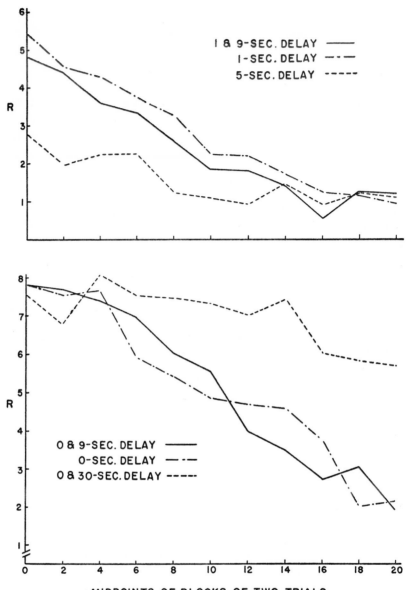

Figure 56. The effect of varied delay of reward on extinction. (Expers. 54A and 55A)

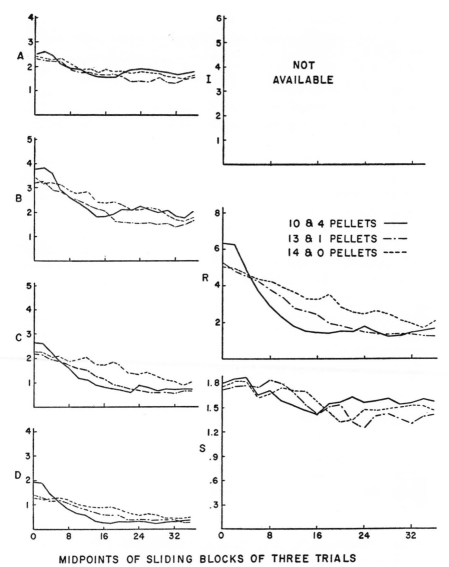

MIDPOINTS OF SLIDING BLOCKS OF THREE TRIALS

Figure 57. The effect of varied amount of reward on extinction, showing groups that differed in the range of variation in reward during acquisition. (Data from Beier, 1958)

1949; and Wilson, Weiss, and Amsel, 1955) appeared both for groups run under conventional conditions without shock and for groups that were given a mild electric shock on every acquisition trial.

The effect of partial reinforcement on resistance to extinction has probably evoked more theoretical activity than any other single phenomenon in the area of learning. Part of the difficulty in understanding this effect stems from the fact that extinction itself is poorly understood. From the present point of view, experimental extinction (at least in instrumental conditioning) reflects the loss of incentive. That is to say, nonreinforcement is a limiting instance of, but continuous with, reinforcing events and extinction is therefore only one of a great many possible changes in the conditions of reinforcement. What is needed is a theory that is general enough to predict the rate at which incentive will become readjusted after any of these changes.

The postulates given in Chapter 5 will undoubtedly have to be supplemented before such a goal is attained. It was assumed there that whenever the incentive is inappropriate to the reward actually received following an S-R event, there is a change in the incentive for that S-R event in the appropriate direction. Viewed through the fractional anticipatory goal-response mechanism, if the r_g is not consonant with the R_G evoked by the reward, then there is an extinction trial of the old and a conditioning trial of the new r_g. Hence there would be a partial change toward the new value.

Partial reinforcement apparently reduces the rate at which this change takes place.[1] One way of accounting for this requires the added assumption that there can be (and typically are, following constant reward) several nonreinforced occurrences of r_g on each extinction trial. Partial reinforcement exposes the subject to nonreinforcement during acquisition and extinguishes the repetitive occurrence of r_g to the cues of nonreinforcement. That is, the rats learn that an empty goal box does not contain food and they therefore stop making r_g repeatedly on such trials.

This account is consistent with the effects of varied reinforce-

1. If one of the accounts of varied reinforcement that was suggested in Chapter 4 is true, namely that reward is inadvertently correlated with speed so that a particular speed is learned as a superstition, then this fact should be taken into account in treating resistance to change following varied reinforcement.

ment on resistance to extinction. In these cases, the repetitive occurrence of r_g is extinguished to the cues of a smaller or longer delayed reward. Such cues, however, are similar to those of nonreinforcement and more so the smaller the reward or the longer it is
delayed. Thus, widely varied reward increases resistance to extinction by reducing the number of occurrences of r_g per nonreinforced trial because of generalization from small-reward or de-
layed-reward trials.

Summary. The several studies of changes in the reward conditions after training with varied reinforcement can be summarized
as follows:

34. Among conditions with the same average delay, resistance
to extinction is an increasing function of the range of variation in
delay of reward.

35. Among conditions with the same average amount, resistance
to extinction is an increasing function of the range of variation in
amount of reward.

36. Partial reinforcement, as the limiting case of increasing the
range of variation in reward, produces the greatest resistance to
extinction.

From Correlated Reinforcement

Conditions of correlated reinforcement are described by a terms
function showing how reward is related to performance. It was
seen in Chapter 8 that speed is affected by this correlation, the
tendency for a rat to run at a particular speed depending on the
reward for that speed relative to the reward for alternative speeds.
It is often difficult to determine when such conditions have been
changed. This is because part of the terms function may remain
the same, and the frequency with which the subject encounters
the change then depends upon his performance. For example, if
rats are experimentally extinguished after first having been
trained under a condition in which reward was given only for
slow responses, the terms function above the cutoff is not changed
since these speeds were never rewarded. Information about the
change is transmitted only when the rat runs slowly.

Extinction after negatively correlated reward. Four of the rats
in Exper. 57D that had been rewarded only when *I*-speed was
below .2 were shifted from four to one trial a day and were then

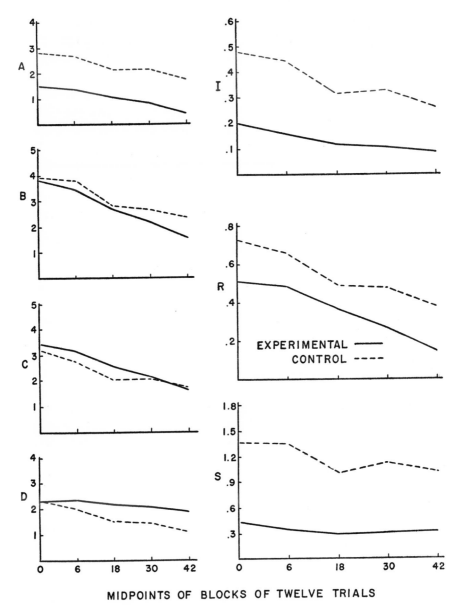

MIDPOINTS OF BLOCKS OF TWELVE TRIALS

Figure 58. Extinction at one trial a day after training at four trials a day on a condition in which reward was given only if *I*-speed was less than .2 (over 5 sec.), compared with matched controls. The zero point shows performance during 12 days at one trial a day before extinction began. (Exper. 57D)

experimentally extinguished along with their matched controls. The results for all response measures are shown in Fig. 58. Descriptively, the over-all effect of extinction was to lead to slower speeds in line with the transition effects that were observed during the acquisition phase. Response times of 10 to 20 seconds became common as the pattern of behavior that had been learned during training was exaggerated. That is, the rats spent more and more time in the start and early segments of the alley, but once clearly underway they ran about as fast as ever to the goal. Indeed, there was virtually no decrease in speed in the last foot of the alley.

Extinction was quite different for the matched-control group. The rats in this group had effectively been on a partial reinforcement condition, and their speeds decreased gradually throughout the alley. In contrast to this progressive loss of incentive in the control rats, the experimental rats apparently maintained incentive and continued actively to behave as if attempting to "solve" the problem.

The three rats in Exper. 58E that had adjusted to this same condition on a one-trial-a-day training schedule also showed a large increase in response time as the immediate effect of extinction. Since widely distributed practice under the $12A,0D < .2I < 0A,\infty D$ condition had produced a general decrement in speed across the entire alley, the further increase in time during extinction was also distributed throughout the alley. The contrast with the extinction performance of the matched-control group was therefore less clear in the measures recorded.

Change to uncorrelated reward. One rat[2] in Exper. 57D that had been rewarded only when I-speed was below .2 was shifted to a condition of constant reward. The effect of this change on performance is shown to the left of the vertical lines in Fig. 59. The very gradual increase in S-speed was accompanied by a decrease in R-speed, which is consistent with the earlier observation that rats under this condition are likely to run slowly if they have started quickly. The over-all effect was an increase in speed, but the change was still far from complete even after 60 days of training at four trials a day. Furthermore, these changes in speed oc-

2. Although only one rat is referred to here, a number of other rats have been run with similar changes in reward and have shown comparable effects. The pattern of results described here is therefore believed to be general.

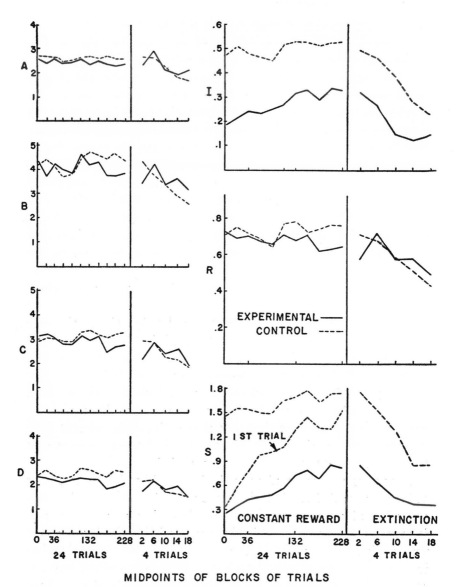

MIDPOINTS OF BLOCKS OF TRIALS

Figure 59. Performance after a change to constant reward following training on a condition in which reward was given only if *I*-speed was less than .2 (over 5 sec.), followed by extinction. (Note that the number of trials per unit distance on the abscissa was changed for extinction.) (Exper. 57D)

curred differentially on trials within the day. The *S*-speed on the first trial of each day has been plotted as a separate curve in Fig. 59, and it can be seen that the rat had adjusted to the new condition insofar as the first trial was concerned, but continued to show the effects of the earlier condition on the later trials of the day.

This training was followed by extinction, and the results are shown to the right of the vertical lines in Fig. 59. The experimental rat returned almost immediately to the earlier pattern of behavior it had learned under the correlated condition. Within ten trials it was behaving like the rats that had been extinguished without the intervening training under constant reward. The transition effect of nonreinforcement had persisted through the 240 trials of continuous reward.

Change in cutoff in negatively correlated reward. Three rats that had learned in Exper. 58C to run under a condition in which reward was given only if *I*-speed was less than .2 were shifted to a condition in which reward was given only if *I*-speed was less than .1. Insofar as the terms functions are concerned, these conditions differ only in that speeds between .2 and .1 which were formerly rewarded are now not rewarded. The effect of this change on performance is shown in the upper graph of Fig. 60.

Speed decreased very gradually. The transition effect of nonreinforcement led to slow speeds and, within a few trials, the rats were occasionally getting reward. However, they did not then suddenly shift to the new level. Instead, average speed gradually decreased as the speeds between .2 and .1 were eliminated.

Comparable results were obtained in Exper. 59C when the cutoff was changed from .5 to .2 *I*-speed in a condition in which a smaller reward was given if speed exceeded the cutoff. These data are plotted in the lower graph of Fig. 60. It will be recalled (see Fig. 43) that this group had originally been placed on a .2 cutoff but had not been materially affected by it. This is the only instance in the present research in which the performance level attained after a change to a condition differed noticeably from that observed during original training under that condition. Presumably this occurred because the rats did not happen to encounter the differential reinforcement sufficiently at the beginning of training to develop a preference for the slow responses. The alternative explanation—namely that the differential in amount of

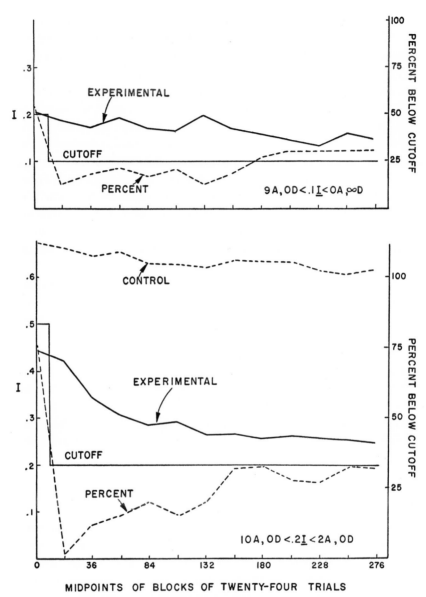

Figure 60. The effect of changing the cutoff in negatively correlated reward. The upper graph shows an increase from 5 to 10 seconds in a condition in which the reward was withheld if speed exceeded the cutoff. (Exper. 58C) The lower graph shows an increase from 2 to 5 seconds in a condition in which a smaller reward was given if speed exceeded the cutoff. (Exper. 59C)

reward was not sufficient to justify the long response interval required—is ruled out by the fact that the rats did run slowly after being exposed adequately to the differential in reinforcement.

We do not yet know how slowly a rat can be induced to run by this procedure of progressively changing the cutoff. However, Bower (1959) did show that, if the cutoff is changed so that it is long relative to the differential reinforcement, the rats will actually speed up and take the poorer reward continuously. Accordingly, there is a limit to how far this procedure can be carried out.

The fact that the changes took place so slowly suggests several possible supplements to the theory being considered. One may be called a generalized partial reinforcement effect. The resistance to extinction of one S-R event that is rewarded continuously may be increased by the nonreinforcement of a similar S-R event (small difference in either the stimulus or the response). This could result from generalization of the training not to make r_g repeatedly when nonreinforced in a similar situation. Thus, stimulus discrimination and response differentiation not only produce a difference in response tendency favoring the rewarded S-R event but lead to relatively persistent behavior. Applied to the present instance, the responses below the original cutoff and above the new cutoff had been rewarded continuously and hence might be expected to extinguish quickly. However, the nonreinforcement of similar responses above the original cutoff and the continued reinforcement of responses below the new cutoff induce resistance to extinction to precisely that region of the terms function that was changed.

A second possible supplement to the theory may be called "acquired distinctiveness of responses." The effects of a reward event are assumed to generalize in gradient fashion from the particular S-R event that occurred to similar S-R events. When a rat runs slowly and is rewarded, generalized incentive accrues to fast responses. The supplementary assumption would be that the extent of this generalization is reduced by response differentiation, which would increase resistance to change because the effect of any new reward encountered would tend to be restricted to the particular S-R event that had occurred. The change would therefore have to be learned for each response more or less independently.

Summary. The studies of the effects of changing the reward after original training under negatively correlated reinforcement may be summarized as follows:

37. If extinction trials are given so the rat cannot get reward no matter what its speed, total response times temporarily increase still further. However, the rats continue to run quickly to the food cup once they get near it.

38. If constant reward is introduced so the rat gets reward no matter what its speed, there is a very gradual increase in speed, the persisting effect of the original condition being progressively more apparent on later trials of the day. Subsequent extinction produces rapid reversion to the pattern of behavior characteristic of the original condition.

39. If the cutoff is changed so the rat must take more time to get the preferred reward,

   a. speed decreases very gradually if the cutoff is still short relative to the differential reinforcement.

   b. speed increases gradually if the cutoff is now long relative to the differential reinforcement.

   c. the rat may be induced to run near a cutoff that would be ineffective if used in original training.

DISCUSSION

When the reward is not constant in the original conditions, the immediate effect of changing the reward conditions can frequently be predicted by amplifying the transition effects observed in performance. Thus, since it was known that rats receiving negatively correlated reward run slowly after a series of "failures," it was not surprising to find that they slowed down when the cutoff was changed or when extinction was begun. In these cases, the discrimination and change-of-reward effects noted in Chapter 4 worked in the same direction. Nonreinforcement, as a cue, was differentially conditioned to slower responses during original learning. And the weakening effect of nonreinforcement on the speed that occurred made the rat more likely to try the slower responses which had originally been rewarded but which had dropped out presumably because they postponed the reward longer than necessary.

The over-all rate at which a rat adjusts to a change in the conditions of reinforcement could be predicted reasonably well by a model based on straightforward statistical reasoning. The model would assume that the rat acts as if it compared the rewards encountered on recent trials with those obtained on previous trials and ascertained the likelihood that the recent events represent a continuation of the earlier conditions. One would have to specify the number of trials to be considered as recent and the number of trials to be used in defining the previous conditions. Given these, together with a confidence level, one could determine when enough information had been made available to conclude that a change had occurred.

The predictions of this model would be quantitatively wrong. In this simple form, it implies that performance does not change until adequate evidence has accumulated, whereupon performance changes radically. The rat's speed often begins to change sooner than the model implies and always does so smoothly and continuously. That is, rather than obeying an arbitrary confidence level, the rat would have to be viewed as adjusting gradually to the changing probability. For example, the transition effects seen in varied reward show that performance changes after one or two trials with a particular reward, even though these events are a part of the original conditions.

More generally, the rat's performance changes much more slowly than this kind of reasoning implies. For example, when constant reward conditions are changed, a single trial is sufficient to determine with certainty that the original condition no longer prevails, but the rat requires a number of trials to adjust to such a change. And particularly with correlated reinforcement, the persistence with which rats cling to their early solution is out of all proportion to the information received that the conditions are no longer the same.

Nevertheless, such a model does permit reasonably good predictions about order relationships in resistance to change. This is already familiar in the comparison of extinction following partial and continuous reinforcement where the discrimination between acquisition and extinction is less clear if reward has been omitted on part of the acquisition trials. Similarly, when part of the terms function in correlated reinforcement is changed, information about the change is only gradually transmitted.

The element that is most conspicuously lacking in such a model is the conception of discrimination as a continuous process. A difference in reward conditions is not discriminable on an all-or-none basis; instead, the number of trials required for a change to be perceived varies with the size of the change. In uncorrelated conditions, the size of the change depends on the difference in amount, delay, or frequency of reward. In correlated conditions, there is the added factor of the similarity of the responses. For example, when a rat that had been rewarded only when its response time exceeded 5 seconds runs in 4 seconds and is rewarded, the effect is not of an insightful nature. Rather, because the responses are similar and the rewards are identical, subsequent behavior is hardly affected at all by the experience. It is presumably for this reason that the behavior acquired under conditions of correlated reinforcement is stable and persistent relative to that produced by the simpler conditions of uncorrelated reinforcement.

Note: On the Change from Negatively to Positively Correlated Reinforcement

Several of the changes previously considered are combined when the conditions are changed from negatively to positively correlated reinforcement. This change is analogous to a reversal in the T-maze or discrimination situation since previously rewarded responses are now nonreinforced, and vice versa.

If the rat had adjusted reasonably well to the original conditions, i.e. was running slowly and getting the better reward frequently, then the change will result in an increase in the frequency of the poorer reward. This will lead to slower running because of the transition effect of the poorer reward and the better reward will become even less frequent. In short, the initial effect of reversing the correlation of the reward will be much the same as a change to constant poorer reward, namely a sizeable decrease in speed as the rat makes the slower responses that had originally received the better reward. Gradually, however, the incentive for the slower responses will be adjusted to the poorer reward and performance will then increase toward the level appropriate to the poorer reward when uncorrelated with speed.

When the original cutoff is reached and the better reward is again encountered, the effect should be like the change to constant better reward, namely a gradual increase in speed that shows up differentially on the several trials of the day. If the criterion speed is then raised, again increasing the frequency of the poorer reward, the entire process as just described should recur in miniature. The extent of this second drop in speed should be inversely related to the extent of the first drop. That is, a rat that was poorly adjusted to the original condition would not suffer an increased frequency of the poorer reward at the advent of the first reversal and hence would not be driven very extensively through the range of slow responses. When a subsequent increase in the criterion does lead to an increase in the frequency of poorer rewards, readjusting the incentive for the slow responses will remain more or less entirely to be done, and hence there will be a large and extensive drop in speed.

The three rats in Exper. 59C that had learned to run slowly under a condition in which a smaller reward was given if speed exceeded the cutoff ($10A,0D < .2I < 2A,0D$) were placed on the opposite correlation so that the larger reward was given for speeds above .2 I-speed. The criterion was then raised for each rat as its speed increased. The observed performance matched in exact detail the description given above.

CHAPTER 10

Conditions of Punishment

THERE are two types of situations that permit the subject to control the occurrence of a noxious stimulus. The most frequently studied is the avoidance situation (see e.g. Sheffield and Temmer, 1950; and Sidman, 1953), in which a noxious stimulus is applied if the subject does not make a designated response within a specified interval of time. In an alley, for example, the rat can avoid an electric shock by getting out of the runway section of the alley quickly enough. The punishment situation (see e.g. Brown, 1948; and Estes, 1944) differs in that a noxious stimulus is applied only if the subject does make the designated response. In an alley, for example, the rat can avoid getting shocked at the goal end by staying in the start and runway sections. Briefly, it might be said that the subject is shocked for responding in the punishment situation and for not responding in the avoidance situation.

The distinction between the punishment and avoidance situations is of practical importance. No other drive-reward condition is necessary in an avoidance situation since the shock itself is sufficient to maintain performance of the designated response. In a punishment situation, on the other hand, the designated response will continue to be made only if it is also relevant to some other drive-reward condition. Whereas the rat in an alley is running away from the source of the shock when the avoidance procedure is used, it is running into the shock when the punishment procedure is used. To keep the rat running in the latter situation, some source of approach tendency is necessary.

The punishment situation involves a conflict between the tendency to respond, based on (say) hunger-food, and the tendency not to respond, based on the noxious stimulus. The noxious stimulus can be made so strong relative to the hunger-food condition that the response will not be made. Miller (e.g. 1951) has made a detailed analysis of this type of conflict. The avoidance situation involves a different sort of conflict, in which the tendency to respond is based on the noxious stimulus and the tendency not to respond is based on the effort required by the response. Presumably, the response can be made so effortful relative to the noxious stimulus that the response will not be made.

In either the punishment or the avoidance situation, the noxious stimulus can be applied for a predetermined length of time or it can be left on until the subject performs a designated escape response. In the latter case, the escape response may or may not be the same as the response that produces or prevents the noxious stimulus. This distinction is important to the extent that the effect of a noxious stimulus depends upon the response evoked by it (see Dinsmoor, 1954).

It is possible that a single analysis could handle the effects of noxious stimulation in the various types of situations but there has been relatively little research designed to support such an analysis. In any event, the remaining discussion in this chapter is restricted to the punishment situation in which no escape response is required.

There is a condition-of-punishment analogue for each of the various conditions of reinforcement previously described. Thus, a fixed punishment can be given regularly, more intense or more immediate for some subjects than for others. The punishment can be varied from trial to trial in intensity or delay, or it can be given on only part of the trials. Finally, the punishment can be correlated with speed of running so that the conditions permit the rat to minimize punishment in the same ways that it can maximize reward in conditions of correlated reinforcement.

Any condition of punishment can be combined with any condition of reinforcement. When both reward and punishment vary, a further consideration is whether there is any correlation between the food and the shock. For example, in a condition involving both partial reward and partial punishment, the food and the shock may be perfectly correlated with each other either positively (food and shock on half the trials and nothing on the other half) or negatively (food alone on half the trials and shock alone on the other half). If the reward and the punishment are not correlated with each other, then there are four equally likely events: food alone, shock alone, both food and shock, and nothing.

The more complex conditions offer a similar set of possibilities. Suppose, for example, that a rat was running under positively correlated reinforcement so that only fast responses were rewarded. Punishment could be given on every trial regardless of speed (constant punishment), it could be given on part of the trials regardless of speed (varied punishment), or it could depend differentially on speed (correlated punishment). In the last type of condition, the presumed effects of the correlations would be antagonistic if negatively correlated punishment were used, since running slowly would minimize punishment while running rapidly would maximize reward. The effects would be complementary were positively correlated punishment used, since running rapidly would simultaneously maximize reward and minimize punishment.

The studies reported here used only a small sample of the possible conditions of punishment. They were undertaken to explore the possible fruitfulness of this research area.

UNCORRELATED PUNISHMENT

Punishment was added to the same experimental situation used in the preceding studies by inserting a grid floor in the last foot of the alley and applying a mild electric shock to the rats' paws. In all the present research, the shock was of 150 msec. duration and, unless otherwise noted, it was delivered at the time the last photobeam in the alley was broken. In uncorrelated conditions the occurrence of the shock was predetermined by the experimenter.

Constant punishment. One group in Exper. 57B was shocked, as well as fed, on every trial, the intensity of the shock starting at a low level and being increased in stages to a moderately intense level. The performance of this group is compared with that of an unpunished control group in Fig. 61. It can be seen that the shock slowed the rats down and led to progressively slower speeds as the intensity was increased (see also Karsh, 1959).

The shock also markedly increased the between-subject differences in speed, the variance of the shock group being 12.93 times larger than the variance of the no-shock group. This effect is itself statistically reliable (d.f. $= 7$ and 7, $p < .01$). However, averaging over the last 20 days of training, the fastest shocked rat was slower than the slowest nonshocked rat, so that the effect on the mean is not mitigated by the effect on the variance.

The effect of a noxious stimulus on performance may well depend upon specific details, such as where in the response chain the shock is applied, when it is introduced during the training, how gradually it is increased in intensity, where on the rat the shock is given (Fowler, 1959), and indeed, even upon the nature of the shocking system (see Campbell and Teghtsoonian, 1958). Nevertheless, for the condition used here:

40. Speed is decreased by the addition of a mild electric shock following the response, speed being a concave downward, decreasing function of shock intensity. This decrease in speed is accompanied by an increase in the between-subject variance.

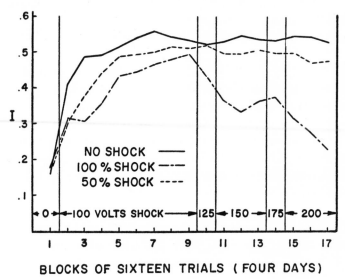

Figure 61. The effects of partial and continuous punishment on performance. The shock intensity was increased in stages as indicated. (Exper. 57B)

Varied punishment. Fig. 61 also shows the performance of a group in Exper. 57B to which the shock was given on only 50 percent of the trials. Compared with no shock, partial shock had a slight over-all depressing effect on speed. However, partial shock also markedly increased the between-subject variance, and in this case produced a bimodality in which the four fastest rats in the partial-shock group were all faster than the fastest rat in the no-shock group, and the four slowest rats in the partial-shock group were all slower than the slowest rat in the no-shock group. Partial punishment at moderate intensities may therefore have a facilitating effect.

Compared with continuous punishment, partial punishment had a less depressing effect on speed. (Over-all analysis of variance of the three groups yielded an F of 11.04, with 2 and 21 d.f., and a Mann-Whitney U-test between the partial and continuous shock groups yielded a $p < .05$.) This difference can only be expected to appear at intermediate levels of shock, since with very strong shocks the rats would stop running even under partial punishment. Nevertheless, over a reasonably broad range we may conclude that:

41. A mild electric shock given on half the trials does not reduce speed as much as the same shock given on every trial.

The results obtained with partial punishment suggest the action of two opposing effects. One is a negative effect, such as that produced by continuous punishment. The other is a positive effect, resulting from a reduction in temporary inhibition because of the stimulus variety that occasional shocks introduce into the situation. The latter effect could produce facilitation when the shock is mild since the aversive effect would not be very strong. Presumably, individual differences in sensitivity to the shock produced the observed effects on variance.

Varied punishment combined with varied reinforcement. Three groups in Exper. 57B were given partial punishment and partial reinforcement. The groups differed in the correlation between the food and the shock, one group $(r = +1)$ getting food and shock on half the trials and nil on the remaining half, one group $(r = -1)$ getting food on half the trials and shock on the remaining half, and the third group $(r = 0)$ getting food and shock on one-fourth of the trials, food on one-fourth, shock on one-fourth, and nil on the remaining fourth. The performance curves of the three groups are shown in Fig. 62.

It might have been predicted that the group for which the food and shock were positively correlated with each other would run the fastest, on the grounds that the shock in that condition could acquire secondary reinforcing properties which might attentuate its aversive properties. Instead, the group for which the food and shock were uncorrelated with each other showed the fastest speed of running, but the large between-subject variances prevented the difference from reaching conventional levels of statistical significance.

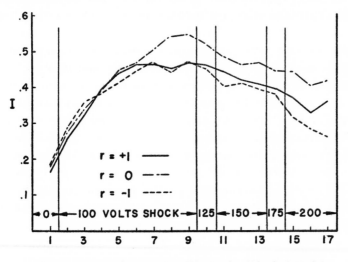

BLOCKS OF SIXTEEN TRIALS (FOUR DAYS)

Figure 62. The effects of partial punishment when combined with partial reinforcement in such a way that the food and shock were uncorrelated with each other, or were perfectly correlated either positively or negatively. The shock intensity was increased in stages as indicated. (Exper. 57B)

Despite the fact that the present data are not conclusive, the importance of the question justifies brief mention of two factors that are consistent with the obtained results. The first is the temporary inhibition effect, such as noted above in connection with partial punishment. The group for which the food and shock were uncorrelated had the most widely varied number of goal events and hence would have the lowest amount of temporary inhibition. The second factor involves the fact that the shock served as an "information" stimulus for the groups for which the food and shock were correlated. The rats in these groups learned the correlation fairly quickly and thereafter they did not even

look into the food cup if the cue indicating nonreward had occurred. It is suggested that an information stimulus functionally
breaks a chain into two chains: running before the stimulus and
running (or not) after it. Since rats slow down as they approach
the end of a chain, and since an information-giving shock at the
last photobeam ends the chain at that point, the rats will begin
to slow down sooner than if no information about the reward
occurs until the food cup is reached. This analysis also applies
to nonnoxious information stimuli and can be tested by measur-
ing the gradient of running speed before an information-giving
stimulus at various distances from the ultimate goal.

Transition effects in varied punishment. It will be recalled
that rats running with partial reinforcement tend ultimately to
run somewhat faster following nonreward than following reward.
Partial punishment produces the opposite transition effect: rats
run faster after trials on which they were not shocked than after
trials on which they were shocked (see also Gwinn, 1949). This
is shown for the group for which the reward was constant in the
upper left graph of Fig. 63. A comparison can be made with the
transition effects in partial reward shown in Fig. 27, since the
punishments were given in precisely the same sequences as the
rewards, and the sequential dependencies were identical.

The groups for which the food and shock were both partial
but correlated with each other showed an appropriate combination of the transition effects. Consider first the group with food
and shock positively correlated. Trials on which neither food nor
shock are received imply faster speed on the next trial, since the
absence of food leads to faster running via the transition effect
of partial reward, and the absence of shock leads to faster running
via the transition effect of partial punishment. The combined
transition effect [1] is clearly evident in the lower left graph of Fig.
63.

The reward and punishment transition effects are placed in
opposition in the condition in which rats receive shock on half
the trials and food on the other half. That is, insofar as shock is

1. This transition effect is relevant to the observation that several rats in this
condition would not run had the food and shock been given on every trial. That
is to say, a rat may run for a combination of food and shock which occurs only part
of the time, whereas it would not run were this event certain.

concerned, shock alone would lead to slower running but, insofar as food is concerned, shock alone would lead to faster running. The opposite is true for the occurrence of food alone. That the shock transition effect is the stronger is indicated in the upper right graph of Fig. 63, where it can be seen that the rats ran slower following shock trials and faster following food trials.[2]

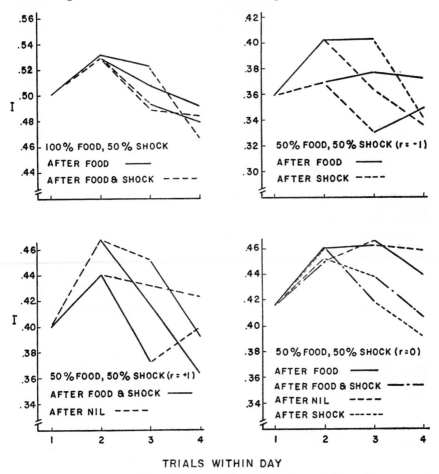

TRIALS WITHIN DAY

Figure 63. Transition effects with massed training of partial punishment and the combination of partial punishment and partial reinforcement. (Exper. 57B)

2. The fact that the transition effect was stronger in this condition than with partial punishment alone could be taken to indicate that the speed unit of measurement is not linearly related to response tendency. Were the units equal, one would expect the transition effect of food to oppose the transition effect of shock and hence to reduce the over-all effect.

Finally, the transition effects for the group for which the food and shock were uncorrelated are shown in the lower right graph of Fig. 63. The nil event favors faster running on the basis of

Table 14. Analysis of variance of third-trial speeds of three groups in Exper. 57B to show the transition effects of partial punishment and combined partial punishment and partial reinforcement. "Tests" refer to the last five blocks of four days over which the analysis was performed.

Source	d.f.	100% food, 50% shock m.s.	F	50% food, 50% shock r = −1 m.s.	F	50% food, 50% shock r = +1 m.s.	F
Rats	7	.3501		.8622		.3101	
Sequences	3	.0122	1.79	.0391	6.86 **	.0466	8.32 **
First trial	1	.0036		.0410	7.19 *	.0411	7.34 *
Second trial	1	.0319	4.69 *	.0757	13.28 **	.0905	16.16 **
Interaction	1	.0012		.0006		.0080	
Rats x sequences	21	.0068		.0057		.0056	
Tests	4	.0233		.0798		.0129	
Rats x tests	28	.0101		.0161		.0309	
Tests x sequences	12	.0036		.0022		.0044	
Rats x tests x sequences	84	.0052		.0044		.0065	

both the food and the shock transition effects, and this condition did indeed tend to lead to the fastest speeds on later trials. The food-shock event implies slower speeds on both accounts, and it did tend to lead to the slowest speeds. The food event and the shock event oppose the transition effects and the data are consistent with the interpretation that the shock effect is the stronger.

Analyses of variance to test the statistical significance of these effects are shown in Table 14. The analyses were performed on the third-trial speeds and may be compared with those in Table 9, which concerned the transition effects in partial reinforcement following the same sequences used here. The analyses show, in all cases, a significant effect of the second-trial event. The effect of the first-trial event is smaller in each case, but is reliable in two of the analyses. Over-all, the trend that emerges may be summarized as follows:

42. Speed varies systematically from trial to trial when punishment occurs on part of the trials, speed being faster following trials without shock.

43. Conditions involving partial punishment and partial reinforcement exhibit transition effects that represent the combined transition effects of food alone and shock alone, the transition effect of shock being stronger than that of food.

CORRELATED PUNISHMENT

In conditions of correlated punishment, some dimension of the punishment depends differentially upon the rat's speed of running. In the present studies the punishment dimension was simply the occurrence or nonoccurrence of an electric shock, negatively correlated punishment meaning shock for fast responses and positively correlated punishment meaning shock for slow responses.

Methodologically, all the statements describing the conditions of correlated reinforcement apply equally to conditions of correlated punishment. The "terms" function in this context describes the way the punishment depends on response speed, and the "incentive" function describes the empirical relationship between speed and uncorrelated punishment. Again, the critical initial question is whether the equilibrium model can correctly predict the effect of correlated punishment, i.e. does speed depend only on the intensity, delay, and frequency of the punishment or does it also depend on the particular correlation between speed and punishment?

Negatively correlated punishment. Negatively correlated punishment involves a conflict similar to those mentioned when discussing the various conditions of negatively correlated reinforcement. Although the differential in shock favors slow responses, fast responses get the reward sooner. Hence, if the shock is weak, its effect might not be sufficient to pull speed down to the cutoff.

One rat in Exper. 57C was run 6 trials a day to a constant 8-pellet reward and negatively correlated punishment. The cutoff speed was selected daily in such a way that the rat would, on the average, be shocked on the fastest 3 trials each day. After 57 days of this condition, the rat was running slightly faster than a matched-control rat.

A second rat was run under this type of condition in Exper. 58B. In this case, a 5-sec. cutoff was enforced from the beginning of training so that shock was applied on any trial when *I*-speed exceeded .2. By the end of 84 days at 6 trials a day, average speed was well below the cutoff and shock was rarely being encountered. However, because the matched-control rat died very early in the experiment, it was not clear that the low performance had resulted from the correlation of shock with speed. To test this interpretation, the conditions were reversed and the shock was now given only when the rat ran slowly.

If punishment acts differentially upon different micromolar responses, then the effects of such a reversal can be predicted. The initial change should be toward slower responses as a result of the accumulated transition effects. However, since the slow responses are now punished, the differential in punishment should be eradicated and speed should then increase toward the level appropriate to 100 percent uncorrelated punishment. Once speed reaches the cutoff, so that the new differential in punishment is encountered and begins to favor fast responses, speed should increase rapidly. Furthermore, if the criterion speed is then raised, speed should increase still further until the criterion gets out of reach, after which speed should drop down to the level appropriate to 100 percent punishment.

This description matches in detail the observed performance. Late in the reversal phase of the experiment, the rat was getting a higher frequency of shocks than at the end of the first phase, but was running appreciably faster. This performance difference is presumably attributable to the reversal in the correlation between speed and shock.

As a further test of this condition, three rats in Exper. 59A were shocked when *I*-speed exceeded .33 (3 seconds). Their performance, shown in Fig. 64, gradually approximated the cutoff. In this case, the major portion of the response time was spent in the last foot of the alley where the effect of shock was typically most apparent. When the cutoff was changed so that shock was given when *I*-speed was above .25 (4 seconds), there was a gradual decrease in speed, particularly in the last foot of the alley, until the rats were doing almost as well on the new cutoff as they had been doing on the old. The matched-control rats in Exper. 59A also ran slowly, partly because they were more disturbed by the shock, but mainly because they inadvertently received negatively correlated punishment as the large transition effects of partial punishment kept their speeds in phase with their experimental mates. Nevertheless, the speeds of the experimental and control groups ultimately differed reliably ($t = 5.37$, d.f. $= 2$, $p < .05$).

It can be concluded that:

44. When a rewarded response receives negatively correlated punishment, so that a shock is given if speed exceeds a cutoff,

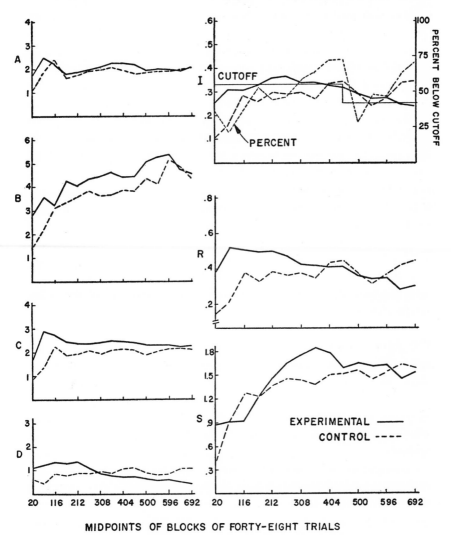

Figure 64. Performance under negatively correlated punishment, compared with that of matched-control subjects. (Exper. 59A)

rats may learn to run slowly near the cutoff and hence deviate from the prediction of an equilibrium model.

Positively correlated punishment. Although speed was seen to increase after a reversal from negatively correlated to positively correlated punishment, we cannot conclude from those data that the performance level produced by the latter condition is different from that produced by uncorrelated punishment. In an effort to test this point, two rats in Exper. 57C were run under positively correlated punishment with the criterion graded daily so that, on the average, each rat would be shocked on the 3 slowest of the 6 trials each day. One rat was given a small reward and the other was given a large reward, but after 47 days of this procedure both rats were running slightly slower than their matched controls. Three rats in Exper. 58B were run under positively correlated punishment with the criterion graded daily so that, on the average, each rat would be shocked on the 4 slowest of the 6 trials each day. Again, no appreciable difference appeared between the experimental and matched-control groups. When the shock was increased in intensity, which was expected to provide greater differential punishment favoring running rapidly, the experimental rats slowed down to an extent closely corresponding to that shown by their matched controls. There is no evidence yet available to show that positively correlated punishment affects performance differently from uncorrelated punishment with the same frequency and intensity.

Correlated punishment and correlated reinforcement. If both the punishment and the reinforcement are correlated with response speed, their effects may be complementary or antagonistic depending on whether or not punishment is minimized by the same performance that maximizes reward. In addition, the shock may serve a specific "informational" function by providing an immediate and distinctive cue indicating the adequacy of the response.

One group of rats was run under a condition in which food and shock were both given only if speed exceeded a criterion that was graded daily so that, on the average, the rats would receive food and shock on the 2 fastest of 6 trials each day. The performance by this group, along with that of its matched-control group, is shown in Fig. 65. The result can be compared with that shown in Fig. 50, where only the correlated reward aspect was used. Adding a shock certainly did not interfere with learning to run rapidly; the shocked group actually attained a somewhat higher terminal performance level than the unshocked group and showed a larger difference from its matched-control group.

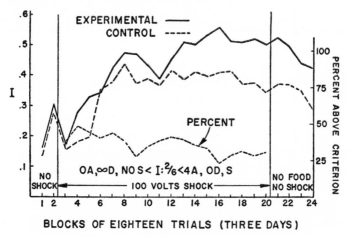

Figure 65. Performance when both food and shock were given only when *I*-speed exceeded a criterion graded daily so as to average success on two of the six trials each day, compared with matched controls. (Exper. 58B)

EXTINCTION FOLLOWING UNCORRELATED PUNISHMENT

The experimental extinction of a response that was both rewarded and punished during training presumably involves two changes which separately would act in opposite directions. That is, speed would be expected to decrease if just the food were omitted and to increase if just the shock were omitted.

The performances during extinction of the three groups that had received continuous reward and different frequencies of punishment during training are shown in Fig. 66. The continuous shock group was performing so far below the unshocked group that a comparison of resistance to extinction is difficult to make. However, continuous shock appears to have produced a somewhat slower relative rate of extinction, which is consistent with the "fixation" effect noted by Farber (1948). The increase in resistance to extinction is clear following partial punishment relative to no punishment, the curves crossing early in extinction and remaining reversed thereafter.

The extinction curves of the three groups for which the reward and the punishment had both been partial during training are

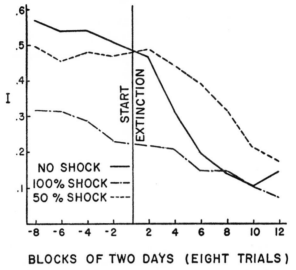

I

NO SHOCK ——
100% SHOCK —·—
50 % SHOCK ----

BLOCKS OF TWO DAYS (EIGHT TRIALS)

Figure 66. Extinction without food or shock after continuous reinforcement and partial, continuous, or no shock. (Exper. 57B)

shown in Fig. 67. The groups did not show very extensive changes in speed during the extinction trials, indicating the combined effect of partial reinforcement and partial punishment on resistance to extinction. Considering the similarity between the training and extinction conditions, one would have predicted a difference among these groups. The group for which the food and shock were positively correlated had encountered the extinction event (no food and no shock) on half of their training trials; the uncorrelated group had encountered this event on one-fourth of their training trials; and the negatively correlated group had never been exposed to the extinction event during training. On this basis, the positively correlated group would be expected to show the least decrement during extinction, but actually it showed the greatest decrement. Apparently the presence of shock on non-rewarded trials during acquisition does not interfere with the training for extinction that the occasional omission of the reward provides.

Many of the rats, and several of the curves, showed a distinct increase in speed early in extinction, which would indicate that the effect of the shock was lost more quickly than the effect of the food. Though somewhat surprising in view of the familiar difficulty in eliminating fears, it is consistent with the transition effects observed during training. This fact, together with the previous results, suggests that shock acts directly to increase the

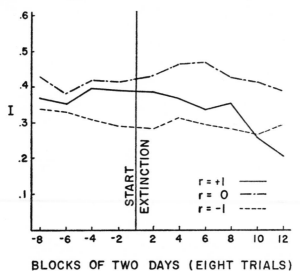

BLOCKS OF TWO DAYS (EIGHT TRIALS)

Figure 67. Extinction without food or shock after training with partial punishment and partial reinforcement combined. (Exper. 57B)

persistence of the approach tendency and does not maintain extinction performance simply through a lessening of the avoidance tendency.

By way of summary of these data,

45. A mild punishment reduces the relative rate at which extinction takes place. The effect is increased if the punishment was encountered on only part of the training trials.

DISCUSSION

The data presented in this chapter are generally consistent with the relatively simple conception that punishment in the type of situation under discussion produces negative incentive. In uncorrelated conditions, punishment decreases performance in proportion to its intensity just as reward increases performance in proportion to its amount. In correlated conditions, punishment is minimized in much the same way that reward is maximized.

The fear response could be used as the mechanism through which punishment produces negative incentive in a manner analogous to the use of the fractional anticipatory goal response as the mechanism underlying positive incentive. Mowrer (1939) applied the fear mechanism to the avoidance situation, and Miller (see e.g. Dollard and Miller, 1950) has made extensive use of it in his analysis of punishment and conflict. Basically, the assumption is that fear is a learnable drive that becomes conditioned to the cues produced by a punished response. Since stopping or avoiding the punished response removes the response-produced cues, incompatible responses are reinforced by a reduction in fear. Were fear to be used as the mechanism for negative incentive,[3] it would be assumed that there is no functional difference between increasing the tendency to make an opposing response and decreasing the tendency to make the punished response.

The effects of punishment do not mirror those of reward in all particulars. Continuous punishment is more detrimental than partial punishment using a same training schedule on which partial reward is better than continuous reward. The transition effect in varied punishment favors the event encountered on the previous trial whereas, with the same sequences, the transition effect in varied reward favors the opposite event. The effects of punishment are more closely confined to the goal end of the alley than are the effects of reward. Presumably, however, all of these differences concern quantitative details and do not imply a basic difference in the way the variables act.

The assignment of the effects of punishment to negative incentive is not intended to discount completely the view popularized by Guthrie (1934) that the effect of punishment depends on the overt response it evokes. That view, which is based on straightforward conditioning principles, assumes that punishment

---

3. Formally, punishment does not affect sINr, but produces another intervening variable, sNIr, which like sFr and sTIr, subtracts from sEr to determine reaction potential.

will interfere with a response to the extent that an incompatible response is produced by the punishment. Although this is certainly an important aspect of punishment, particularly during the early trials, it would appear not to be completely adequate because of the evidence on correlated punishment. The overt response evoked by a shock is independent of the correlation of the shock with speed, yet performance varies systematically with this correlation. The negative incentive approach, coupled with the micromolar assumption, therefore seems more consistent with the ultimate performance levels attained in the various conditions of punishment.

However, the evidence yet available is too fragmentary to develop a formal conceptualization of the effects of punishment. In addition to negative incentive value, an electric shock may have response-evocation, informational, and stimulus variety properties. A comprehensive account of punishment will have to include all these effects.

NOTE: ON THE EFFECT OF CONTEXT ON
RELATIVE INCENTIVE VALUE

It has been argued that the relative incentive value of two events can be correctly inferred from a response measure such as running speed, since increases in speed get the event more quickly but require more effort. If this position is accepted, then the data presented can be reorganized in such a way as to suggest that relative incentive value depends in part upon the context in which the event occurs.

Consider the following four events: food, food and shock, nil, and shock. Were these events given on every trial, running speed would indicate that their relative incentive values rank in the order as listed. That is, rats run faster to food alone than to food and shock, but if the shock is not too intense, the latter condition is superior to the nil event that produces the baseline level of performance. Shock without food completely inhibits the response.

In Table 15 these four events are compared in two other contexts. The left column shows the terminal performance levels of four groups all of which received food on half the trials and one of the four events on the other half, and the right column makes a similar comparison when the common event was food and shock.

The rank orders of the events differ in the two columns, and both differ from the order listed above for constant conditions. This failure of the events to maintain the same order is taken to indicate a dependence of relative incentive value on the context provided by other events encountered in the situation.

Table 15. Terminal *I*-speeds arranged to make two comparisons of four goal-box events. The numbers in parentheses came from the same group. (Exper. 57B)

Event	50% food alone and 50%:	50% food and shock and 50%:
Food alone	.536	(.490)
Food and shock	(.490)	.311
Nil	.598	.373
Shock alone	.327	.397

A specific illustration of the complexity this introduces can be seen by comparing the two values in the bottom row of Table 15. Both groups received partial reinforcement, one also receiving partial shock (negatively correlated with the food) and the other receiving continuous shock. In the context of partial reinforcement, the continuous shock group actually ran somewhat faster than the partial shock group. The same conclusion is suggested by the last two entries in the right column of Table 15, this time with the shock positively correlated with the food. Whereas it was shown previously that continuous shock was significantly more detrimental than partial shock in the context of continuous reward, the opposite conclusion would seem to be indicated in the context of partial reinforcement.

CHAPTER 11

The Free Behavior Situation

THE CONCEPT of the free behavior situation was discussed in *Behavior Theory and Social Science,* written jointly with David L. Olmsted, Burton S. Rosner, Richard D. Schwartz, and Carl M. Stevens. Subsequently, Rosner and I began exploratory work in the area, developed suitable equipment for the continuous duty required, and determined the general feasibility of the problem. The recent research and present write-up are my responsibility, but Rosner read an early draft of this chapter and helped develop the methods and ideas discussed.

A FREE BEHAVIOR SITUATION, in general, is one in which the subject can freely perform a response that is relevant to some need and which contains all the sources of satisfaction of that need. It can be viewed as a "correlated drive" condition, since the subject's drive level depends upon his performance in much the same way that reward depends upon performance in conditions of correlated reinforcement. Thus the subject can lower his prevailing level of drive by doing more work or can reduce his work output at the expense of tolerating a higher level of drive.

The familiar free-responding situation in which (say) a thirsty rat presses a bar for water is not a free behavior situation because the experimenter controls the subject's drive level by a supplementary watering. It can be made into a free behavior situation by leaving the bar continuously available and requiring the rat to work for whatever water it receives by pressing the bar. In non-free behavior research, such as the alley studies previously described, the measured response is of only short-term significance to the subject's needs, since any differential in reward achieved in the apparatus is promptly counteracted by a compensating differential in maintenance diet. In such situations, therefore, the rat is actually working to get the reward a few minutes sooner. In contrast, the subject in a free behavior situation must work or do without whatever the reward is altogether.

We shall consider three major independent variables in the free behavior situation. The schedule of reinforcement could be any of those developed by Skinner (see Ferster and Skinner, 1957), but we have so far studied only fixed ratio schedules. Similarly, any of the conditions of reinforcement previously discussed could be used, but we have so far studied only constant amounts of water given as reward. Finally, there is the force required to depress the bar.

All these variables may be conceptualized as jointly setting the "terms" on which the rat is working. The rat must exert at least the required force the specified number of times to get a water drop of the selected size. If the force requirement is increased, the reinforcement ratio increased, or the drop size decreased, then the rat must do more work to maintain the previous level of water intake. In general, the experimenter can set any combination of terms and observe the equilibrium level of performance that these conditions produce.

There are a number of more complex free behavior situations. Other schedules of reinforcement, e.g. variable interval, or other conditions of reinforcement, e.g. correlated amount of reward, can be used. A supplementary constant amount of water can be given daily irrespective of bar-pressing behavior. The manipulandum need not be continuously available, but instead can be inserted (or made functional) for a specified period of time each day. Several manipulanda can be used, e.g. one bar might require a greater force or a higher ratio but provide a larger drop of water. Several drives can be used, e.g. the rat must press one bar to get food and another to get water. The conditions to be described concern only a small sample of the wide variety of possible free behavior situations.

There are reasons for questioning whether the concepts that are familiar in extant behavior theories are directly applicable to the free behavior situation. The common dependent variables, latency (or speed, or rate), probability, amplitude, and resistance to extinction, are not of primary importance, although they may describe interesting local details of free behavior. Rather, the most pertinent behavioral datum is the amount of work done as measured by daily water intake. In addition to determining the drive level, the subject also controls the number and distribution of trials, which requires that notions such as habit and reactive inhibition be treated differently. The experimenter controls the amount of reward per response unit and hence determines the incentive for responding, but the effect is quite the opposite of that found in non-free behavior research since the total response output decreases if the size of the reward is increased.

Nevertheless, one might attempt to extend conventional theories to deal with the free behavior situation; for example, an equilibrium model such as that described for correlated reward conditions might be devised for correlated drive conditions. There are several alternative types of miniature models, among them the three proposed in *Behavior Theory and Social Science*. However, the present report has been cast primarily at the empirical level because there are not yet enough data available to support the selection and test of a formal, theoretical treatment.

THE AD LIB. DRINKING FREE BEHAVIOR SITUATION

A water bottle freely accessible in a rat's home cage constitutes a simple free behavior situation: the rat can drink at any time and hence determine its prevailing level of thirst. The terms can be manipulated by varying the size of the hole in the tube to the water bottle and thus presumably affecting the effort per unit of water of the consummatory response itself.

In a brief study using this procedure six rats were housed in standard individual activity wheels with food (ground Purina mash) freely available. Six tubes were prepared[1] from 9-mm. glass tubing with holes of 1, 2, 3, 4, 5, or 6 mm. diameter. Each rat had each tube on its water bottle for two successive days with the order counterbalanced across rats by a Latin-square of sequences. Daily records of weight and activity, as well as food and water intake, were taken.

Mean water intake on the second day with each tube is shown as a function of the size of the hole in the tube in the upper graph of Fig. 68. It will be seen that distinctly less water was taken from the smallest tube than from any of the others. There is also a suggestion of nonmonotonicity in the function, because water intake decreased slightly when the relatively large tubes were used. The differences in water intake were reliable at beyond the

1. The equipment for this study was prepared by Milton Trapold.

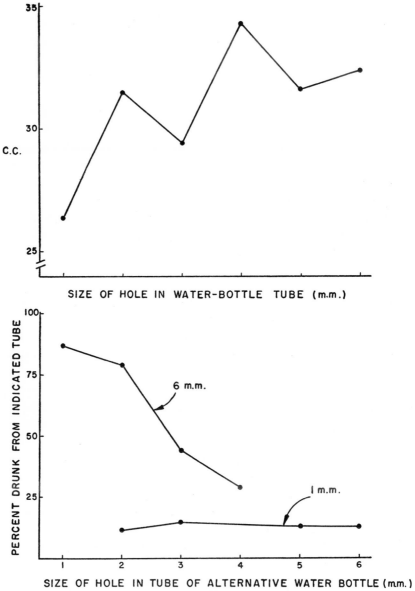

Figure 68. Daily water intake as a function of the size of the hole in the bottle tube (upper graph), and percent drunk from a large or small tube as a function of the size of the hole in the alternative tube (lower graph).

.01 level ($F = 8.00$, d.f. $= 5$ and 20) and remained reliable at beyond the .05 level even with the 1 mm. tube excluded ($F = 3.34$, d.f. $= 4$ and 20). No consistent effects of tube size on weight, activity, or food intake were noted.

Following the tests with each size tube singly, a choice free behavior situation was set up by making two water bottles available. They were placed on the side of the cage opposite the food bin. To counterbalance slight position preferences, the bottles were left in the same position for two days and then reversed for two days. The amount of water taken from each bottle on the second day in each position was observed.[2]

Only some of the possible combinations were tested. The results, which are summarized in the lower graph of Fig. 68, tend to confirm the single-bottle data. Very little water was taken from the smallest tube, even when the next smallest tube was the alternative. From the other end, however, intake from the largest tube decreased as the size of the alternative increased and there was a clear preference for a tube of intermediate size to the largest one.

The apparently aversive feature of a large drinking tube makes the ad lib. drinking situation complicated for the study of free behavior.[3] Another finding that adds to the complexity of the situation is that there are apparently other features of the tube besides the size of the hole that affect preference. When there was a choice between two tubes having holes of the same size, preferences as high as 80 percent sometimes occurred. Some unidentified feature such as smoothness, curvature of the tip (the tubes themselves were straight), or the like must also be important.

The bar-pressing free behavior situation inserts an instrumental response into the chain of going to the water source and making the consummatory response. The instrument not only provides a convenient way to manipulate the terms on which the rat is working, but also avoids the kinds of complications found in the ad lib.

2. A preference of 100 percent would not be expected using this procedure since the rat had to try both bottles and thus take some water from a less preferred tube. Preferences were generally higher on the second day as the rats learned which bottle was in which position.

3. This finding may also be relevant to studies of the effect of the size of the drinking tube on T-maze and straight alley behavior (see e.g. Wike and Barrientos, 1957).

drinking situation. It has, however, produced a number of technical and procedural problems for which the following descriptions represent the current solution.

THE BAR-PRESSING FREE BEHAVIOR APPARATUS

Each rat lived alone in a one-foot cube box, two (opposite) sides and the bottom of which were of ½″ hardware cloth. The other two sides and the top were of ¼″ sheet aluminum. The box was placed inside a 16″ x 16″ x 24″ box made entirely of Celotex and painted flat black. A white 7-watt bulb inside the Celotex box was operated on a 12-hour light, 12-hour dark cycle. There were 3 such boxes with comparable equipment.

Water delivery system. A ½″ diameter brass rod that protruded ½″ into one of the solid sides of the box had been filed flat on the top and drilled with a water cup ¼″ in diameter and ¼″ deep. A #64 jeweler's drill hole from the bottom of the cup met a hole drilled lengthwise part way into the brass rod. The opposite end of the rod was threaded and attached directly to a solenoid valve. The input to the valve was connected by a rubber tube to a 125 cc. aspirator bottle, above which a 1,000 cc. bottle was arranged on the inkwell principle to maintain a constant water level in the 125 cc. bottle. Distilled water (see Young and Falk, 1956) flowed by gravity into the cup when the valve was open.

The amount of water that flowed into the cup was determined jointly by the size of the opening in the valve and by the length of time it was open. Once adjusted to provide a smooth flow of water (too large an opening produced a water spout), the size of the opening in the valve was not changed. Instead, the amount of water per drop was controlled by the setting of a Hunter timer that was wired with an internal hold so that it was made for the set time by a momentary impulse and was then automatically reset for the next delivery. The minimum practicable volume of water per drop was about .005 cc., and the maximum volume that the cup could hold was about .1 cc. Since the system was not calibrated to permit accurate setting for a predetermined volume of water, the average drop size actually given on any setting was calculated throughout the research by dividing the total quantity of water delivered over a period of time by the number of deliveries during that time.

The "work" system. A bar of ⅛″ solid brass was bent in a plane parallel with the floor and completely surrounded the rod containing the water cup. The bar was attached directly to the arm of a microswitch so that the weight of the bar alone depressed the switch. An adjustable counterspring held the bar above the make-point of the switch, and the spring's tension determined the force required to depress the bar. The minimum practicable force was about 20 gm. dead weight, and the maximum was 150 gm.

It should be noted that this arrangement virtually eliminated any incompatibility between bar-pressing and the consummatory response. The rats typically addressed the water cup with their front paws resting on the bar and they could press and drink almost simultaneously. The complete range of motion of the bar was 1″, but a depression of ¾″ tripped the microswitch (with an audible click), and a release of ½″ from that point reset the switch. Thus, at least a ½″ excursion per press (to within ¼″ of the upper and lower limits) was required.

The ratio system. A continuous 44-pole stepping switch,[4] activated by the microswitch attached to the bar, stepped at the end of the impulse and hence at the release of the bar. The switch could follow impulses at better than 8 per second, well above the maximum rate at which the rats could work the bar.

Each pole of the stepper was wired to a terminal which, when plugged, fired the reinforcement timer. The ratio was set by plugging terminals spaced the selected number of poles apart. The minimum ratio was 1:1 and the maximum 43:1. Ratios not evenly divisible into 44 were achieved by using extra double-jump leads that effectively reduced the number of poles on the stepping switch.

The response-recording system. A continuously cumulating Veeder-Root counter, equipped with a printing dial, stepped at each delivery of reinforcement. The cumulated count was stamped each hour through a typewriter ribbon onto moving adding-machine paper by means of a solenoid.[5] A brief impulse to the solenoid was delivered at the combined make of microswitches on two constant speed disks, one turning at 1 RPH (making for 1

---

4. These switches, as well as some of the other electrical equipment, were generously supplied by the Southern New England Telephone Company.

5. The printing counters were designed and built primarily by Gus Ogren.

minute/revolution) and the other at 1 RPM (making for 1 second/revolution). The number of reinforcements delivered in any interval was then obtained by subtraction.

Procedure. The rat was first put into the free behavior box with the ratio set at 1:1, the force at 20 gm., and the water at about .02 cc. per drop. If the rat's operant level of bar-pressing failed to get the response started, shaping trials were given. Twelve grams of ground Purina mash were given at the same time daily in a spill-proof cup.[6] The terms for the water were shifted every 2 or 3 days over a wide range of ratios, forces, and drop sizes during the first 4 to 6 weeks.[7] Then selected terms were set and left in force for 14 to 20 days to permit a stable performance level to be attained. Equilibrium was estimated by averaging over the last 10 days on any condition.

Free Bar-pressing Behavior

After preliminary training in the apparatus, three rats were placed on the lenient terms of a 1:1 ratio on a 20-gm. bar for a water drop of about .025 cc. They consumed 26.65, 22.70, and 36.50 cc. per day respectively. These values compare favorably with those found in ad lib. drinking on a reduced food regimen, which suggests that the addition of a bar response need not materially affect the amount of water taken daily.

If more demanding terms are used, however, a significant decrease in water intake occurs. For example, when the drop size for the above three rats was reduced to about .005 cc., water consumption fell to 24.36, 17.92, and 21.98 cc. per day respectively. Even on such reduced water intake, a rat can complete its food ration

---

6. The reduced feeding was instituted to help keep the rats on a 24-hour rhythm, to maintain a constant body weight in order to reduce long-term drifts in water need, and to control food intake because of the close dependence on it of water intake. The importance of this last relationship is attested to by the fact that, on several days when the rats were inadvertently not fed, water intake dropped to about 10 percent of normal.

7. This "basic training" was instituted after it was found that rats that had worked on (say) a 1:1 ratio with a 20-gm. bar for a month or so (50,000 or more continuously reinforced responses) were often unable to shift directly to even a 10:1 ratio or a 50-gm. bar, both of which are well within their range of physical ability. Apparently, the rats learn the terms so well that they will die in the cage with the bar rather than try a slightly more demanding response.

and maintain a constant body weight. This is true down to a water intake level of 10 to 12 cc. per day.

The terms can, of course, be made so demanding that the rats stop pressing the bar, cannot eat their food, and hence would die if left alone. For example, although the rats can survive adequately on a 1:1 ratio with a 150-gm. bar, or on a 20:1 ratio with a 20-gm. bar, they are typically unable to manage on a 20:1 ratio with a 150-gm. bar. Indeed, some rats fail with a 20-gm bar at a 40:1 ratio, although rats in other non-free research have gone well above this level.

The amount of water taken varies considerably from day to day, ranging from 5 percent to 10 percent on either side of the mean values given. Comparable variation was found in the ad lib. drinking situation and is probably partly attributable to uncontrolled variations in humidity. Therefore, although the rat reaches a stable equilibrium in the sense that there are no apparent long-term drifts in average water intake, day-to-day intake does not become very highly stabilized.

A question of stability with greater systematic import concerns the replicability of the equilibrium level from occasion to occasion. It is comparable to the question asked about changes in reward conditions, i.e. is the equilibrium level determined solely by the prevailing terms or is it also affected by the prior terms on which the rat has worked?

There are certainly temporary effects of the immediately preceding conditions. A rat shifted from very demanding to more lenient terms takes in more than the eventual equilibrium amount of water for a few days. Another deviation from replicability arises when a rat that has worked only at a 1:1 ratio is shifted to a higher ratio (say, 10:1). When the 1:1 ratio is reinstituted, stable equilibrium frequently exceeds the original 1:1 level, which can be attributed to the added skill that a high ratio induces the rat to learn; the more skillful way of responding requires less work and hence permits a higher level of water intake.

However, looking only at stable levels after several days on a condition and using rats that have had preliminary training covering a wide sample of conditions, the degree of replicability appears to fall well within the limits set by the day-to-day variation already

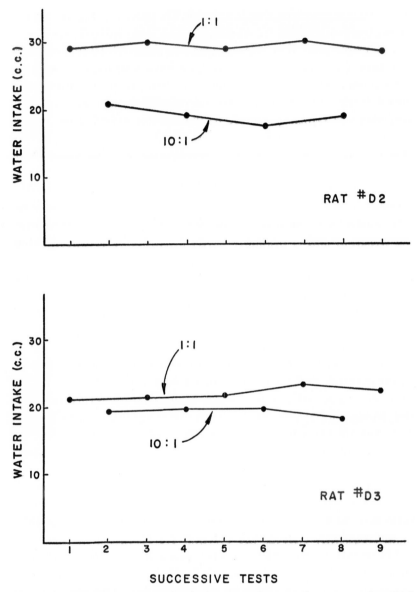

Figure 69. Equilibrium water intake on successive tests for two rats for which the terms were shifted repeatedly between a 1:1 and a 10:1 ratio, with the force and drop size held constant.

noted. Data supporting this contention are shown in Fig. 69, where the equilibrium levels for two rats [8] that were shifted repeatedly between a 1:1 and 10:1 ratio are represented. Because these data were collected over a six-month period, during which the rats' ages and the prevailing average humidity changed substantially, the degree of replicability seems adequate. Certainly, at least, occasion-to-occasion differences in equilibrium do not override the differences produced by the terms.

Toward a Descriptive Equation for Free Bar-pressing Behavior

Water intake in the free bar-pressing behavior situation is some joint function of the force requirement of the bar, the reinforcement ratio, and the size of the water drop. The simplest equation that might apply in such a situation would assert that intake is proportional to the prevailing terms described in grams of work per cc. of water by multiplying the force times the ratio and dividing by the drop size. Were such a description adequate, the rat would halve its intake if any component of the terms were doubled. The data do not conform to such a simple account.

However, there is no reason to believe that this type of approach would be inadequate if more complex functions were used. In an attempt to get preliminary data bearing on the development of such an equation, three rats were run under the eight terms formed by two levels of each of the three independent variables. The results are arrayed for each rat and each condition in Fig. 70. These data probably do not justify very exact treatment; because there was only one observation period for each condition, sequence effects and long-term changes in water need cannot be ruled out. However, they do suggest several significant features of the descriptive equation.

The force variable did not have much differential effect over the range used. Average intake was 21.93 cc. per day with a 40-gm. bar and 21.37 cc. per day with an 80-gm. bar. The difference is small because the three rats did not show the same results, one rat taking more water with the lighter bar, one taking more water with

8. The third rat running at this time showed a continual drift upward in water intake and then died of whirling disease. One of the rats in the ad lib. drinking study also later died of this disease after showing a marked increase in water intake.

the heavier bar, and one showing no clear preference. Such an outcome might be taken to indicate that the force variable produced only random effects, but the consistency of the data within each animal's record suggests an alternative interpretation: the relationship between force and intake is nonmonotonic with the optimum

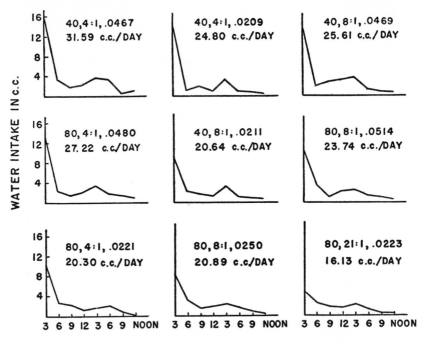

THREE HOURS ENDING AT INDICATED TIME

Figure 70a. Performance of rat #F1 under a variety of terms in the free behavior situation. The rat was fed at noon, and the lights were on from 3:00 P.M. to 3:00 A.M.

condition being at a force somewhat above zero. This interpretation is reasonable if one recognizes that the defined response requires the release of the bar and that the total effort in pressing and releasing the bar should be smallest when the counterspring perfectly matches the resting weight of that part of the rat situated over the bar.[9] If the force were lower, so that the rat's weight

9. This account may be peculiar not only to free behavior but also to the particular physical arrangement of the bar and water cup in the present apparatus. Even in general, however, the force required to press a bar can be reduced below zero by making the rat pull the bar up.

exceeded the counterspring of the bar, then it would take less work to press but more to release. Conversely, higher forces would take more work to press but less to release. Since both components must be performed, it is the aggregate work that is affected by the force variable.

The ratio variable had an appreciable effect, average water intake being 22.75 cc. per day at a 4:1 ratio and 20.55 cc. per day at

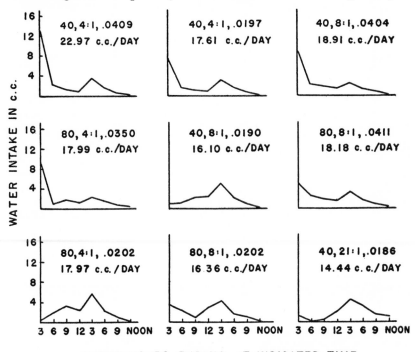

THREE HOURS ENDING AT INDICATED TIME

Figure 70b. Performance of rat #F2 under a variety of terms in the free behavior situation. The rat was fed at noon, and the lights were on from 3:00 P.M. to 3:00 A.M.

an 8:1 ratio. The effect was consistent, appearing in all comparisons for all rats. In terms of absolute size, however, doubling the number of presses required to get a drop of water reduced intake by only about 10 percent.

The size of the water drop had a greater differential effect, average intake being 23.62 cc. per day with the larger drop and 19.68 cc. per day with the smaller drop. The sizes were not precisely replicated, and the larger drop was slightly more than twice the size of the smaller drop. However, these inadequacies would not seem to be sufficient to account for the greater effect of the drop-size variable. At least, the data suggest that doubling the number of presses per drop does not affect intake to the same extent as halving the size of the drop. If substantiated, the discrepancy would be particularly interesting since both changes involve the same over-all difference in work in the sense that, during the course of a day,

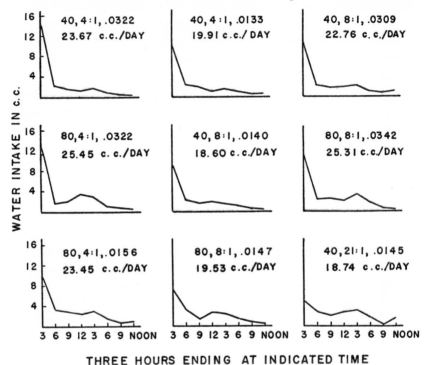

THREE HOURS ENDING AT INDICATED TIME

Figure 70c. Performance of rat #F3 under a variety of terms in the free be-havior situation. The rat was fed at noon, and the lights were on from 3:00 P.M. to 3:00 A.M.

the same number of presses would get the same amount of water. It also suggests a possible relationship to the data on varied amount of reward, where it was also found that performance may be better if larger rewards are given less frequently.

The interactions among these variables appear to be multiplica-tive. Balancing out the force variable because of its more complex effect, water intake at the higher ratio was 90.37 percent of the intake at the lower ratio when the drop size was small and 90.33

percent when the drop size was large. Accordingly, the total descriptive equation will probably be the product of the functions of the three variables.

DISCUSSION

The data show clearly that a rat will reduce its water intake, and presumably therefore tolerate a higher prevailing level of thirst, if it is required to do more work to get water. This is true even when the rat has virtually nothing else to do during its waking hours and has ample time to get all the water it wants. The decrease in water intake seems reasonable if one considers the dynamics of the situation.

Presumably, principles such as those discussed in the previous chapters determine the rat's tendency to press the bar. The more demanding the terms, the lower this response tendency either through the effects of force and ratio on effort or of drop size on incentive. Therefore, on the one hand, the response will get started only after the drive has risen to a higher level as a result of deprivation and, on the other hand, the response will stop sooner as the reduction in drive lowers the response tendency.

This kind of approach could be formally implemented by tracking response tendency over time. In addition to assumptions about the rate at which drive increases during deprivation and decreases during drinking, it would be necessary to use two "thresholds," one for starting the response and one for stopping it. Such an analysis would be ordinally consistent with the obtained data in that the more demanding terms would require a higher level of drive to keep response tendency within the prescribed bounds. Furthermore, it could also imply the observed leveling of the intake pattern produced by more demanding terms since the cumulating temporary inhibition would cause a burst of drinking to stop sooner so that the higher residual drive would cause another burst after a shorter period of rest.

However, a number of problems should be considered before a formal quantitative model based on such notions can be built. One concerns individual differences in the effects of the independent variables. For example, some rats are more "sensitive" to the ratio variable than other rats. An instance of this can be seen in Fig. 69, in which rat D2 shows a larger decrease in intake than rat D3 when the ratio was increased from 1:1 to 10:1. That this difference did not result from different units of measurement is indicated by the fact that rat D2 took more water than rat D3 at the 1:1 ratio but not at the 10:1 ratio. Indeed, when later tested at a 21:1 ratio, the difference was reversed, with rat D3 taking more water.

Also several associated variables might reasonably be expected to affect the pattern of water intake. The light used in the present research was quite dim, and a brighter light might produce a more radical diurnal cycle. The time the food is given relative to the light cycle may also affect the amount of water consumed at different times of the day. The amount of food given could affect not only the total intake but also the daily pattern of drinking, as a larger food diet would, at the same time, increase the need for water and reduce the tendency for the competing response of eating to occur. Systematic study of these factors must precede the development of a dynamic model of the free behavior situation.

CHAPTER 12

Problems for Future Research

THE ATTEMPT to determine general principles that will correctly describe the relationship between performance and the conditions of reinforcement is a continuing task. The research reported in this book has been largely exploratory, and the questions raised by the results far outnumber the answers given. Although some of the questions have been mentioned in previous chapters, it seems appropriate to indicate briefly several directions that appear promising for future research.

LEARNING AND PERFORMANCE AS RESEARCH EMPHASES

Most research in the field of learned behavior has been directed primarily at the laws or principles of learning. The experimenter typically is careful to provide some obvious reason for learning to occur, such as reward only for the correct response, so that he can study the way various learning conditions affect the acquisition of the response. The present emphasis on performance is somewhat different. In this case, the experimenter is careful to use learning conditions under which it is known that a subject can learn, so that he can study the way performance is affected by reward, motivation, and work variables.

The two problems are not completely separable; the distinction is one of emphasis. Consider, for example, an experiment in discrimination learning in which more reward is given following response to a grey stimulus than to a white one. If a significant preference for the grey stimulus is obtained, it is clear that the learning conditions (e.g. the stimulus difference) are sufficient and also that the performance conditions (e.g. the reward difference) are sufficient. If no preference is obtained, the failure may be due to an insufficiency in the learning conditions, the performance conditions, or both. A decision can be made only if one or the other of the conditions has elsewhere been shown to be sufficient.

At a quantitative level, however, it must be added that the sufficiency of conditions is not all-or-none in character; both the learning and the performance conditions vary in degree of sufficiency. In general, the assumption is that the likelihood of one S-R event depends jointly on its relative advantage and its relative discriminability compared to other S-R events. Although the emphasis in the present type of research is on the effect of the conditions of reinforcement on performance, the interrelationships with the learning conditions are necessarily also involved.

Systematic and Methodological Extensions

The research reported in the previous chapters has sampled only a few of the possible conditions of reinforcement. There is a clear need to replicate the findings and to extend them along several lines. One such line of research would be aimed at systematically determining the functions about which the available data provide only isolated information. For example, the studies of varied reward were confined to variation between two equally likely values, whereas an adequate account should also deal with unequal variations among a number of values. Similarly, performance in conditions of negatively correlated reward is clearly some joint function of the cutoff value, the reward for fast responses, and the reward for slow responses, but we know only a few of the features of this function. Indeed, all the data require this kind of systematic elaboration.

A closely related line of research would be concerned with types of conditions that have not yet been studied at all. Besides the variety of terms functions described in Chapter 7, reward can be correlated with performance in other ways. For example, trial-to-trial variation in speed might be reduced by giving more reward the closer speed is to the speed on the previous trial. Resistance to nonreinforcement might be enhanced by giving more reward the larger the number of immediately preceding nonreinforced trials. The gradient of speed of running toward the goal might be altered by correlating reward with speed differently in different sections of the alley. In general, any aspect of performance can be selectively reinforced in several ways, but how the organism will adjust to such conditions is still an open question.

A final class of problems that should be mentioned in this context concerns the use of information stimuli. Ferster and Skinner (1957) have described some effects on rate of responding of using stimuli, such as the brightness of a light, as external clocks and counters. Were such stimuli added to the alley, the rat would not have to rely solely on internal cues to gauge the correctness of its performance. Furthermore, an information stimulus need not bear a perfect relationship to the conditions of reinforcement; e.g. a tone might be sounded for six seconds in a condition in which the rat had to take only five seconds in the alley to maximize reward. Also other techniques, such as adding weights to the animals or tilting the alley, might alter the distinctiveness of responses of different speeds and hence affect the rat's ability to adjust to complex conditions of reinforcement.

INTEGRATION OF CONDITIONS OF CORRELATED REINFORCEMENT WITH TRIAL-AND-ERROR AND DISCRIMINATION LEARNING

The major thesis advanced in this book is that the same principles of performance that apply to trial-and-error and discrimination learning also govern selection among quantitatively different responses. If this thesis is true, the three types of situations can be used to cross-check empirical findings and to provide interesting tests of some aspects of the theoretical approach.

For example, the micromolar theory assumes that speed is an increasing function of the amount of uncorrelated reward because, in effect, rats are willing to do more work to get a large reward quickly. This analysis can be tested in a trial-and-error analogue by offering rats a choice between two bars, one of which is harder to press but has a shorter delay of reward associated with it. If the amount of reward is independent of which bar is pressed, the likelihood of pressing the harder bar should be an increasing function of the amount of reward.

The combination of correlated reinforcement with trial-and-error or discrimination learning poses a novel training problem about which virtually no information is available. Suppose, for example, that correlated reinforcement is being used to train a rat to run fast in one alley and slow in the other. Although the rat can presumably learn to perform adaptively in such a situation, we do not yet know what procedure will produce the adjustment most quickly. The rat might first be taught the appropriate skill in one alley before the second alley is introduced, or the terminal conditions might be imposed in full force from the very beginning of training. The optimal procedure may well depend on the type of conditions, with the successive introduction of the components being better if one aspect of the problem is particularly difficult.

Once adequate procedures are known for training a rat to perform appropriately in two alleys, the question of choice among different conditions of reinforcement can be considered. This question is particularly important to the further development of the micromolar approach because there is currently no provision for predicting preference between qualitatively different S-R events (e.g. choice between two alleys). One possible solution would be to cast all the micromolar responses of both alleys into a single analysis and simultaneously determine the alley-speed combination that is most likely to occur. Alternatively, the decisions might be made sequentially, the rat being viewed as first selecting the alley on the basis of some parameter of the competing sEr profiles and then selecting the micromolar response most appropriate in the chosen alley. Data from a variety of choice situations will be needed to guide the development of the approach in this area.

As a preliminary to research on more complex conditions, two studies of choice behavior were run. One was concerned primarily with the effect of the distribution of practice on conventional maze learning. Two groups were run six trials each week, one group being given one trial a day while the other group was given all six trials in one day. The first and fifth were choice trials, and the remaining trials were forced so as to equate experience in the two alleys and to permit the separate measurement of running speed. The major results of the study are shown in Fig. 71, where it can be seen that the distributed-trials group learned as quickly as the massed-trials group insofar as the latter group's first trial was concerned. Massed trials improved performance on the second choice trial of the day, which is consistent with the observation that in conditions of correlated reinforcement rats are better at selecting among quantitatively different responses on later trials of the day. It should also be noted that the differences in running speed bore no simple and consistent relation to choice behavior.

The second study compared learning when the differential reinforcement was based on delay of reward, on amount of reward, or on both delay and amount of reward. These data, shown in

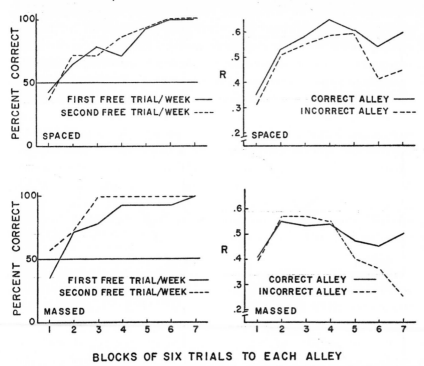

BLOCKS OF SIX TRIALS TO EACH ALLEY

Figure 71. Choice and *R*-speeds for groups given six trials a week, the spaced group having one trial a day and the massed group having all six trials in one day. The first and fifth trials each week were free and the remaining trials were forced to equate the number of trials in the two alleys. Reward in the correct alley was 4 pellets at 0 seconds delay; there was no food reward in the incorrect alley. (Exper. 56F)

Fig. 72, are consistent with the expectation that trial-and-error learning is faster the larger the difference in reward. Again, choice behavior was a more sensitive index of the developing differential in response tendency than was running speed.

INTEGRATION OF THE FREE-RESPONDING AND DISCRETE-TRIALS PROCEDURES

The procedure used in the present research involved discrete trials: the rats were removed from the apparatus after each trial. In terms of empirical objectives, the most closely related research has been done by Skinner and his associates using the free-respond-

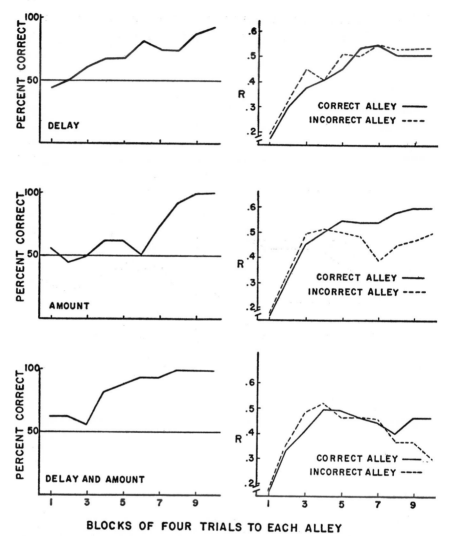

Figure 72. Choice and *R*-speeds for groups given a choice based on differential delay (5 pellets at 1-sec. or 5-sec. delay), differential amount (9 pellets or 1 pellet at 5-sec. delay), or differential delay and amount (9 pellets at 1-sec. delay or 1 pellet at 9-sec. delay). Rats were run 8 trials a day; the first and fifth trials were free and the remaining trials were forced to equate number of trials in the two alleys. (Exper. 57A)

ing procedure in a bar-pressing or key-pecking situation. The differences between these procedures are thought to be mainly of degree rather than kind. This can be shown by drawing alley analogies to the various schedules described by Skinner and, contrariwise, by designing bar-pressing situations analogous to the conditions used in the alley. The few examples given here are intended to illustrate a possible direction along which the data obtained with the free-responding and discrete-trials procedures might be successfully integrated.

It should be emphasized at the outset that there is no intended implication that one situation is better than the other for yielding reliable behavioral laws. They are the two most widely used situations for studying simple instrumental learning, and both have yielded valuable results. The relationship between the results has been somewhat obscured by the use of independent language systems. The following remarks aim toward coordinating definitions to suggest kinds of research that might bridge the differences in the procedures.

Discrete trials vs. free responding. In the alley, the rat is typically removed from the apparatus between trials; in the Skinner box, the rat is typically left in the box with the manipulandum freely available. At first thought, the difference seems to be mainly in intertrial interval, with the discrete-trials procedure treating the distribution of practice as an independent variable controlled by the experimenter whereas the free-responding procedure involves an effectively zero intertrial interval since the rat can respond again at once. However, such an assertion raises the problem of defining a "trial."

From an S-R point of view, a trial is the contiguity of a stimulus and a response. The discrete-trials procedure involves a controlled sequence of events: presentation of the stimulus, occurrence of the response, removal of the stimulus. Since an occurrence of the response to whatever stimuli are present between trials is not rewarded, discrete trials involve a discrimination of the trial stimuli from the between-trial stimulus complex. Presumably, the stimulus change attendant on putting a rat in and taking it out of an alley is sufficiently large to make this discrimination relatively easy.

From a larger point of view, however, the difference between the trial stimuli and the between-trial stimuli is a manipulatable variable. Suppose, for example, that the rat is placed in an alley between trials. If the between-trial alley were different from the trial alley, the situation would be viewed as conventional single-presentation discrimination learning. On the other hand, if the trial and between-trial alleys were the same, the situation would be described as a partial reinforcement condition. In the former case, there would be two S-R events and performance would be measured in each separately; in the latter case, there would be only one S-R event, and a single over-all measure of performance would then be taken.

Consider now an interval schedule in the free-responding situation, where reward is set up periodically by a clock. If temporal cues are not considered, then there is no basis in an interval schedule for the subject to discriminate when a reward has been set up, and such a schedule would be viewed as a form of partial reinforcement with a zero intertrial interval. However, the situation is not so simple when temporal cues are considered.

If the interval is fixed at (say) one minute, then the trial stimuli are the box plus the cue of one-minute-since-last-reward. Because these are somewhat different from earlier cues, a discrimination can be formed. It is analogous to rewarding a rat in a black alley and placing it between trials in a succession of alleys beginning with white and each getting darker until the next trial in the black alley. The scallop reported to result from fixed interval schedules is consistent with the expectation that the rat would run faster in the darker alleys.

Variable interval schedules are still more complex. Suppose the reward is set up one, two, or three minutes after the previous reward. The analysis up to the first minute is the same as for the fixed interval schedule insofar as the similarity of these cues to the one-minute trial cues is concerned, but the latter are themselves rewarded only one-third of the time. The other two-thirds of the time, the rat moves on to the one-to-two minute between-trial stimuli, to which it will respond on the basis of similarity to reinforced trial cues. The two-minute cues give a trial with 50 percent reward, and so on to the three-minute cues which, when they occur, are rewarded continuously.

An alley analogue to this variable interval schedule would use (say) a dozen progressively brighter alleys. The rat would be placed in alleys 1, 2, 3, and 4 successively, being rewarded a third of the time in alley 4. If rewarded there, the rat would be returned to alley 1, but if not, it would be moved on to alleys 5, 6, 7, and 8. Half of the time the rat would be rewarded in alley 8 and then returned to alley 1, and half of the time it would be moved on to alleys 9, 10, 11, and 12, in the last of which it would always be rewarded and returned to alley 1. Performance in such a situation would depend on principles concerning partial reinforcement, single-presentation discrimination learning, and generalization to stimuli intermediate between reinforced stimuli.

In ratio schedules, the subject can begin the next required behavior chain immediately following the previous reward. Such schedules are therefore properly viewed as the limiting case of discrete trials with a zero intertrial interval.

For some problems a discrete-trial procedure is better, and for others free-responding is advantageous. For example, the alley analogue of a variable interval schedule would permit testing the rat in the alleys rearranged in order, whereas the stimuli in the free-responding schedule are constrained to follow a time course of change. On the other hand, free-responding permits a continuous gradation of the stimuli as well as the use of procedures in which the rat can be given direct control over the occurrence of trial stimuli.

There is, of course, nothing about the running response which requires discrete trials and nothing about the bar-pressing response which requires free responding. Running may be done in an activity wheel, the alley may be made continuous, or retracing can be allowed so that breaking a photobeam becomes the unit of response. The Skinner box can include an external stimulus change to identify a trial and a converse change to terminate a trial, or the subject or the bar can be removed after each trial.

Of particular importance to the present research, the discrete-trials procedure is more appropriate to research on the amount and delay of reward. When the amount of reward is not the same for all subjects, the ideal procedure is to equalize the differential between trials in order to prevent a cumulative effect of drive reduction. When delay of reward is varied, termination of the trial stimulus insures that the same S-R sequence cannot occur in the delay interval and permits equalizing the interval between the reward and the succeeding response without large variations in the intertrial interval. It is perhaps more than coincidence that the schedules described by Skinner almost exclusively involve frequency of reward and do not treat reward as continuously variable in dimensions such as amount and delay. This suggests a distinction between schedules of reinforcement and conditions of reinforcement.

Conditions of reinforcement vs. schedules of reinforcement. As used here, conditions of reinforcement refer to the relationship between some dimension of the reward (amount, delay, or frequency) and some dimension of the response (speed or amplitude). In all the cases we have considered, the response unit is held constant—the rat runs down the alley—and the conditions of reinforcement describe the consequences of this response. Some of the procedures included by Skinner as schedules of reinforcement use other sorts of variables.

Ratio schedules vary the length of the behavior chain, i.e. the response required to obtain the reward. Comparing performance under different reinforcement ratios is analogous to comparing performance in alleys of different lengths. Similarly, variable ratio schedules vary the length of the chain from trial to trial for the same subject. Such procedures are quite distinct operationally from partial reinforcement conditions. The distinction in the alley context would be between running a rat down a two-foot alley and rewarding it every fourth time compared with running it in an eight-foot alley under continuous reinforcement.

Interval schedules, as has been argued, involve primarily control over the intertrial interval and the associated distinctiveness of the trial stimuli. They also vary the number of trials to the negative stimulus: the longer the interval, the more nonreinforced trials can occur to the between-trial cues. Long fixed intervals suffer, therefore, not only because the trial stimuli are less distinctive, resulting in more generalization of the effect of extinction to the between-trial stimuli, but also because of a concomitant increase in the amount of this effect, resulting from the increased relative frequency of negative stimuli. These reasons may account for the fact that long fixed intervals do not show the typical advantage of distributed practice. There is no reason to doubt that a rat would respond well enough on a one-hour fixed interval schedule if distinctive external cues were provided to indicate when reward was set up.

Variable interval schedules also involve partial reinforcement, as described earlier. A number of other schedules fall partly or entirely within the concept of conditions of reinforcement. Of particular relevance to the conditions that were the major concern of the present research is the differential reinforcement of response rate. Such schedules, in which the subject must press at a high (or low) rate in order to obtain reward, are comparable to what are here called conditions of discontinuously correlated delay and amount of reward.

Speed vs. rate. There would appear to be a close similarity between the measures used in the two types of situations since both depict the ratio of response per unit of time.[1] Speed is measured by holding the response constant and observing the time required to complete it, while rate typically involves holding time constant and observing the number of responses that occur in that time.

Weiss (1958) recorded speed in a bar-pressing situation. A guillotine door in front of the bar served to isolate discrete trials, and a succession of Standard electric timers recorded starting time from the opening of the door to the first press, and pressing time separately for each press in a short fixed ratio. Weiss found that the gradient of speed of pressing showed the kind of increasing-then-decreasing function observed in the gradient of speed of running. This finding not only indicates one comparability in the two situations but also suggests that the decrease in speed near the end of an alley does not result solely from the fact that the rat has to slow down in order not to run into the end wall. A terminal decrease in speed appears to be a general characteristic in the performance of short homogeneous behavior chains with terminal reinforcement.

RELATIVE QUANTIFICATION OF PERFORMANCE VARIABLES

Laws and theories that are stated in terms of exact numbers have an enormous advantage over less quantitative formulations,

---

1. There is an important difference between average speed with average rate since the former is obtained as the mean of the reciprocals of the times, whereas the latter is typically obtained as the reciprocal of the mean of the times.

not only because they can be used to make exact predictions but also because they can be applied to situations in which several variables that act differently upon performance are varied simultaneously. The possible fruitfulness of Hull's quantification methodology has already been mentioned although adequate attempts to use it have not yet been made. Another approach to the problem would be to develop a relative quantification of the performance variables by the procedure of pitting them against each other.

Consider, for example, the amount and the delay of reward. The type of statement that would give a relative quantification of these two variables would assert that a specified difference in amount of reward is equal to a specified difference in delay of reward, insofar as their effects on performance are concerned. Specifically, the difference between a 4-pellet amount and an 8-pellet amount might be found to be equivalent to the difference between 6-sec. delay and 2-sec. delay. There are several procedures that can be used to generate such statements and to test their generality.

The simplest procedure is to use constant reward conditions and to find delay-amount combinations that produce the same running speed in different groups of subjects. A closely related procedure is to train the subjects initially with one delay-amount combination, and then find other combinations to which the animals can be shifted without an over-all change in performance.[2] Three additional procedures involve the paradigms of correlated reinforcement, trial-and-error learning, or discrimination learning. Delay-amount combinations can be sought for which the rat is indifferent as to which is given for fast and which for slow responses, which is given in the right and which in the left alleys, or which is given in the white and which in the black alleys.

As with any attempt to achieve a general quantification, the interactions among the variables involved, and among them and other variables, plays a major role. That is to say, the results should not be peculiar to a particular length of alley, to a particular level

2. This procedure has the interesting additional feature that, since the two changes act in opposite directions, the relative rates of change of the two components can be assessed by temporary changes in performance. Trapold (Exper. 58C) attempted to use this procedure, but since other animals for which only one dimension of the reward was changed did not show a change in performance, the results were inconclusive.

of drive, etc. There are no data yet available to indicate just how far such a procedure can be carried, but unless consistent relationships of this kind underlie observed performance, the cause of quantification will probably require a radically different conception from any yet proposed.

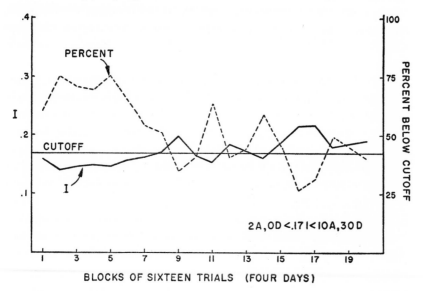

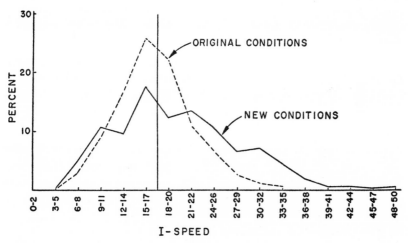

Figure 73. Performance under antagonistic correlations of delay and amount with a larger but delayed reward given if *I*-speed exceeded .17 (6 sec.). Rats were originally trained by Bower under a 10A,0D < .17*I* < 10A,30D condition. (Exper. 59F)

A brief study of this type of problem was run using rats that had been trained by Bower (1959) under a condition in which a 10-pellet amount was given immediately if they exceeded 6 seconds in the alley, and was delayed 30 seconds otherwise (10A,0D < .17I < 10A,30D). The rats were shifted to a condition in which the correlation of delay with speed remained negative, but the amount, which was initially uncorrelated, was now correlated positively with speed: the reward for slow responses was reduced to 2 pellets (2A,0D < .17I < 10A,30D). The performance of these animals is shown in Fig. 73, and it can be seen in the upper graph that speed gradually increased to a level at which the two reward events occurred about equally often. The fluctuations in the average performance curve which reflect the variable behavior observed in these animals are depicted in the lower graph of Fig. 73; it can be seen that there was a much larger variance in the speed distribution when both the amount and the delay were correlated to produce antagonistic effects than under the original correlated delay condition. However, such conditions must be used from the beginning of training in order to be sure that the results are not affected by a persisting transition effect leading to slower running following a delayed reward.

ETCETERA

The descriptions given in this chapter have been intended mainly to suggest several broad classes of problems. The range of possibilities within each class is enormous; the interested reader can generate instances for himself as easily as he could read any attempted methodical enumeration of them. At the other extreme, no mention has been made of the more distant problems, such as the use of complex conditions of reward and punishment in the free behavior situation.

Other species should be studied in analogous situations, since the more complicated problems may exceed the potential skill of the rat and even tax the ingenuity of the human. Other drive-reward conditions should be used to determine the generality of the principles. And variations in associated factors such as light cycle, temperature, and vitamin balance must ultimately be brought into the picture if it is to be complete.

It is hoped that this brief recital will counteract any possible implication that our empirical knowledge of these simple situations is either complete or nearly so. Indeed, the amount of research that could be done is overwhelming. Fortunately, however, this fact is offset by the indications in the available data that a reasonably comprehensive account can be formulated without an exhaustive study of all the possible conditions.

CHAPTER 13

General Summary and Conclusions

THIS BOOK has been aimed at both empirical and theoretical goals and an attempt has been made to keep them separate. On the empirical side, the goals have been to give a reasonably comprehensive description of the large number of possible ways a response can be rewarded and to report the effects on performance of some of these conditions of reinforcement. On the theoretical side, the goals have been to examine the micromolar assumption that quantitatively different behaviors are different responses with separate response tendencies and to see whether this extension of the S-R reinforcement theory fits the data more adequately than the familiar assumption that quantitative variations in a response index the strength of that response (e.g. the stronger a rat's tendency to run down an alley, the faster it will run).

More than a thousand rats were trained to run down a short straight alley and over a hundred different conditions of reinforcement were used. The major results of these researches have been summarized in the 45 numbered paragraphs distributed throughout the book. Briefly, it was found that when reward was constant on all trials, performance was faster the larger the amount and the shorter the time of delay of reward. When the reward was varied from trial to trial in amount or delay, performance varied from trial to trial systematically with respect to the rewards encountered on the previous trials, and there was no simple relationship between average performance and the performance produced by constant reward at the mean value. When the reward was correlated with performance so that response speed affected the amount or delay of reward, the rats tended to run at the speed that received the maximal reward, and the extent to which performance converged skillfully on the optimal level depended on the size of the differential in reward.

It is clear at the empirical level that performance depends in part upon the conditions of reinforcement. The relationship, however, is a complex one. Consider, for example, the problem of inferring the reinforcement history of a subject known to be performing at a given stable level after a large number of trials. The reward might have been constant at the size that produces that level of performance. Alternatively, a larger reward might have been given on only part of the trials. The reward might have been varied between several sizes, in which case a number of combinations, differing in both mean and variance, could produce that performance level. The reward might have been correlated with speed so that performance at that level received the maximal reward, or the observed performance might represent a compromise between two more highly rewarded speeds. The problem of inferring reward from performance is insolvable; a large number of different conditions produce the same level of performance.

The converse problem of predicting performance from reward is solvable but hardly less complex. Although the behavior is lawful in the sense that each particular condition of reinforcement consistently produces a specifiable performance level, there are no obvious constancies at the next higher level of abstraction. Consider, for example, the problem of predicting the stable performance level of a subject given a specified total quantity of reward during training. The reward could have been given in any of a number of ways, and performance could range from very slow to very fast depending on which way was used. Thus it appears that a completely empirical approach would result in a catalog describing the outcome of each possible condition. Predictions could then be made only about conditions that were replications of, or close interpolations between, conditions that had been previously studied and hence were listed in the catalog.

At a somewhat more abstract level, however, it seems likely that a reasonably simple theory can adequately subsume the available data and also be used to make predictions about novel conditions. This theory is a micromolar one in which a separate response tendency is computed for each speed of responding. The major positive determinant of differential response tendency is incentive, which depends jointly on three variables: (a) the duration of that particular response, (b) the length of time for which the reward is delayed after the response, and (c) the amount of reward. The major negative determinant of differential response tendency is effort, which is assumed to be greater for fast than for slow responses. The probability of any response speed then depends upon its response tendency—incentive minus effort—in comparison with that of other response speeds.

According to such a theory, rats should run fast when the delay and amount of reward are not correlated with response speed, because fast responses have a shorter duration and hence get the reward sooner. When there is a correlation between the delay or amount of reward and response speed, rats should tend to run at that speed which gets the maximal reward. Furthermore, the extent to which they acquire this skill should depend on the degree of differential reinforcement, since the larger the reward given to one speed relative to that given other speeds, the greater the difference in the incentive component of response tendency. In general, the micromolar theory assumes that rats adjust to the various conditions of reinforcement in terms of the principles of maximization of reward and minimization of effort.

In contrast to the micromolar approach, the conventional macromolar type of theory assumes that different speeds reflect different strengths of a single molar response. That is to say, the larger and more immediate the reward at the end of an alley, the stronger the response tendency to run, and hence the faster the response. This conception was used to develop an equilibrium model from which performance in conditions of correlated reinforcement could be predicted. The basic assumption of this model is that, if speed depends upon reward according to some determinant incentive function and if the conditions make the reward depend upon speed according to some explicit terms function, then performance must stabilize at that level which receives just that reward which produces just that speed. However, tests showed the model to be generally incorrect: the rats adjusted to the demands of the conditions better than the model predicted. Accordingly, it is concluded that the micromolar approach offers the greater hope for a generally adequate theory of learned behavior.

Two reactions to this conclusion can be anticipated. One is that this same conclusion could have been arrived at without any laboratory work simply by considering familiar kinds of behavior. For example, any normal adult human can, at command, raise his arm slowly or rapidly. In attempting to account for this, and count-less similar examples, the need for a micromolar approach be-comes obvious. The great number of skillful adjustments to com-plex conditions of correlated reinforcement could hardly be under-stood unless quantitatively different behaviors are treated as being learnable as separate responses.

It is true that the answers to some theoretically important ques-tions about behavior can be determined, or at least constrained, by attending to everyday experience. For example, it is clear that people can make very intricate stimulus discriminations and re-sponse differentiations, and if a laboratory test failed to demon-strate such adjustment, one would be inclined to question the choice of subject or procedure rather than to doubt the possibility of the phenomenon. However, natural illustrations do not permit systematic descriptions and seldom involve the kinds of controls that are necessary to support detailed theoretical arguments. Such observations are a supplement to, but not a substitute for, the laboratory.

The second reaction to the conclusion favoring the micromolar approach is diametrically opposed to the first. Everyday illustra-tions are discounted for lack of control, and the laboratory demon-strations are discounted because the rats were allowed to perform rituals in meeting the quantitative criteria. The argument would be that a macromolecular approach is adequate provided care is taken to see that the behaviors are qualitatively identical before interpreting quantitative differences as reflecting differences in response strength.

This argument was considered in Chapter 6. To the discussion there it can be added that, even though rats learn a distinctive way of responding, it is not clear that *that* response obeys macro laws. That is to say, one can reject the comparison with uncorrelated re-ward because the responses are qualitatively different, but one must still account for the systematic data within the correlated conditions. For example, the amount of reward does not notice-ably affect the topography of the response when the reward is de-layed if speed exceeds a cutoff, but the speed of this response is not an increasing function of the amount of reward. Similarly, within a broad range, the topography of the response is independ-ent of the cutoff and the delay for fast responses, but speed varies systematically with these variables. Such results suggest a micro-molar approach to the selection of the speed of whatever topography of response the rats perform. They do not, however, rule out the possibility of some successful elaboration of a macromolecular theory.

The present data do permit the rejection of an equilibrium model based on the simplest macromolar assumption that all behaviors that complete a molar response in the same total time can be aggregated together and treated as indicating the same strength of that response. The data are consistent with the simplest micromolar assumption that all such behaviors can be aggregated together into a separate response class. The message of the micromolar approach is this: organisms always learn the quantitative details of a response as well as its qualitative features and perform the response according to the principle of maximization of reward. Whether some more complex formulation will be necessary remains to be determined by future research.

*Designs and Procedures of the Researches
in the Double-Alley Maze*

Exper. 54A. The effect of varied delay of reward on running
   speed
Experimenters: Logan, Beier, Ellis
Subjects: 23 male and female hooded rats
Procedure: white or black alley, 9 gm/day (male) and 8 gm/day
   (female) maintenance

Design:
    I. 1 tr/day, 50 trials
        Gp. A: (N = 7) 50%a: 4 pellets at 1-sec. delay
                       50%b: 4 pellets at 9-sec. delay
                       Sequence: abaababbab or oppo-
                       site, repeated
        Gp. B: (N = 8) 4 pellets at 1-sec. delay
        Gp. C: (N = 8) 4 pellets at 5-sec. delay
   II. 1 tr/day, 20 trials
        Gps. A, B, C: extinction
  III. 1 tr/day, 35 trials
        Gps. A, B, C: 4 pellets at 1-sec. delay
  IV. 1 tr/day, 40 trials
        Gps. A, B, C: extinction
   V. 1 tr/day, 80 trials
        Gp. A: extinction
  VI. 1 tr/day, 9 trials
        Gp. A: 4 pellets at 1-sec. delay
 VII. 1 tr/day, 2 days
        Gp. A: test with both doors open

Exper. 54B. The effect of varied amount of reward on running
   speed

Experimenters: Logan, Beier, Kincaid
Subjects: 24 male hooded rats
Procedure: white or black alley, 9 gm/day maintenance

Design:
 I. 1 tr/day, 50 trials
    Gp. A: (N = 8) 50%a: 7 pellets at 2-sec. delay
           50%b: 1 pellet at 2-sec. delay
           Sequence: abaababbab or oppo-
           site, repeated
    Gp. B: (N = 8) 7 pellets at 2-sec. delay
    Gp. C: (N = 8) 4 pellets at 2-sec. delay
 II. 1 tr/day, 10 trials
    Gps. A, B, C: extinction

Exper. 54C. Effect of unit of reward on running speed
Experimenters: Kover, Beier
Subjects: 12 female hooded rats
Procedure: white alley, 9 gm/day maintenance

Design:
 I. 1 tr/day, 70 trials
    Gp. A: (N = 6) ½ gm. in 1 piece
    Gp. B: (N = 6) ½ gm. in 6 pieces
 II. 1 tr/day, 26 trials
    Gp. A: ½ gm. in 6 pieces
    Gp. B: ½ gm. in 1 piece

Exper. 54D. Performance without reward
Experimenters: Logan, Beier
Subjects: 6 male hooded rats
Procedure: white or black alley, 9 gm/day maintenance

Design:
 I. 1 tr/day, 37 trials
    All rats: no food reward in alley
 II. 1 tr/day, 36 trials
    All rats: choice trials, no food in either alley
 III. 1 tr/day, 27 trials
    All rats: tests without reward under high
       (H = 48 hrs.), regular (R = 24 hrs.),

and low (L = 3 hrs.) deprivation, in
order HLLLRRHLLRRHHHHLL-
RRHLRHHLRR

Exper. 55A. Effect of range of variation in delay of reward
Experimenter: Kincaid
Subjects: 15 male hooded rats
Procedure: white alley, 9 gm/day maintenance

Design:
I. 10 tr/day, 130 trials
      Gp. A: (N = 5) 50%a: 1 pellet at 0-sec. delay
                      50%b: 1 pellet at 9-sec. delay
                      Sequence: 5 long, 5 short, differ-
                      ent sequence each day
      Gp. B: (N = 5) 50%a: 1 pellet at 0-sec. delay
                      50%b: 1 pellet at 30-sec. delay
                      Sequence: 5 long, 5 short, differ-
                      ent sequence each day
      Gp. C: (N = 5) 1 pellet at 5-sec. delay
II. 10 tr/day, 20 trials
      Gps. A, B, C: extinction

Exper. 55B. Running speed as a joint function of length of food
  deprivation and magnitude of reinforcement
Experimenter: Weiss
Subjects: 72 male albino rats
Procedure: white alley. One 40-minute feeding every 48 hours
  maintenance. [Diet: 20% B-3F casein, 30% lard, 50% ground
  Purina, plus 1 drop/16.5 gms. each of $CuSO_4$ (.125%), $MnSO_4$
  (5%), $Fe_2(SO_4)_3$ (5%), Abdec multiple vitamins]

Design:
I. 1 tr/2 days, 55 trials
      Gp. A: (N = 6) 1 pellet at 0-sec. delay, 2 hrs.
                      deprivation
      Gp. B: (N = 6) 12 pellets at 0-sec. delay, 2 hrs.
                      deprivation
      Gp. C: (N = 6) 1 pellet at 0-sec. delay, 12 hrs.
                      deprivation

Gp. D: (N = 6)   3 pellets at 0-sec. delay, 12 hrs. deprivation

Gp. E: (N = 6)   6 pellets at 0-sec. delay, 12 hrs. deprivation

Gp. F: (N = 6) 12 pellets at 0-sec. delay, 12 hrs. deprivation

Gp. G: (N = 6)   1 pellet at 0-sec. delay, 24 hrs. deprivation

Gp. H: (N = 6) 12 pellets at 0-sec. delay, 24 hrs. deprivation

Gp. I: (N = 6)   1 pellet at 0-sec. delay, 48 hrs. deprivation

Gp. J: (N = 6)   3 pellets at 0-sec. delay, 48 hrs. deprivation

Gp. K: (N = 6)   6 pellets at 0-sec. delay, 48 hrs. deprivation

Gp. L: (N = 6) 12 pellets at 0-sec. delay, 48 hrs. deprivation

II. 1 tr/2 days, 16 trials

Rats reassigned among conditions in I

Exper. 55C. Choice between constant and varied reward

Experimenter: Rosenwald

Subjects: 16 male albino rats

Procedure: both alleys (every fourth trial free choice, others forced), 10gm/day maintenance

Design:

I. 1 tr/day, 160 trials

Gp. A: (N = 8) Alley A: 5 pellets at 0-sec. delay

Alley B: 50%a: 9 pellets at 0-sec. delay

50%b: 1 pellet at 0-sec. delay

Gp. B: (N = 8) Alley A: 5 pellets at 5-sec. delay

Alley B: 50%a: 5 pellets at 1-sec. delay

50%b: 5 pellets at 9-sec. delay

Exper. 55D. Comparison of controlled delay and controlled latency of reinforcement

Experimenters: Logan, Beier, Kincaid

Subjects: 74 male albino and 47 male hooded rats

Procedure: white or black alley, 12 gm/day (albino) or 9 gm/day (hooded) maintenance

Design:

    I. 1 tr/day, 57 trials

           Gp. A: (N = 12) 2 pellets at 0-sec. delay
           Gp. B: (N = 10) 2 pellets at 1-sec. delay
           Gp. C: (N = 10) 2 pellets at 2-sec. delay
           Gp. D: (N = 10) 2 pellets at 3-sec. delay
           Gp. E: (N = 11) 2 pellets at 5-sec. delay
           Gp. F: (N = 10) 2 pellets at 10-sec. delay
           Gp. G: (N = 10) 2 pellets at 30-sec. delay
           Gp. H: (N = 10) 2 pellets at 2-sec. latency
           Gp. I: (N = 9) 2 pellets at 4-sec. latency
           Gp. J: (N = 10) 2 pellets at 6-sec. latency
           Gp. K: (N = 9) 2 pellets at 10-sec. latency
           Gp. L: (N = 10) 2 pellets at 20-sec. latency

    II. 1 tr/day, 24 trials (following 30-day rest)

           Gps. A through G: original conditions under 16
                      gm/day maintenance

    III. 1 tr/day, 24 trials

           Gps. A through G: extinction

    IV. 1 tr/day, 8 trials (following 14-day rest)

           Gps. A through G: extinction

    V. 1 tr/day, 40 trials

           Gps. A through G: 2 pellets at 3-sec. delay

Exper. 55E. Effect of varied amount of reward on running speed and extinction

Experimenters: Logan, Beier, Kincaid

Subjects: 24 male hooded rats

Procedure: white or black alley, 9 gm/day maintenance

Design:

    I. 1 tr/day, 62 trials

           Gp. A: (N = 8) 50%a: 9 pellets at 4-sec. delay

> 50%b: 1 pellet at 4-sec. delay
> Sequence: abaababbab or opposite, repeated

Gp. B: (N = 8) 9 pellets at 4-sec. delay
Gp. C: (N = 8) 5 pellets at 4-sec. delay

  II. 1 tr/day, 34 trials

      Gps. A, B, C: extinction

 III. 1 tr/day, 56 trials

      Gps. A, B, C: 9 pellets at 4-sec. delay

  IV. 1 tr/day, 40 trials

      Gp. A: 50%a: 9 pellets at 4-sec. delay
              50%b: 1 pellet at 4-sec. delay

      Gp. B: extinction

Exper. 56A. Comparison of varied amount of reward and partial reinforcement

Experimenters: Logan, Beier, Kincaid

Subjects: 24 male hooded rats

Procedure: white alley, 10 gm/day maintenance

Design:

   I. 1 tr/day, 60 trials

      Gp. A: (N = 8) 9 pellets at 4-sec. delay
      Gp. B: (N = 8) 50%a: 9 pellets at 4-sec. delay
                      50%b: 1 pellet at 4-sec. delay
      Gp. C: (N = 8) 50%a: 9 pellets at 4-sec. delay
                      50%b: no food reward
                      Sequence: abaababbab or opposite, repeated

  II. 1 tr/day, 45 trials

      All groups: extinction

 III. 1 tr/day, 42 trials

      All groups: relearning, original conditions

  IV. 1 tr/day, 80 trials

      Gp. A: continued unchanged
      Gps. B and C: conditions reversed

Exper. 56B. A comparison of controlled latency and controlled delay of reinforcement

Experimenters: Logan, Beier, Dodd

Subjects: 23 male hooded rats
Procedure: white alley, 12 gm/day maintenance

Design:

 I. 1 tr/day, 86 trials
   Gp. A: (N = 12) 2 pellets at 13-sec. latency
   Gp. B: (N = 11) 2 pellets at 12-sec. delay

 II. 1 tr/day, 12 trials (starting 2 weeks after castration)
   Gp. A: (N = 8) 2 pellets at 12-sec. delay, 125 testosterone/day
   Gp. B: (N = 7) 2 pellets at 12-sec. delay, 5 testosterone/day
   Gp. C: (N = 8) 2 pellets at 12-sec. delay, 0 testosterone/day

 III. 1 tr/day, 3 trials
   All groups: food satiated, no reward, 12-sec. confinement

Exper. 56C. Uncorrelated and negatively correlated delay of reward
Experimenters: Logan, Beier, Barry, Weiss
Subjects: 137 male rats, half hooded and half albino
Procedure: white alley, 12 gm/day maintenance

Design:

 I. 1 tr/day, 57 trials
   Gp. A: (N = 11) 2 pellets at 0-sec. delay
   Gp. B: (N = 12) 2 pellets at 1-sec. delay
   Gp. C: (N = 23) 2 pellets at 3-sec. delay
   Gp. D: (N = 12) 2 pellets at 10-sec. delay
   Gp. E: (N = 11) 2 pellets at 30-sec. delay
   Gp. F: (N = 11) no food reward
   Gp. G: (N = 16) 2 pellets at 4-sec. latency
   Gp. H: (N = 17) 2 pellets at 5-sec. interval
   Gp. I: (N = 12) $2A,0D < .33R < 2A,10D$
   Gp. J: (N = 12) $2A,0D < .33R < 0A,\infty D$

 II. 1 tr/day, 22 trials
   Gp. A: (N = 11) 12 pellets at 0-sec. delay
   Gp. B: (N = 12) 12 pellets at 1-sec. delay
   Gp. C: (N = 13) 12 pellets at 3-sec. delay

Gp. C*: (N = 10)   2 pellets at 3-sec. delay
Gp. D: (N = 12) 12 pellets at 10-sec. delay
Gp. E: (N = 11) 12 pellets at 30-sec. delay
Gp. F: (N = 11) 12 pellets at 0-sec. delay
Gp. G: (N = 9) 12 pellets at 4-sec. latency
Gp. G*: (N = 7)   2 pellets at 4-sec. latency
Gp. H: (N = 9) 12 pellets at 5-sec. interval
Gp. H*: (N = 8)   2 pellets at 5-sec. interval
Gp. I: (N = 6) $12A,0D < .33R < 12A,10D$
Gp. I*: (N = 6) $2A,0D < .33R < 2A,10D$
Gp. J: (N = 12) $2A,0D < .33R < 0A \infty D$

III. 1 or 6 tr/day, 34 days
Gp. J: (N = 6) $2A,0D < .33R < 0A, \infty D$
(1 tr/day)
Gp. J*: (N = 6) $2A,0D < .33R < 0A, \infty D$
(6 tr/day)

IV. 1 tr/day, 16 trials
Gps. J and J*: $2A,0D < .33R < 0A, \infty D$

Exper. 56D. Effect of change from controlled delay to correlated delay (controlled latency)
Experimenters: Logan, Beier
Subjects: 16 male hooded rats
Procedure: white or black alleys, 10 gm/day maintenance

Design:
I. 1 tr/day, 84 trials
Gp. A: (N = 8) 1 pellet at 4-sec. delay
Gp. B: (N = 8) 7 pellets at 4-sec. delay
II. 1 tr/day, 48 trials
Gp. A: 1 pellet with latency controlled at mean under *I*
Gp. B: 7 pellets with latency controlled at mean under *I*

Exper. 56E. A comparison of partial and varied amount of reward
Experimenters: Logan, Beier
Subjects: 8 male hooded rats
Procedure: white or black alleys, 9 gm/day maintenance

Design:
    I. 1 tr/day, 50 trials
        Gp. A: (N = 7) 50%a: 9 pellets at 4-sec. delay
                     50%b: no reward
    II. 1 tr/day, 44 trials
           Gp. A: 50%a: 9 pellets at 4-sec. delay
                 50%b: 1 pellet at 4-sec. delay

Exper. 56F. Effect of distribution of practice on trial-and-error learning
Experimenter: Logan
Subjects: 16 male hooded rats
Procedure: both alleys (first and fifth of each 6 trials free), 10 gm/day maintenance

Design:
    I. 6 tr/week, 98 trials, 4 pellets, 0-sec. delay in correct alley
           Gp. A: (N = 8) 1 tr/day for 6 days, 1 day rest/ week
           Gp. B: (N = 8) 6 tr/day for 1 day, 6 days rest/ week

Exper. 57A. Choice between differential delay and/or differential amount of reward
Experimenters: Hill, Peckham
Subjects: 24 male hooded rats
Procedure: both alleys (every fourth trial free), 12 gm/day maintenance

Design:
    I. 8 tr/day, 80 trials
           Gp. A: (N = 8) Alley A: 9 pellets at 1-sec. delay
                        Alley B: 1 pellet at 1-sec. delay
           Gp. B: (N = 8) Alley A: 5 pellets at 1-sec. delay
                        Alley B: 5 pellets at 9-sec. delay
           Gp. C: (N = 8) Alley A: 9 pellets at 1-sec. delay
                        Alley B: 1 pellet at 9-sec. delay
    II. 8 tr/day, 80 trials
           All groups: reversal

Exper. 57B. Effect of uncorrelated punishment on speed of running

Experimenters: Logan, Peckham, Gonzalez, McLellan

Subjects: 64 male albino rats

Procedure: black alley, 12 gm/day maintenance

Design:

    I. 4 tr/day, 16 trials

        All rats: 4 pellets at 0-sec. delay, no shock

    II. 4 tr/day, 128 trials

        Gp. A: (N = 8) 4 pellets at 0-sec. delay, no shock

        Gp. B: (N = 8) 50%a: 4 pellets at 0-sec. delay, no shock

                            50%b: no food, no shock

        Gp. C: (N = 8) 4 pellets at 0-sec. delay, 100-volt shock

        Gp. D: (N = 8) 50%a: 4 pellets at 0-sec. delay, 100-volt shock

                            50%b: 4 pellets at 0-sec. delay, no shock

        Gp. E: (N = 8) 50%a: 4 pellets at 0-sec. delay, 100-volt shock

                            50%b: no food, 100 volts shock

        Gp. F: (N = 8) 50%a: 4 pellets at 0-sec. delay, 100-volt shock

                            50%b: no food, no shock

        Gp. G: (N = 8) 50%a: 4 pellets at 0-sec. delay, no shock

                            50%b: no food, 100-volt shock

                            Sequence: aabb, abba, baab, bbaa or reverse, repeated

        Gp. H: (N = 8) 25%a: 4 pellets at 0-sec. delay, 100-volt shock

                            25%b: 4 pellets at 0-sec. delay, no shock

                            25%c: no food, 100-volt shock

                            25%d: no food, no shock

                            Sequence: (adbc, cbda, dcab, bacd) or (cbda, adbc, bacd, dcab), repeated

III. 4 tr/day, 16 trials
>> All shock groups: 125 volts
IV. 4 tr/day, 48 trials
>> All shock groups: 150 volts
V. 4 tr/day, 16 trials
>> All shock groups: 175 volts
VI. 4 tr/day, 48 trials
>> All shock groups: 200 volts
VII. 4 tr/day, 48 trials
>> All groups: no food, no shock

Exper. 57C. Correlated and uncorrelated reward and punishment
Experimenter: Logan
Subjects: 16 male hooded rats
Procedure: black alley, 12 gm/day

Design:
I. 6 tr/day, 144 trials
>> Gp. A: (N = 1) 8 pellets at 0-sec. delay, no shock
>> Gp. B: (N = 1) 1 pellet at 0-sec. delay, no shock
>> Gp. C: (N = 1) 8 pellets at 0-sec. delay, 100% shock
>> Gp. D: (N = 1) 1 pellet at 0-sec. delay, 100% shock
>> Gp. E: (N = 1) 8 pellets at 0-sec. delay, 100% shock (delayed 5 sec.)
>> Gp. F: (N = 1) 1 pellet at 0-sec. delay, 100% shock (delayed 5 sec.)
>> Gp. G: (N = 1) $8A,0D,S < I: \frac{3}{6} < 8A,0D,0S$
>> Gp. H: (N = 1) matched-control on G
>> Gp. I: (N = 1) $1A,0D,S < I:\frac{3}{6} < 1A,0D,0S$
>> Gp. J: (N = 1) matched-control on I
>> Gp. K: (N = 1) $8A,0D,0S < I: \frac{3}{6} < 8A,0D,S$
>> Gp. L: (N = 1) matched-control on K
>> Gp. M: (N = 1) $8A,0D,0S < I: \frac{3}{6} < 0A,\infty D,S$
>> Gp. N: (N = 1) matched-control on M
>> Gp. O: (N = 1) $8A,0D,S < I: \frac{3}{6} < 0A,\infty D,0S$
>> Gp. P: (N = 1) matched-control on O
II. 6 tr/day, 216 trials
>> Gps. G through P: same conditions as I

Exper. 57D. Discontinuously correlated delay of reinforcement
Experimenters: Logan, Beier, Peckham
Subjects: 46 male albino rats
Procedure: white alley, 12 gm/day maintenance

Design:
- I. 4 tr/day, 240 trials
  - Gp. A: (N = 6) 1A,0D < .2I < 1A,10D
  - Gp. B: (N = 6) matched-control on A
  - Gp. C: (N = 6) 12A,0D < .2I < 12A,10D
  - Gp. D: (N = 6) matched-control on C
  - Gp. E: (N = 6) 1A,0D < .2I < 0A,∞D
  - Gp. F: (N = 6) matched-control on E
  - Gp. G: (N = 5) 12A,0D < .2I < 0A,∞D
  - Gp. H: (N = 5) matched-control on G
- IIa. 4 tr/day, 144 trials
  - Gps. A, B, E, F: (N = 4/gp) shift to 12 pellets
- IIb. 1 tr/day, 75 trials
  - Gps. C, D, G, H: (N = 4/gp) extinction after 12 more days on original conditions
- IIc. 4tr/day, 320 trials
  - Gps. G, H: (N = 1/gp) 256 trials of 100% reward, then 164 trials of extinction

Exper. 57E. Performance of inbred mice
Experimenters: Logan, Beier
Subjects: 6 grey mice
Procedure: white or black alleys, 4 gm/day maintenance

Design:
- I. 1 tr/day, 36 trials
  - All mice: 2 pellets at 2-sec. delay
- II. 1 tr/day, 16 trials
  - All mice: 2 pellets at 0-sec. delay

Exper. 58A. Activity and running speed
Experimenter: Logan
Subjects: 6 male albino rats
Procedure: Individual activity wheels and white alley

Design:
- I. 30 days

Ad lib. food in activity wheels, nipple size on water bottle varied between 1, 2, 3, 4, 5, and 6 mm.

II. 30 days

Ad lib. food in activity wheels, two water bottles available with different nipple sizes

III. 52 days

12 gm/day food in activity wheels, large water bottle

IV. 32 days, 12 gm/day maintenance, 1 tr/day

No food reward in alley

V. 32 days, 12 gm/day maintenance, 1 tr/day

8 pellets at 0-sec. delay

Exper. 58B. Positively correlated reward and punishment
Experimenters: Logan, Gonzalez
Subjects: 31 male hooded rats
Procedure: black alley, 12 gm/day maintenance

Design:

I. 6 tr/day, 360 trials

Gp. A: (N = 4) 0A, ∞D < *I*: 2/6 < 4A,0D
Gp. B: (N = 4) control gp. A
Gp. C: (N = 4) 0A, ∞D < *I*: 4/6 < 4A,0D
Gp. D: (N = 4) control gp. C
Gp. E: (N = 4) 0A, ∞D, 0S < *I*: 2/6 < 4A,0D, 100S
Gp. F: (N = 3) control gp. E
Gp. G: (N = 3) 4A,0D,100S < *I*: 2/6 < 4A,0D,0S
0S, 36 tr.; 100S, 180 tr.; 125S, 90 tr.; 150S, 18 tr.; 175S, 36 tr.
Gp. H: (N = 3) control gp. G
Gp. I: (N = 1) 4A,0D,0S < .2*I* < 4A,0D,150S

II. 6 tr/day, 72 trials

Gps. A through F: extinction, no food, no shock
Gp. G: 4A,0D,200S < *I*: 2/6 < 4A,0D,0S
Gp. H: control gp. G
Gp. I: 4A,0D,0S < .2*I* < 4A,0D,150S

III. 6 tr/day, 360 trials

Gp. I: 4A,0D,150S < .2*I* < 4A,0D,0S

Exper. 58C. Rate of change in performance with changes in the conditions of reinforcement

Experimenter: Trapold

Subjects: 56 male albino rats

Procedure: white alley, 12 gm/day maintenance

Design:

    I. 1 tr/day, 65 trials

          All rats: 5 pellets at 0-sec. delay

    II. 1 tr/day, 18 trials

          Gp. A: (N = 8) 5 pellets at 0-sec. delay

          Gp. B: (N = 8) 9 pellets at 0-sec. delay

          Gp. C: (N = 8) 1 pellet at 0-sec. delay

          Gp. D: (N = 8) 5 pellets at 4-sec. delay

          Gp. E: (N = 8) 50%a: 9 pellets at 0-sec. delay

                                50%b: 1 pellet at 0-sec. delay

          Gp. F: (N = 8) 9 pellets at 4-sec. delay

          Gp. G: (N = 8) no food reward

    IIIa. 1 tr/day, 19 trials

          Gps. A, B, C, G: same conditions, half in large individual living cages and half in small individual living cages

    IIIb. 4 tr/day, 240 trials

          Gp. F: $9A,0D < .2I < 0A, \infty D$

    IVa. 1 tr/day, 14 trials

          Gps. A, B, C: same conditions as IIIb, maintenance to 18 gm/day

    IVb. 4 tr/day, 240 trials

          Gp. F: (N = 4) $9A,0D < .1I < 0A, \infty D$

Exper. 58D. Effect of pre- and post-reward detention

Experimenter: Gonzalez

Subjects: 60 male albino rats

Procedure: white alley, 12 gm/day maintenance

Design:

    I. 1 tr/day, 105 trials

          Gp. A: (N = 12) 5 pellets at 2-sec. delay, immediate removal

Gp. B: (N = 12) 5 pellets at 2-sec. delay, 30-sec. post-reward detention

Gp. C: (N = 12) 5 pellets at 30-sec. delay, immediate removal

Gp. D: (N = 12) no reward, immediate removal

Gp. E: (N = 12) no reward, 30-sec. detention

Exper. 58E. Discontinuously correlated delay and amount of reward with widely distributed practice
Experimenters: Logan, Gonzalez
Subjects: 8 male hooded rats
Procedure: white alley, 12 gm/day maintenance

Design:

    I. 1 tr/day, 240 trials

        Gp. A: (N = 4) $12A,0D < .2I < 0A,\infty D$

        Gp. B: (N = 4) matched-control on A

    II. 1 tr/day, 60 trials

        All groups: extinction

Exper. 59A. Negatively correlated punishment
Experimenter: Logan
Subjects: 6 male albino rats
Procedure: black alley, 12 gm/day maintenance

Design:

    I. 4 tr/day, 184 trials

        Gp. A: (N = 3) $4A,0D,0S < .33I < 4A,0D,200S$

        Gp. B: (N = 3) matched-control on A

    II. 6 tr/day, 300 trials

        Same as I

    III. 6 tr/day, 240 trials

        Gp. A: $4A,0D,0S < .25I < 4A,0D,200S$

        Gp. B: matched-control on A

Exper. 59B. Positively correlated reinforcement
Experimenters: Logan, Brooks
Subjects: 6 male albino rats
Procedure: black alley, 12 gm/day maintenance

Design:

    I. 4 tr/day, 268 trials

Gp. A: $(N = 3)$ $0A, \infty D <$ criterion $< 4A, 0D$ (criterion increased through arbitrary stages)

Gp. B: $(N = 3)$ matched-control on A

II. 4 tr/day, 96 trials

Gp. A: $0A, \infty D <$ criterion $< 1A, 0D$

Gp. B: matched-control on A

Exper. 59C. Negatively correlated amount of reward
Experimenters: Logan, Brooks
Subjects: 6 male albino rats
Procedure: white alley, 12 gm/day maintenance

Design:

I. 4 tr/day, 76 trials

Gp. A: $(N = 3)$ $10A, 0D < .2I < 2A, 0D$

Gp. B: $(N = 3)$ matched-control on A (matched on delay of reinforcement)

II. 4 tr/day, 192 trials

Gp. A: $10A, 0D < .5I < 2A, 0D$

Gp. B: matched-control on A (matched on delay for 112 trials; matched on interval of reinforcement thereafter)

III. 4 tr/day, 288 trials

Gp. A: $10A, 0D < .2I < 2A, 0D$

Gp. B: matched-control on A (matched on interval)

IV. 4 tr/day, 200 trials

Gp. A: switch to $2A, 0D <$ criterion $< 10A, 0D$ (criterion stepped through arbitrary stages as speed increased)

Gp. B: matched-control on A (matched on delay)

Exper. 59D. Controlled interval of reinforcement
Experimenters: Logan, Brooks
Subjects: 6 male albino rats
Procedure: white alley, 12 gm/day maintenance

Design:

I. 4 tr/day, 500 trials

Gp. A: (N = 3) 10 pellets at 5-sec. interval
Gp. B: (N = 3) matched-control with same delays
as mates in A.

Exper. 59E. Effect of drive in negatively correlated reward
Experimenter: Logan
Subjects: 4 male albino rats (originally trained by Bower with 4
trials a day under a $10A,0D < .17I < 0A,\infty D$ condition)
Procedure: white alley

Design:
    I. 1 tr/day, 16 days
        All rats: $10A,0D < .17I < 0A,\infty D$
    II. 1 tr/day, 48 days
        Gp. A: (N = 2) same condition, 16 gm/day main-
tenance
        Gp. B: (N = 2) same condition, 10 gm/day main-
tenance
    III. 4 tr/day, 48 days
        Same as II
    IV. 4 tr/day, 48 days
        All rats: switch to uncorrelated reward in black
alley

Exper. 59F. Performance under antagonistically correlated delay
and amount of reward
Experimenter: Logan
Subjects: 3 male albino rats (originally trained by Bower under
a $10A,0D < .17I < 10A,30D$ condition)
Procedure: white alley, 12 gm/day maintenance

Design:
    I. 4 tr/day, 320 trials
        All rats: $2A,0D < .17I < 10A,30D$

Associated Bibliography

BARRY, H., III (1958) Effects of strength of drive on learning and on extinction. *J. Exp. Psychol., 55,* 473–81.

BARRY, H., III, AND LOGAN, F. A. (1957) Latent learning in a straight alley. *Psychol. Reports, 3,* 88.

BEIER, E. M. (1958) Effects of trial-to-trial variation in magnitude of reward upon an instrumental running response. (Ph.D. dissertation, Yale Univ.)

BOWER, G. H. (1959) Correlated delay of reinforcement. (Ph.D. dissertation, Yale Univ.)

LOGAN, F. A., BEIER, E. M., AND ELLIS, R. A. (1955) Effect of varied reinforcement on speed of locomotion. *J. Exp. Psychol., 49,* 260–6.

LOGAN, F. A., BEIER, E. M., AND KINCAID, W. D. (1956) Extinction following partial and varied reinforcement. *J. Exp. Psychol., 52,* 65–70.

WEISS, R. F. (1958) Response speed, amplitude, and resistance to extinction as joint functions of work and reinforcement ratio. (Ph.D. dissertation, Yale Univ.)

General References

AMSEL, A., AND ROUSSEL, J. (1952) Motivational properties of frustration: I. Effect on a running response of the addition of frustration to the motivational complex. *J. Exp. Psychol., 43,* 363–8.

ANDERSON, A. C. (1932) Trace discrimination in the white rat. *J. Comp. Psychol., 13,* 27–55.

ANDERSON, E. E. (1941) The externalization of drive: I. Theoretical considerations. *Psychol. Rev., 48,* 204–9.

ANGER, D. (1956) The dependence of interresponse times upon the relative reinforcement of different interresponse times. *J. Exp. Psychol., 52,* 145–61.

ARNOLD, W. J. (1945) An exploratory investigation of primary response generalization. *J. Comp. Psychol., 38,* 87–102.

BERGMANN, G., AND SPENCE, K. W. (1941) Operationism and theory in psychology. *Psychol. Rev., 48,* 1–14

BERNSTEIN, L. (1957) The effects of variations in handling upon learning and retention. *J. Comp. Physiol. Psychol., 50,* 162–7.

BLODGETT, H. C. (1929) The effect of the introduction of reward upon the maze performance of rats. *Univ. Calif. Publ. Psychol., 4,* 113–34.

BLODGETT, H. C., AND McCUTCHAN, K. (1948) Relative strength of place and response learning in the T-maze. *J. Comp. Physiol. Psychol., 41,* 17–24.

BROWN, J. S. (1948) Gradients of approach and avoidance responses and their relation to level of motivation. *J. Comp. Physiol. Psychol., 41,* 450–65.

BROWN, J. S., AND FARBER, I. E. (1951) Emotions conceptualized as intervening variables—with suggestions toward a theory of frustration. *Psychol. Bull., 48,* 465–95.

BROWN, W. L., AND GENTRY, G. (1948) The effects of intra-maze delay. II. Various intervals of delay. *J. Comp. Physiol. Psychol., 41,* 403–7.

BROWN, W. L., GENTRY, G., AND BOSWORTH, L. L. (1949) The effects of intra-maze delay. IV. A gap in the maze. *J. Comp. Physiol. Psychol., 42,* 182–91.

BRUNSWICK, E. (1939) Probability as a determiner of rat behavior. *J. Exp. Psychol., 25,* 175–97.

BUGELSKI, R. (1938) Extinction with and without sub-goal reinforcement. *J. Comp. Psychol., 26,* 121–34.

CAMPBELL, B. A., AND TEGHTSOONIAN, R. (1958) Electrical and behavioral effects of different types of shock stimuli on the rat. *J. Comp. Physiol. Psychol., 51,* 185–92.

CAMPBELL, D. T. (1954) Operational delineation of "what is learned" via the transposition experiment. *Psychol. Rev., 61,* 167–74.

CAPALDI, E. J. (1958) The effect of different amounts of training on the resistance to extinction of different patterns of partially reinforced responses. *J. Comp. Physiol. Psychol., 51,* 367–71.

CONRAD, D. G., SIDMAN, M., AND HERRNSTEIN, R. J. (1958) The effects of deprivation upon temporally spaced responding. *J. Exp. Analysis Beh., 1,* 59–66.

COTTON, J. W. (1953) Running time as a function of amount of food deprivation. *J. Exp. Psychol., 46,* 188–97.

COTTON, J. W., AND LEWIS, D. J. (1957) Effect of intertrial interval on acquisition and extinction of a running response. *J. Exp. Psychol., 54,* 15–20.

CRESPI, L. P. (1944) Amount of reinforcement and the level of performance. *Psychol. Rev., 51,* 341–57.

CRUM, L., BROWN, W. L., AND BITTERMAN, M. E. (1951) The effect of delayed partial reinforcement on resistance to extinction. *Amer. J. Psychol., 64,* 228–37.

DEMBER, W. N., AND FOWLER, H. (1958) Spontaneous alternation behavior. *Psychol. Bull., 55,* 412–28.

DINSMOOR, J. A. (1954) Punishment: I. The avoidance hypothesis. *Psychol. Rev., 61,* 34–46.

DOLLARD, J., AND MILLER, N. E. (1950) *Personality and psychotherapy.* New York, McGraw-Hill.

ESTES, W. K. (1944) An experimental study of punishment. *Psychol. Monogr., 57,* No. 263.

ESTES, W. K. (1955) Statistical theory of spontaneous recovery and regression. *Psychol. Rev., 62,* 145–54.

FARBER, I. E. (1948) Response fixation under anxiety and non-anxiety conditions. *J. Exp. Psychol. 38,* 111–31.

FEHRER, E. (1956) Effects of amount of reinforcement and of pre and post reinforcement delays on learning and extinction. *J. Exp. Psychol., 52,* 167–76.

FERSTER, C. B., AND SKINNER, B. F. (1957) *Schedules of reinforcement.* New York, Appleton-Century-Crofts.

FINGER, F. W. (1942) The effect of varying conditions of reinforcement upon a simple running response. *J. Exp. Psychol., 30,* 53–68.

FINGER, F. W., REID, L. S., WEASNER, M. H. (1957) The effect of reinforcement upon activity during cyclic food deprivation. *J. Comp. Physiol. Psychol., 50,* 495–8.

FOWLER, H., JR. (1959) The effect of strength of punishment and distribution of trials on the acquisition of a running response. (Ph.D. dissertation, Yale Univ.)

FRIEDES, D. (1957) Goal-box cues and pattern of reinforcement. *J. Exp. Psychol., 53,* 361–71.

GLANZER, M. (1953a) Stimulation satiation: an explanation of spontaneous alternation and related phenomena. *Psychol. Rev., 60,* 257–68.

GLANZER, M. (1953b) The role of stimulus satiation in spontaneous alternation. *J. Exp. Psychol., 45,* 387–93.

GRICE, G. R. (1948) The relation of secondary reinforcement to delayed reward in visual discrimination learning. *J. Exp. Psychol., 38,* 1–16.

GRINDLEY, G. C. (1929) Experiments on the influence of the amount of reward on learning in young chickens. *Brit. J. Psychol., 20,* 173–80.

GUILFORD, J. P. (1936) *Psychometric methods.* New York, McGraw-Hill.

GUTHRIE, E. R. (1934) Reward and punishment. *Psychol. Rev., 41,* 450–60.

GUTHRIE, E. R. (1935) *The psychology of learning.* New York, Harper.

GWINN, G. T. (1949) The effects of punishment on acts motivated by fear. *J. Exp. Psychol., 39,* 260–9.

HARLOW, H. F. (1949) The formation of learning sets. *Psychol. Rev., 56,* 51–65.

HARLOW, H. F. (1950) Analysis of discrimination learning by monkeys. *J. Exp. Psychol., 40,* 26–39.

HILGARD, E. R. (1956) *Theories of learning.* New York, Appleton-Century-Crofts.

HILL, W. F. (1956) Activity as an autonomous drive. *J. Comp. Physiol. Psychol., 49,* 15–19.

HULL, C. L. (1939) The goal gradient hypothesis and maze learning. *Psychol. Rev., 32,* 25–43.

HULL, C. L. (1943) *Principles of behavior.* New York, Appleton-Century.

HULL, C. L. (1952) *A behavior system.* New Haven, Yale Univ. Press.

HULL, C. L. et al. (1947) A proposed quantification of habit strength. *Psychol. Rev., 54,* 237–54.

HULSE, S. H., JR. (1958) Amount and percentage of reinforcement and duration of goal confinement in conditioning and extinction. *J. Exp. Psychol., 56,* 48–57.

HUMPHREYS, L. G. (1939) Acquisition and extinction of verbal expectations in a situation analogous to conditioning. *J. Exp. Psychol., 25,* 294–301.

JENKINS, W. O., AND STANLEY, J. C., JR. (1950) Partial reinforcement: a review and critique. *Psychol. Bull., 47,* 193–234.

KARN, H. W., AND PORTER, J. M. JR. (1946) The effects of certain pretraining procedures upon maze performance and their significance for the concept of latent learning. *J. Exp. Psychol., 36,* 461–70.

KARSH, E. B. (1959) The effect of intensity of punishment and number of rewarded and punished trials on running speed in a conflict situation. (Ph.D. dissertation, Yale Univ.)

KATZ, S. (1957) Stimulus aftereffects and the partial reinforcement extinction effect. *J. Exp. Psychol., 53,* 167–72.

KENDLER, H. H. (1952) "What is learned?"—a theoretical blind alley. *Psychol. Rev. 59,* 269–77.

KENDLER, H. H., et al. (1957) Nonreinforcements versus reinforcements as variables in the partial reinforcement effect. *J. Exp. Psychol., 53,* 269–76.

KLING, J. W. (1956) Speed of running as a function of goal-box behavior. *J. Comp. Physiol. Psychol., 49,* 474–6.

KOBRICK, J. L. (1956) The relationships among three measures of response strength as a function of the numbers of reinforcements. *J. Comp. Physiol. Psychol., 49,* 582–6.

KOCH, S. (1954) Clark L. Hull. In Estes, et al., *Modern learning theory.* New York, Appleton-Century-Crofts.

LAWRENCE, D. H. (1949) Acquired distinctiveness of cues: I. Transfer between discriminations on the basis of familiarity with the stimulus. *J. Exp. Psychol., 39,* 770–84.

LEWIS, D. J. (1956) Acquisition, extinction, and spontaneous recovery as a function of percentage of reinforcement and intertrial intervals. *J. Exp. Psychol., 51,* 45–53.

LOGAN, F. A. (1952) The role of delay of reinforcement in determining reaction potential. *J. Exp. Psychol., 43,* 393–9.

LOGAN, F. A. (1956) A micromolar approach to behavior theory. *Psychol. Rev., 63,* 63–73.

LOGAN, F. A. (1959) The Hull-Spence approach. In S. Koch, ed., *Psychology: a study of a science,* Study 1, Vol. 2. New York, McGraw-Hill.

LOGAN, F. A., OLMSTED, D. L., ROSNER, B.S., SCHWARTZ, R. D., AND STEVENS, C. M. (1955) *Behavior theory and social science.* New Haven, Yale Univ. Press.

LONGENECKER, E. D., KRAUSKOPF, J., AND BITTERMAN, M. E. (1952) Extinction following alternating and random partial reinforcement. *Amer. J. Psychol., 65,* 580–7.

MANDLER, G., AND KESSEN, W. (1959) *The language of psychology.* New York, Wiley.

McGEOCH, J. A., AND IRION, A. L. (1952) *The psychology of human learning.* New York, Longmans, Green.

METZER, R., COTTON, J. W., AND LEWIS, D. J. (1957) Effect of reinforcement magnitude and of order of presentation of different magnitudes on runway behavior. *J. Comp. Physiol. Psychol., 50,* 184–8.

MILLER, N. E. (1951) Comments on theoretical models illustrated by the development of a theory of conflict behavior. *J. Pers., 20,* 82–100.

MILLER, N. E. (1959) Liberalization of basic S-R concepts: extensions to conflict behavior, motivation, and social learning. In S. Koch, ed., *Psychology: a study of a science,* Study 1, Vol. 2, 196–292. New York, McGraw-Hill.

MILLER, N. E., AND STEVENSON, S. S. (1936) Agitated behavior of rats during experimental extinction and a curve of spontaneous recovery. *J. Comp. Psychol., 21,* 205–31.

MORGAN, C. T., AND FIELDS, P. E. (1938) The effect of variable preliminary feeding upon the rat's speed of locomotion. *J. Comp. Psychol., 26,* 331–48.

MOWRER, O. H. (1939) A stimulus-response analysis of anxiety and its role as a reinforcing agent. *Psychol. Rev., 46,* 553–66.

NOTTERMAN, J. M. (1951) A study of some relations among aperiodic reinforcement, discrimination training, and secondary reinforcement. *J. Exp. Psychol., 41,* 161–9.

NOTTERMAN, J. M. (1959) Force emission during bar pressing. *J. Exp. Psychol., 58,* 341–7.

PAVLOV, I. P. (1927) *Conditioned reflexes.* G. V. Anrep, trans. London, Oxford Univ. Press.

PEREBOOM, A. C., AND CRAWFORD, B. M. (1958) Instrumental and competing behavior as a function of trials and reward magnitude. *J. Exp. Psychol., 56,* 82–5.

PERIN, C. T. (1943) A quantitative investigation of the delay-of-reinforcement gradient. *J. Exp. Psychol., 32,* 38–51.

PERKINS, C. C., JR. (1947) The relation of secondary rewards to gradients of reinforcement. *J. Exp. Psychol., 37,* 377–92.

PETERSON, L. R. (1956) Variable delayed reinforcement. *J. Comp. Physiol. Psychol., 49,* 232–4.

RAMOND, C. K. (1954) Performance in instrumental learning as a joint function of delay of reinforcement and time of deprivation. *J. Exp. Psychol., 47,* 248–50.

REID, L. S., AND FINGER, F. W. (1955) The rat's adjustment of 23-hour food deprivation cycles. *J. Comp. Physiol. Psychol., 48,* 110–13.

RESTLE, F. (1957) Discrimination of cues in mazes: a resolution of the "place-vs.-response" question. *Psychol. Rev. 64,* 217–28.

RESTLE, F. (1958) Toward a quantitative description of learning set data. *Psychol. Rev., 65,* 77–91.

REYNOLDS, B. (1945) Extinction of trace conditioned response as a function of the spacing of trials during acquisition and extinction series. *J. Exp. Psychol., 35,* 81–95.

REYNOLDS, B. (1949) The acquisition of black-white discrimination habit under two levels of reinforcement. *J. Exp. Psychol., 39,* 760–9.

REYNOLDS, B. (1950) Resistance to extinction as a function of the amount of reinforcement present during acquisition. *J. Exp. Psychol., 40,* 46–52.

ROZEBOOM, W. W. (1958) "What is learned?"—an empirical enigma. *Psychol. Rev., 65,* 22–33.

SCHOENFELD, W. N., et al. (1950) Unconditional response rate of the white rat in a bar-pressing apparatus. *J. Comp. Physiol. Psychol., 43,* 41–8.

SCHRIER, A. M. (1958) Comparison of two methods of investigating the effect of amount of reward on performance. *J. Comp. Physiol. Psychol., 51,* 725–31.

SEWARD, J.P., AND WELDON, R. J. (1953) Response latency as a function of change in delay of reward. *J. Comp. Physiol. Psychol., 46,* 184–9.

SHEFFIELD, F. D., AND TEMMER, H. W. (1950) Relative resistance to extinction of escape training and avoidance training. *J. Exp. Psychol.,* *40,* 287–98.

SHEFFIELD, V. F. (1949) Extinction as a function of partial reinforcement and distribution of practice. *J. Exp. Psychol., 39,* 511–26.

SIDMAN, M. (1953) Avoidance conditioning with brief shock and no exteroceptive warning signal. *Science, 118,* 157–8.

SIDMAN, M. (1956) Time discrimination and behavioral interaction in a free operant situation. *J. Comp. Physiol. Psychol., 49,* 469–73.

SKINNER, B. F. (1938) *The behavior of organisms.* New York, Appleton-Century.

SKINNER, B. F. (1948) "Superstition" in the pigeon. *J. Exp. Psychol., 38,* 168–72.

SKINNER, B. F. (1950) Are theories of learning necessary? *Psychol. Rev., 57,* 193–216.

SMEDSLUND, J. (1953) The problem of "what is learned?" *Psychol. Rev., 60,* 157–8.

SPENCE, K. W. (1947) The role of secondary reinforcement in delayed reward learning. *Psychol. Rev. 54,* 1–8.

SPENCE, K. W. (1951a) Theoretical interpretations of learning. In C. P. Stone, ed., *Comparative psychology,* 239–91. New York, Prentice Hall.

SPENCE, K. W. (1951b) Theoretical interpretations of learning. In S. S. Stevens, ed., *Handbook of experimental psychology.* New York, Wiley.

SPENCE, K. W. (1952) The nature of the response in discrimination learning. *Psychol. Rev., 59,* 89–93.

SPENCE, K. W. (1956) *Behavior theory and conditioning.* New Haven, Yale Univ. Press.

THURSTONE, L. L. (1927) A law of comparative judgment. *Psychol. Rev., 34,* 273–86.

TOLMAN, E. C. (1932) *Purposive behavior in animals and men.* New York, Century.

TOLMAN, E. C. (1955) Principles of performance. *Psychol. Rev., 62,* 315–26.

TOLMAN, E. C., AND HONZIK, C. H. (1930) Introduction and removal of reward and maze performance in rats. *Univ. Calif. Publ. Psychol., 4,* 257.

TOLMAN, E. C., RITCHIE, B.F., AND KALISH, D. (1946) Studies in spatial learning. II. Place versus response learning. *J. Exp. Psychol., 36,* 221–9.

TOLMAN, E. C., RITCHIE, B. F., and KALISH, D. (1947) Studies in spatial learning. IV. The transfer of place learning to other starting paths. *J. Exp. Psychol., 37,* 39–47.

WALKER, E. L. (1958) Action decrement and its relation to learning. *Psychol. Rev., 65,* 129–42.

WEINSTOCK, S. (1954) Resistance to extinction of a running response following partial reinforcement under widely spaced trials. *J. Comp. Physiol. Psychol., 47,* 318–22.

WEINSTOCK, S. (1958) Acquisition and extinction of a partially reinforced running response at a 24-hour intertrial interval. *J. Exp. Psychol., 56,* 151–8.

WENDT, G. R. (1936) An interpretation of inhibition of conditioned reflexes as competition between reaction systems. *Psychol. Rev., 43,* 258–81.

WIKE, E. L., AND BARRIENTOS, G. (1957) Selective learning as a function of differential consummatory activity. *Psychol. Reports, 3,* 255–8.

WILKE, E. L., AND McNAMARA, H. J. (1957) The effects of percentage of partially delayed reinforcement on the acquisition and extinction of an instrumental response. *J. Comp. Physiol. Psychol., 50,* 348–51.

WILSON, M. P., AND KELLER, F. S. (1953) On the selective reinforcement of spaced responses. *J. Comp. Physiol. Psychol., 46,* 190–3.

WILSON, W., WEISS, E. J., AND AMSEL, A. (1955) Two tests of the Sheffield hypothesis concerning resistance to extinction, partial reinforcement, and distribution of practice. *J. Exp. Psychol., 50,* 51–60.

WOLFE, J. B., AND KAPLON, M. D. (1941) Effect of amount of reward and consummative activity on learning in chickens. *J. Comp. Psychol., 31,* 353–61.

YOUNG, P. T., AND FALK, J. L. (1956) The acceptability of tap water and distilled water to nonthirsty rats. *J. Comp. Physiol. Psychol., 49,* 336–9.

ZEAMAN, D. (1949) Response latency as a function of the amount of reinforcement. *J. Exp. Psychol., 39,* 466–83.

Index

Acquired distinctiveness of cues, 201
Activity, 35, 42
Alternation, 113
Antagonistic correlations, 134, 208, 254
Apparatus: delay box, 23; double-alley maze, 22, 28; free behavior, 230
Avoidance situation, 206

Baseline performance, 38, 44ff., 50, 53
Behavioral summation, 104, 106

Chaining delay of reinforcement, 45, 170
Change-of-reward effect, 82, 202
Choice behavior, 244
Complementary correlations, 134, 208
Compromise response, 158
Conflict, 159, 206, 215
Contrast, 91, 188

Detention in goal box, 61, 185
Discrimination effect, 82, 202
Drive, 35, 43, 81, 97, 99, 104, 113, 179, 225
Drive stimulus, 104

Effort, 97, 99, 106, 207
Equilibrium analysis, 135ff., 152, 159, 162, 258
Error variance, 37ff., 100, 233
Escape response, 207
Experimenter differences, 33
Exploratory behavior, 42
Extinction: after discrimination training, 201; after negatively correlated reward, 195; after uncorrelated punishment, 219; as a function of amount of reward, 185; as a function of delay of reward, 185; as a function of partial reinforcement, 191, 197; as a function of varied amount of reward, 191; as a function of varied delay of reward, 191

Fear, 30, 42, 54, 221, 222
Feedback, 11, 96, 104
Fixation, 219
Force, of bar press, 226, 235
Fractional anticipatory goal response, 90, 99, 105, 194, 222
Free behavior situation, 225ff.
Frustration, 81, 88, 102

Generalization, 97, 106, 183
Goal gradient, 129, 251
Graded criteria, 10, 174

Habit, 97, 105

Incentive, 97, 98, 105; concept of, 3ff.; effect of context on, 223; effect of drive on, 113; negative, 222
Incentive function, 136, 215
Incompatible responses, 45, 60, 223
Independence of path, 12, 199, 233
Individual differences, 37, 43, 52, 208, 239; in amount function, 55; in delay function, 51; in equilibrium model, 139
Information stimulus, 211, 218, 243
Inhibition, 97, 105; conditioned, 100; in negatively correlated reinforcement, 182; reactive, 100; temporary, 100, 107, 210, 211
Interaction: amount of reward and drive, 59; delay and amount of reward, 55, 158; delay of reward and drive, 58; ratio and drop size, in free behavior, 238
Intertrial interval, 44, 62ff., 244

Laboratory, 21ff.
Latent learning, 32, 177
Learning conditions, 94, 241

Macro vs. micro, 121
Missing data, 27
Molar vs. molecular, 120

Oscillation, 100, 107, 114, 138

Partial reinforcement, 7, 77ff., 188, 250
Performance conditions, 94, 241
Prefeeding, 62
Pretraining, 25, 32
Procedure, 26
Punishment, 18, 206ff.; constant, 208; correlated, 215ff.; partial, 209

Qualitative vs. quantitative, 92
Quantification, 149, 251ff.

Re-extinction, 188
Reinforcement (see also Reward): condition of, 3, 136, 250; handling, 42; primary, 104; schedules of, 226, 250; uncorrelated, 133; vs. contiguity, 98
Relearning, 188
Resistance to change, 13, 191, 194, 202ff., 221